OXFORD

GCSE Maths

Foundation

PLUS

Dave Capewell
Formerly Westfield School, Sheffield

Geoff Fowler
Mathematics Strategy Manager, Birmingham

Peter Mullarkey
Netherhall School, Maryport, Cumbria

Katherine Pate
Maths Publishing Consultant

OXFORD
UNIVERSITY PRESS

UNIVERSITY PRESS

Great Clarendon Street, Oxford OX2 6DP

Oxford University Press is a department of the University of Oxford.
It furthers the University's objective of excellence in research, scholarship,
and education by publishing worldwide in

Oxford New York

Auckland Cape Town Dar es Salaam Hong Kong Karachi
Kuala Lumpur Madrid Melbourne Mexico City Nairobi
New Delhi Shanghai Taipei Toronto

With offices in

Argentina Austria Brazil Chile Czech Republic France Greece
Guatemala Hungary Italy Japan South Korea Poland Portugal
Singapore Switzerland Thailand Turkey Ukraine Vietnam

Oxford is a registered trade mark of Oxford University Press
in the UK and in certain other countries

British Library Cataloguing in Publication Data

Data available

ISBN 0 19 915088 5

ISBN 978 019 9150885

10 9 8 7 6 5 4 3 2

Typeset by MCS Publishing Services Ltd, Salisbury, Wiltshire

Printed and bound by Rotolito Lombarda

Acknowledgements

The graph on page 269 is reproduced from www.statistics.gov.uk.

The publisher would like to thank Edexcel for their kind permission to
reproduce past exam questions. Edexcel Ltd. accepts no responsibility
whatsoever for the accuracy or method of working in the answers given.

This high quality material is endorsed by Edexcel and has been through a
rigorous quality assurance programme to ensure that it is a suitable companion
to the specification for both learners and teachers.
This does not mean that its contents will be used verbatim when setting
examinations nor is it to be read as being the official specification – a copy of
which is available at www.edexcel.org.uk

The Publisher would also like to thank Peter Hind for his authoritative guidance
in preparing this book.

The image on the cover is reproduced courtesy of Jupiter images/Creatas.

The Publisher would like to thank the following for permission to
reproduce photographs:

p42 Tom Brakefield/Stock Connection Blue/Alamy; **p65** Elmtree Images/Alamy;
p71 Robert Estall/Corbis; **p76** Oxford University Press; **p106** Ashley Cooper/Alamy;
p111 Custom Medical Stock Photo/Science Photo Library; **p155** Honda;
p176 NASA/Oxford University Press; **p199** Steve Bicknell Style Library/Alamy ;
p279 Corel/Oxford University Press; **p297** Oxford University Press;
p314l Ordnance Survey; **p314r** Andrew Brown/Corbis; **p338** David Martyn
Hughes/Alamy; **p355** Araldo de Luca/Corbis.

Figurative artwork is by Peter Donelly.
Technical artwork is by MCS Publishing Services Ltd.

About this book

This book has been specifically written to help you get your best possible grade in your Edexcel GCSE Mathematics examinations. It is designed for students who have achieved level 5 at Key Stage 3 and are looking to progress to a grade C at GCSE, Foundation tier.

The authors are experienced teachers and examiners who have an excellent understanding of the Edexcel two-tier specification and so are well qualified to help you successfully meet your objectives.

The book is made up of units that are based on the Edexcel specification, and provide coverage of the National Curriculum strands at Key Stage 4.

The units are:

Each unit contains double page spreads for each lesson. These are shown on the full contents list.

Problem solving is integrated throughout the material as suggested in the National Curriculum.

How to use this book

This book is made up of units of work that are colour-coded:
Algebra (green), Data (blue), Number (orange) and Shape, space and
measures (pink).

Each unit starts with an overview of the content, so that you know
exactly what you are expected to learn.

This unit will show you how to

- Understand place value and order numbers, representing them as positions on a number line
- Multiply and divide numbers by powers of ten
- Represent decimal numbers as positions on a number line
- Read scales, dials and timetables

The first page of a unit also provides prior knowledge questions to help
you revise before you start – then you can apply your knowledge later
in the unit:

Before you start ...

You should be able to answer these questions.

1 Put these numbers in order from lowest to highest.

    0.37   0.4   0.312   0.35

Review

Key stage 3

Inside each unit, the content develops in double page spreads that all
follow the same structure.

Each spread starts with a list of the learning outcomes and a summary of
the keywords:

N1.1   Place value

This spread will show you how to:

- Understand place value and order numbers, representing them as positions on a number line
- Multiply and divide numbers by powers of ten

Keywords
Digit
Order
Place value

Key points are highlighted in the text so you can see the facts you need
to learn:

- Area of triangle = $\frac{1}{2} \times$ base $\times$ height

  The **height** must be **perpendicular** to the **base**.

Perpendicular means at right angles.

Examples showing the key skills and techniques you need to develop are shown in boxes. Also, margin notes show tips and reminders you may find useful:

Simplify these expressions:

a $4x + 2y - 2x + 3y$ **b** $7p - 3q + 5q - p$ **c** $5c - 2b + 2c - 3b$

a $4x + 2y - 2x + 3y$
$= 4x - 2x + 2y + 3y$
$= 2x + 5y$

b $7p - 3q + 5q - p$
$= 7p - p + 5q - 3q$
$= 6p + 2q$

c $5c - 2b + 2c - 3b$
$= 5c + 2c - 2b - 3b$
$= 7c - 5b$

Rearrange, keeping terms and their signs together.

Each exercise is carefully graded, set at three levels of difficulty:
- The first few questions are mainly repetitive to give you confidence, and simplify the content of the spread
- The questions in the middle of the exercise consolidate the topic, focusing on the main techniques of the spread
- Later questions extend the content of the spread – some of these questions may be problem-solving in nature, and may involve different approaches.

At the end of the unit is an exam review page so that you can revise the learning of the unit before moving on. The key Edexcel objectives are identified:

D2 Exam review

Key objectives
- Draw and produce, using paper and ICT, diagrams for continuous data, including scatter graphs and stem-and-leaf diagrams
- Distinguish between positive, negative and zero correlation using lines of best fit

Summary questions, including past exam questions, are provided to help you check your understanding of the key concepts covered and your ability to apply the key techniques.

An Edexcel formula page is provided near the end of the book so you can see what information you will be given in the exam.

You will find the answers to all exercises at the back of the book so that you can check your own progress and identify any areas that need work.

Contents

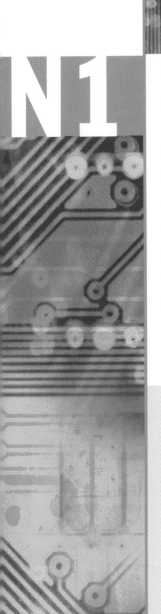

N1

This unit will show you how to

- Understand place value and order numbers, representing them as positions on a number line
- Multiply and divide numbers by powers of ten
- Represent decimal numbers as positions on a number line
- Read scales, dials and timetables
- Order negative numbers using a number line
- Add, subtract, multiply and divide with negative numbers
- Express a whole number as a product of its factors
- Understand and use simple divisibility tests
- Find the highest common factor and least common multiple of two numbers

Before you start ...

You should be able to answer these questions.

1 Put these numbers in order from lowest to highest.

    0.37   0.4   0.312   0.35

2 What number is the arrow pointing to?

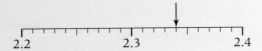

3 Put these numbers in order starting with the smallest.

    −8, −1, 2, −5, −3, 4

4 Calculate.

  a 10 − 3   **b** −6 − 4

  c 3 × (−4)   **d** −6 ÷ 2

5 Write all the factors of 48.

Review

Key stage 3

Key stage 3

Key stage 3

Key stage 3

Key stage 3

This spread will show you how to:

- Understand place value and order numbers, representing them as positions on a number line
- Multiply and divide numbers by powers of ten

Keywords
Digit
Order
Place value

- The value of each **digit** in a number depends upon its **place value**.

In the number 37.65:

Thousands 1000	Hundreds 100	Tens 10	Units 1	•	tenths $\frac{1}{10}$	hundredths $\frac{1}{100}$
		3	7	•	6	5

You write this number in words as thirty-seven point six five.

The digits stand for:

	3 tens	7 units	6 tenths	5 hundredths
37.65 =	30 +	7 +	$\frac{6}{10}$ +	$\frac{5}{100}$
=	30 +	7 +	0.6 +	0.05

You can use a place value table to compare or **order** two or more numbers.

Example

Put these numbers in order from lowest to highest.

0.47   0.5   0.512   0.55   0.52

Look at each number to see the place value of the first non-zero digit.

0.47   0.5   0.512   0.55   0.52

You can see that 0.47 is the smallest number. The other four numbers all have a 5 in the first decimal place, so now look at the second digit.

0.50   0.512   0.55   0.52

You can now order the numbers: 0.47   0.5   0.512   0.52   0.55

The digit 4 stands for 4 tenths and the digit 5 stands for 5 tenths.

You can use a place value table to multiply and divide.

- To multiply a number by 100, move all the digits two places to the left.

6.7 × 100

Hundreds	Tens	Units	•	tenths
		6	•	7
6	7	0	•	

× 100

The 0 holds the digits in place.

6.7 × 100 = 670

- To divide a number by 10, move all the digits one place to the right.

73.2 ÷ 10

Tens	Units	•	tenths	hundredths
7	3	•	2	
	7	•	3	2

÷ 10

73.2 ÷ 10 = 7.32

1 Write each of these numbers in words.

    a 456   **b** 13 200   **c** 115 020   **d** 460 340   **e** 4 325 400

    f 55 670 345   **g** 45.8   **h** 367.03   **i** 4503.34   **j** 2700.02

2 Write each of these numbers in figures.

    a five hundred and thirty-eight

    b two thousand and thirty-one

    c fifteen thousand, six hundred and three

    d two hundred and eighty thousand, four hundred and fifty-three

    e four hundred and seventeen point three

    f one million, seven hundred and seventeen thousand, three hundred and thirty-eight

    g five hundred and thirty-seven point four zero three

    h three and three hundredths

3 What number lies exactly halfway between

    a 25 and 26   **b** 1.8 and 1.9   **c** 30 and 70

    d 4.9 and 5   **e** 1.25 and 1.5   **f** 0.7 and 0.71?

4 Put these lists of numbers in order, starting with the smallest.

    a   5.103   5.099   5.2   5.12   5.007

    b   0.545   0.55   0.525   0.5   0.509

    c   7.302   7.403   7.35   7.387   7.058

    d   0.4   4.2   0.42   42   2.4

    e   27.6   26.9   27.06   26.97   27.1

    f   13.3   14.15   13.43   13.19   14.03

5 Calculate each of these without using a calculator.

    a 3.2×100 **b** 0.4×10 **c** $152 \div 100$ **d** $14.6 \div 100$

    e 2.37×10 **f** 24.3×100 **g** $1.23 \div 100$ **h** $45.9 \div 10$

    i 3.4×1000 **j** 13.56×10 **k** $0.236 \div 10$ **l** 1.745×10

    m 0.0392×10 **n** $72.8 \div 100$ **o** $12.4 \div 1000$ **p** 0.0814×100

6 Use the information given to work out each of these calculations without using a calculator.

    a $23 \times 42 = 966$ What is 2.3×42?

    b $91 \times 103 = 9373$ What is 9.1×103?

    c $39 \times 57 = 2223$ What is 0.39×57?

    d $34 \times 71 = 2414$ What is 340×71?

This spread will show you how to:

- Represent decimal numbers as positions on a number line
- Read scales, dials and timetables

Keywords
Estimate
Number line
Scale
Timetable

- You can represent decimal numbers as a position on a **number line**.

The arrow is pointing between 4 and 5.

There are 10 spaces between 4 and 5.
10 spaces represent 1 unit.
1 space represents $1 \div 10 = \frac{1}{10} = 0.1$ unit.
The arrow is pointing to the number 4.3.

The arrow is pointing between 2.2 and 2.3.

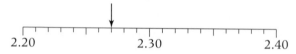

There are 10 spaces between 2.2 and 2.3.
10 spaces represent 0.1 unit.
1 space represents $0.1 \div 10 = 0.01$ unit.
The arrow is pointing to the number 2.27.

You can write 2.2 as 2.20, and so on.

You can **estimate** a measurement from a **scale**.

The reading is between 4 and 5 cm.
There are only two spaces between 4 and 5 cm.
The pointer is a little under a quarter of the way between 4 and 5.
A good estimated reading is 4.2 cm.

Most of the scales you read are number lines.

You need to be able to read **timetables** for buses and trains.

How long does it take for the 07:40 train from Clitheroe to get to Colne?

Station	Time of leaving	Team of leaving	Time of leaving
Clitheroe	07:10	07:40	08:10
Blackburn	07:28	07:58	08:28
Nelson	08:23	08:53	09:23
Colne	08:41	09:11	09:41
Bradford	09:52	10:22	10:52

The train leaves Clitheroe at 07:40.
It arrives at Colne at 09:11.

From 07:40 to 08:00 = 20 minutes
From 08:00 to 09:00 = 60 minutes
From 09:00 to 09:11 = 11 minutes
Total journey time = 91 minutes = 1 hour 31 minutes

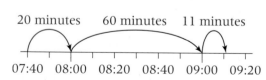

Example

1 Write the number each of the arrows is pointing to.

a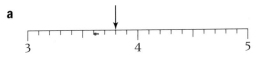

b

c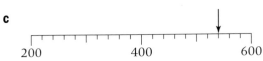

d

2 Write the reading shown on each scale.

a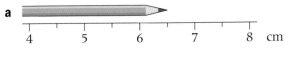

b

c

d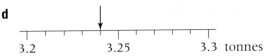

3 Use the scales to write a good estimated reading for each question.

a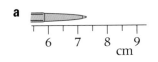

b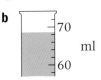

c

d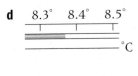

e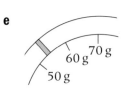

f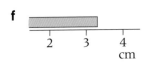

g

h

4

Carlisle–Hexham bus timetable			
Carlisle	09:25	11:50	15:00
Crosby on Eden	09:41	12:11	15:21
Lanercost Priory	09:58	12:28	15:38
Birdoswald Fort	10:10	12:40	15:50
Chesters Fort	11:18	13:48	16:58
Hexham	11:32	13:59	17:09

a What time does the 11:50 bus from Carlisle arrive at Hexham?

b What time does the 15:50 bus from Birdoswald Fort leave Crosby on Eden?

c How long does it take the 09:25 bus from Carlisle to travel to Hexham?

d Harry catches the 12:28 bus at Lanercost Priory. He gets off at Chesters Fort. How long is his journey?

This spread will show you how to:

- Order negative numbers using a number line
- Add, subtract, multiply and divide with negative numbers

Keywords
Add
Negative numbers
Order
Subtract

- **Negative numbers** are numbers below zero.

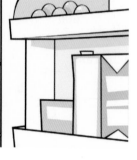

The temperature in the fridge is −5°C or 5 degrees below freezing.

You can order negative numbers using a number line.

Example

Place these numbers in **order**, starting with the smallest.

−13, −14, 2, −5, −3, 4

−14 is further away from zero than −13, so it is smaller.

The correct order is −14, −13, −5, −3, 2, 4.

You can use a number line to help you **add** or **subtract** from a negative number.

To add, you move to the right.

To subtract, you move to the left.

Example

Calculate   **a** 5 − 12   **b** −3 + 8   **c** −5 − 4

a Start at 5 and subtract 12 (move to the left).

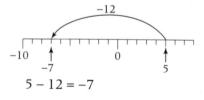

5 − 12 = −7

b Start at −3 and add 8 (move to the right).

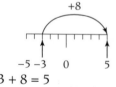

−3 + 8 = 5

c Start at −5 and subtract 4.

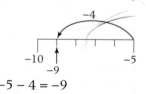

−5 − 4 = −9

There are two rules for adding and subtracting negative numbers.

- Adding a negative number is the same as subtracting a positive number.

- Subtracting a negative number is the same as adding a positive number.

18 + −3 = 18 − 3 = 15

18 − −3 = 18 + 3 = 21

1   Put these lists of numbers in order from lowest to highest.

a	−13	−6	0	17	−12	15
b	0	−5	−6	−8	−3	−7
c	2	1	−2	4	3	−5
d	−1.5	3	9	−3	2	−8
e	−3	2	−5	−4.5	3	−2
f	3	8	6	−9	−1	2
g	−1	−3	0	−4.5	5.5	−2.5
h	−5	−5.1	−6	−5.8	−5.7	−5.4

2   Calculate these.

a $4 + 12$ b $5 - 12$ c $7 - 3$ d $14 + 23$

e $34 - 17$ f $8 - 15$ g $-3 + 12$ h $-23 + 12$

i $-15 + 7$ j $-13 + 34$ k $-5 - 3$ l $-5 + 3$

m $-12 - 6$ n $21 - 17$ o $-8 + 3$ p $-4 + 8 - 2$

q $-12 - 3 - 5$ r $13 - 8 + 5$ s $-5 + 4 - 7$ t $-12 - 4 - 12$

3   Find the number that lies exactly halfway between each of these pairs of numbers.

a 28 and 34   b −5 and −17   c −6 and 14   d −18 and 4

e 3 and 8   f −4 and 9   g −20 and 35   h −3.5 and 2.5

4   Copy and complete each of these number patterns.

a $7 + 3 = 10$ b $7 - 3 = 4$ c $12 + 3 = 15$ d $12 - 3 = 9$
 $7 + 2 = 9$ $7 - 2 = 5$ $12 + 2 = 14$ $12 - 2 = 10$
 $7 + 1 = 8$ $7 - 1 = 6$ $12 + 1 = \underline{\quad}$ $12 - 1 = \underline{\quad}$
 $7 + 0 = 7$ $7 - 0 = 7$ $12 + 0 = \underline{\quad}$ $12 - 0 = \underline{\quad}$
 $7 + -1 = \underline{\quad}$ $7 - -1 = \underline{\quad}$ $12 + -1 = \underline{\quad}$ $12 - -1 = \underline{\quad}$
 $7 + -2 = \underline{\quad}$ $7 - -2 = \underline{\quad}$ $12 + -2 = \underline{\quad}$ $12 - -2 = \underline{\quad}$
 $7 + -3 = \underline{\quad}$ $7 - -3 = \underline{\quad}$ $12 + -3 = \underline{\quad}$ $12 - -3 = \underline{\quad}$
 $7 + -4 = \underline{\quad}$ $7 - -4 = \underline{\quad}$ $12 + -4 = \underline{\quad}$ $12 - -4 = \underline{\quad}$

Write what you notice.

5   Calculate each of these.

a $13 + -5$ b $6 + -8$ c $12 + -3$ d $4 + -4$

e $-5 + -8$ f $-3 + -11$ g $-11 + -3$ h $15 - -5$

i $4 - -8$ j $-2 - -5$ k $-12 - -7$ l $-14 - -8$

m $-16 - -20$ n $-13 + -12$ o $-13 - -12$ p $13 + -12$

q $-12 + 7 - 4$ r $-12 + -7 - 4$ s $-12 - -7 - 4$ t $-12 - 7 + -4$

This spread will show you how to:

- Add, subtract, multiply and divide with negative numbers

Keywords

Divide
Multiply
Negative number

You can use a number line to help you multiply or divide **negative numbers**.

- -2×4 can be represented on a number line as four lots of -2.

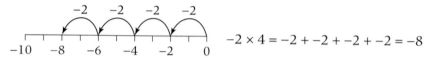

$$-2 \times 4 = -2 + -2 + -2 + -2 = -8$$

- **Negative number** × positive number = negative number.

- $-16 \div -4$ can be represented on a number line as 'how many lots of -4 are needed to make -16?'

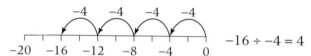

$$-16 \div -4 = 4$$

- Negative number ÷ negative number = positive number.

To **multiply** a negative number by a negative number, look for patterns in multiplication tables.

-5×2	=	-10		-5×0	=	0
-5×1	=	-5		-5×-1	=	5

- Negative number × negative number = positive number.

As you multiply -5 by smaller and smaller numbers, the answer gets bigger.
The pattern indicates that -5×-1 is 5.

Remember these rules:

- Negative × positive = negative
  $-2 \times 4 = -8$
- Negative × negative = positive
  $-2 \times -4 = 8$
- Positive ÷ negative = negative
  $-8 \div -2 = -4$
- Negative ÷ positive = negative
  $-8 \div 2 = -4$
- Negative ÷ negative = positive
  $-8 \div -2 = 4$

If the signs are different the answer will be negative.
If the signs are the same the answer will be positive.

1 Copy and complete these multiplication tables.

a $4 \times 3 = 12$
$4 \times 2 = 8$
$4 \times 1 = 4$
$4 \times 0 = 0$
$4 \times -1 = -4$
$4 \times -2 = \underline{}$
$4 \times -3 = \underline{}$
$4 \times -4 = \underline{}$

b $-7 \times 3 = -21$
$-7 \times 2 = -14$
$-7 \times 1 = \underline{}$
$-7 \times 0 = \underline{}$
$-7 \times -1 = \underline{}$
$-7 \times -2 = \underline{}$
$-7 \times -3 = \underline{}$
$-7 \times -4 = \underline{}$

2 Choose a number card to make each of these calculations correct.

$\boxed{-2} \quad \boxed{2} \quad \boxed{4} \quad \boxed{-3} \quad \boxed{-4} \quad \boxed{3}$

a $7 \times \boxed{} = -14$
b $-30 \div \boxed{} = -15$
c $-5 \times \boxed{} = 15$
d $-27 \div \boxed{} = -9$
e $\boxed{} \times -5 = 20$
f $-6 \times \boxed{} = -24$

3 Calculate these.

a 3×-2 **b** 6×5 **c** 3×-7 **d** -4×-2 **e** -5×4

f -6×-4 **g** 8×-3 **h** -6×-7 **i** -8×-2 **j** -5×-10

k $-10 \div -2$ **l** $-40 \div 5$ **m** $-30 \div -6$ **n** $-45 \div -9$ **o** $54 \div -6$

p -9×7 **q** -7×7 **r** -8×-9 **s** $72 \div -8$ **t** $-42 \div 7$

u $-12 \div 3$ **v** $100 \div -10$ **w** $-81 \div -9$ **x** -7×8 **y** $-130 \div 10$

4 Here are a set of multiplication and division questions that have been marked by the teacher.
Explain why each of the answers that has been marked wrong is incorrect and write the correct answer.

a $4 \times -5 = 20$ ✗
b $3 \times -2 = -6$ ✓
c $-5 \times -6 = -30$ ✗
d $-14 \times -2 = -28$ ✗
e $7 \times -3 = -21$ ✓
f $8 \times 5 = 20$ ✗
g $7 \times -5 = 35$ ✗
h $-40 \div -5 = -8$ ✗
i $30 \div -5 = -6$ ✓
j $-14 \times -5 = -70$ ✗

5 Calculate these, using either a mental or a written method.
Remember to check the sign of your answer.

a -8×15 **b** -12×-11 **c** 25×-9 **d** 21×-7 **e** -9×13

f -19×7 **g** -23×18 **h** $-240 \div 6$ **i** $221 \div -17$ **j** -21×3.2

This spread will show you how to:

- Express a whole number as a product of its factors
- Understand and use simple divisibility tests
- Find the highest common factor and least common multiple of two numbers

Keywords

Factor
Highest common
  factor
Least common
  multiple
Multiple
Product

Any whole number can be written as the **product** of two factors.

$48 = 4 \times 12$ so 4 and 12 are **factors** of 48.

You can use simple divisibility tests to find the factors of a number.

Here are some simple tests:

Factor	Test	120
2	the number ends in a 0, 2, 4, 6 or 8	120
3	the sum of the digits is divisible by 3	$1 + 2 + 0 = 3$
4	the last two digits of the number are divisible by 4	$20 \div 5 = 4$
5	the number ends in 0 or 5	120
6	the number is divisible by 2 *and* by 3	60, 40
7	there is no simple check for divisibility by 7	
8	half of the number is divisible by 4	15
9	the sum of the digits is divisible by 9	–
10	the number ends in 0	120

A factor divides
into a number
exactly, with no
remainder.

Factors of 120:
  1×120
  2×60
  3×40
  4×30
  5×24
  6×20
  8×15
  10×12

The multiples of 15 are 15, 30, 45, 60, ...

- You can find the **highest common factor** (HCF) of two numbers by listing all the factors of both numbers.
- You can find the **least common multiple** (LCM) of two numbers by listing the first few multiples of each number.

The **multiples** of a
number can be
divided exactly by
the number,
leaving no
remainder.

Example

Find the HCF and LCM of 10 and 15.

The factors of 10 are: 1   2   5   10
The factors of 15 are: 1   3   5   15

1 and 5 are **common factors** of 10 and 15.
5 is the highest common factor of 10 and 15.

The first six multiples of 10 are: 10   20   30   40   50   60
The first six multiples of 15 are: 15   30   45   60   75   90

30 and 60 are **common multiples** of 10 and 15.
30 is the least common multiple of 10 and 15.

1 Look at this list of numbers.

2	3	4	5	6	8	10
12	15	16	17	18	19	20

    a Write all the numbers that are factors of 20.
    b Write all the numbers that are factors of 192.
    c Write all the numbers that are multiples of 5.
    d Write all the numbers that are prime numbers.

2 Write all the factor pairs of each of these numbers.
    a 24   **b** 45   **c** 66   **d** 100   **e** 120
    f 132   **g** 160   **h** 180   **i** 360   **j** 324
    k 224   **l** 264   **m** 312   **n** 325   **o** 432

3 Write the first three multiples of each of these numbers.
    a 17   **b** 29   **c** 42   **d** 25   **e** 47
    f 35   **g** 90   **h** 120   **i** 95   **j** 208

4 Find a number between 300 and 400 that has exactly 15 factors.

5 Find the highest common factor of
    a 6 and 4   **b** 25 and 40   **c** 18 and 30   **d** 24 and 56
    e 30 and 75   **f** 36 and 54   **g** 50 and 125   **h** 24, 36 and 72
    i 30, 75 and 105

6 Find the least common multiple of
    a 6 and 4   **b** 5 and 8   **c** 12 and 18   **d** 15 and 25
    e 14 and 21   **f** 30 and 75

7 **a** Two hands move around a dial. The faster hand moves around in 24 seconds, and the slower hand in 30 seconds. If the two hands start together at the top of the dial, how many seconds does it take before they are next together at the top?

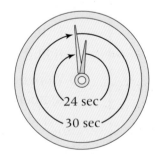

    b A wall measures 234 cm by 432 cm.
    What is the largest size of square tile that can be used to cover the wall, without needing to cut any of the tiles?

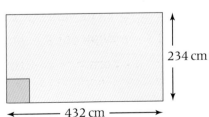

Exam review

Key objectives

- Multiply or divide any number by powers of ten
- Understand and use positive and negative numbers, both as positions and translations on a number line
- Add, subtract, multiply and divide integers and then any number

1 a Mark the following numbers on the related number line:

   i 1387   **ii** 1.387   **iii** 13.87   **iv** 0.1387   (4)

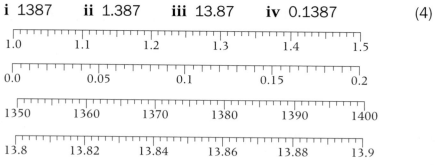

b Use the above numbers and the signs × and ÷ to complete the following calculations:

   i $1387 \div 1000 = ?$ **ii** $? \times 100 = 13.87$

   iii $1.387 \; ? \; 10 = 0.1387$ **iv** $1.387 \times 1000 = ?$ (4)

2 Sally wrote down the temperature at different times on 1st Jan 2003.

Time	Temperature
midnight	−6°C
4 am	−10°C
8 am	−4°C
noon	7°C
3 pm	6°C
7 pm	−2°C

  a Write down

    i the highest temperature

    ii the lowest temperature.   (2)

  b Work out the difference in the temperature between

    i 4 am and 8 am   **ii** 3 pm and 7 pm.   (2)

At 11 pm that day the temperature had fallen by 5 °C from its value at 7 pm.

  c Work out the temperature at 11 pm.   (1)

(Edexcel Ltd., 2004)

S1

This unit will show you how to

- Know rough metric equivalents to imperial measures
- Convert measurements from one unit to another
- Calculate the area and perimeter of rectangles, triangles and shapes made from rectangles and triangles
- Use formulae to find the area of any parallelogram
- Use formulae of rectangles, triangles and parallelograms to find the area of any trapezium
- Calculate the circumference and area of a circle
- Calculate the volume of cuboids and shapes made from cuboids

Before you start ...

You should be able to answer these questions.

Review

1 Evaluate.

a 60×10	**b** 71×1000	**c** 4.8×10
d 26.3×100	**e** 4.5×1000	**f** $600 \div 100$
g $750 \div 10$	**h** $6500 \div 1000$	**i** $32 \div 10$

Unit N1

2 Evaluate.

a $6 \times \frac{8}{5}$ **b** $9 \times 2\frac{1}{2}$ **c** $6 \times 1\frac{3}{4}$

Key stage 3

3 Evaluate.

a $5.8 + 2$ **b** $14.8 + 0.7$ **c** $6.4 + 2.6$

Key stage 3

4 Measure this line

a in millimetres   **b** in centimetres

Key stage 3

5 Calculate the perimeter and area of this rectangle.

8 cm

5 cm

Key stage 3

6 Find the volume of this shape.

Key stage 3

This spread will show you how to:

● Know rough metric equivalents to imperial measures
● Convert measurements from one unit to another

Keywords
Capacity
Convert
Equivalents
Imperial
Length
Mass
Metric

You can measure **length**, **mass** and **capacity** using **metric** and **imperial units**.

You can **convert** between metric units by multiplying or dividing by 10, 100, 1000, . . .

1 lb of bananas

Paris 40 km

● **Length** is a measure of distance.

Metric units		Imperial units	Equivalents
millimetre (mm)	10 mm = 1 cm	inch (")	5 miles ≈ 8 km
centimetre (cm)	100 cm = 1 m	foot (')	1 inch ≈ 2.5 cm
metre (m)	1000 m = 1 km	yard (3 ft = 1 yd)	1 yard ≈ 1 m
kilometre (km)		mile	1 foot ≈ 30 cm

≈ means approximately equal to.

1 metre is a bit longer than 1 yard.

● **Mass** is a measure of the amount of matter in an object. Mass is linked to weight.

Metric units		Imperial units	Equivalents
gram (g)	1000 g = 1 kg	ounce (oz)	1 ounce ≈ 30 g
kilogram (kg)	1000 kg = 1 tonne	pound (lb)	1 kg ≈ 2.2 lb
tonne (t)		stone	
		ton	

1 lb of jam   1 kg of sugar

● **Capacity** is a measure of the amount of liquid a 3-D shape will hold.

Metric units		Imperial units	Equivalents
millilitre (ml)	1000 ml = 1 litre	pint	1 pint ≈ 600 ml
centilitre (cl)	100 cl = 1 litre	gallon	1.75 pints ≈ 1 litre
litre			1 gallon ≈ 4.5 litres

1 pint   1 litre of
of milk   lemonade

Example

Calculate the approximate length of a 12 inch ruler in

a centimetres   **b** millimetres.

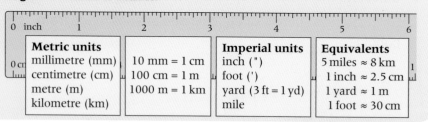

a 1" ≈ $2\frac{1}{2}$ cm
  12" ≈ $2\frac{1}{2} \times 12 = 30$ cm

b 1 cm = 10 mm
  30 cm = 30 × 10 = 300 mm

cm ⟶ ×10 ⟶ mm
÷ 10

1 Choose one of these metric units to measure each of these items.

millimetre	gram	millilitre	centimetre
kilogram	centilitre	metre	tonne
litre	kilometre		

a your height

b amount of tea in a mug

c your weight

d length of a suitcase

e weight of a suitcase

f distance from Paris to Madrid

g quantity of drink in a can

h amount of petrol in a car

i weight of an elephant

j weight of an apple.

Write the appropriate abbreviation next to your answers.

2 Convert these measurements to the units shown.

a 20 mm = ___ cm

b 400 cm = ___ m

c 450 cm = ___ m

d 4000 m = ___ km

e 0.5 cm = ___ mm

f 4.5 kg = ___ g

g 6000 g = ___ kg

h 6500 g = ___ kg

i 2500 kg = ___ t

j 3 litres = ___ ml

3 Convert these distances to miles.

a Berlin 16 km

b Dusseldorf 40 km

c Bonn 88 km

d Dresden 84 km

4 Convert these measurements to centimetres.

a 1 inch   **b** 5 inches   **c** 6 inches   **d** 12 inches   **e** 36 inches

5 Use 1 kg ≈ 2.2 lb to convert these weights to pounds.

a 2 kg   **b** 40 kg   **c** 50 kg   **d** 0.5 kg   **e** 2.5 kg

6 Use 1 oz ≈ 30 g to convert ounces to grams in these recipes.

a
Lemon Curd

6 oz butter
12 oz caster sugar
6 lemons
6 eggs

b
Cumberland Pudding

8 oz rice
4 oz raisins
3 oz sugar
4 oz currants
1 egg
beef marrow

c
Chocolate Crunchies

6 oz self-raising flour
2 oz cornflour
2 oz cornflakes
1 oz drinking chocolate
6 oz margarine
3 oz sugar

7 The speed limit on a motorway in the UK is 70 miles per hour. Calculate the speed limit in kilometres per hour.

70

Perimeter and area of a rectangle and a triangle

This spread will show you how to:

● Calculate the area and perimeter of rectangles, triangles and shapes made from rectangles and triangles

Keywords
Area
Base
Perimeter
Perpendicular
  height
Square units

● The **perimeter** of a shape is the distance around it.

Perimeter is a length, so it is measured in mm, cm, m or km.

● The **area** of a shape is the amount of space it covers.

Area is measured in **square units**: mm², cm², m² or km².

You can find the area of a rectangle using:

● **Area of a rectangle = length × width**

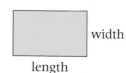
width
length

This formula also works for a square.

You can find a formula for the area of any triangle.

For this triangle ...
base

complete the rectangle ...

the area has doubled.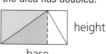
height
base

The area of a triangle is half the area of the surrounding rectangle.

● **Area of triangle = ½ × base × height**

The height must be perpendicular to the base.

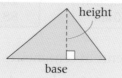
height
base

Perpendicular means at right angles.

You can find the area of a compound shape by splitting it into rectangles and triangles.

Example

Calculate the perimeter and area of each shape.

a
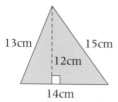
13cm   15cm
12cm
14cm

b
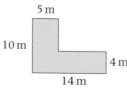
5 m
10 m
4 m
14 m

The two missing lengths are:
10 − 4 = 6 m
and
14 − 5 = 9 m

a Perimeter = 15 + 13 + 14
  = 42 cm
  Area = ½ × base × height
  = ½ × 14 × 12
  = 84 cm²

b Perimeter = 5 + 6 + 9 + 4 + 14 + 10
  = 48 m
  Area = area of green rectangle
  + area of orange rectangle
  = 10 × 5 + 9 × 4
  = 50 + 36 = 86 m²

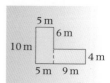
5 m
10 m
6 m
4 m
5 m   9 m

1 Calculate the perimeter and area of each rectangle.
Give the units of your answers.

a 4 m
2 m

b 8 cm 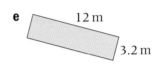 1.5 cm

c 13.5 mm
6 mm

d 5.4 cm
8 cm

e 12 m
3.2 m

2 Calculate the area of each triangle.

a 4cm
6cm

b 6m
10m

c 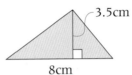 3.5cm
8cm

d 9mm
16mm

e 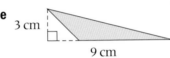 3 cm
9 cm

3 Calculate the missing lengths. Give the units of your answers.

a 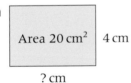 Area 20 cm² | 4 cm
? cm

b 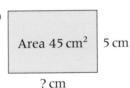 Area 45 cm² | 5 cm
? cm

c ? m
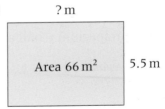 Area 66 m² | 5.5 m

4 Calculate the perimeter and area of each shape.
State the units of your answers.

a 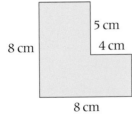 5 cm
8 cm | 4 cm
8 cm

b 10 cm 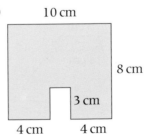 8 cm
3 cm
4 cm | 4 cm

c 8 cm | 8 cm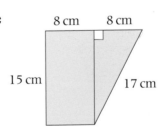
15 cm | 17 cm

Area of a parallelogram and a trapezium

This spread will show you how to:

- Use formulae to find the area of any parallelogram
- Use formulae of rectangles, triangles and parallelograms to find the area of any trapezium

Keywords
Area
Base
Parallelogram
Perpendicular
    height
Trapezium

You can find the formula for the **area** of any **parallelogram**.

For this parallelogram ...

cut off one triangle ...

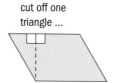

and fit it on the other end ... to make a rectangle.

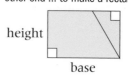

- **Area of parallelogram = base × perpendicular height.**

The height must be perpendicular to the base.

You can find the formula for the area of any **trapezium**.

You can fit two **congruent** trapeziums together to make a parallelogram.

Congruent means identical.

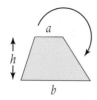   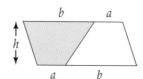

The base of the parallelogram is $a + b$ and the height is h.
Area of parallelogram = $(a + b) \times h$
Area of trapezium = half area of parallelogram.

- **Area of trapezium = $\frac{1}{2} \times (a + b) \times h$**

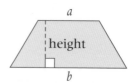

The height is the perpendicular distance between the parallel sides.

Example

Calculate the area of each shape.

a

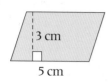

b

a Area of parallelogram = 5×3
$= 15 \text{ cm}^2$

b Area of trapezium = $\frac{1}{2}(3 + 7) \times 4$
$= 5 \times 4$
$= 20 \text{ cm}^2$

1 Calculate the area of each parallelogram.

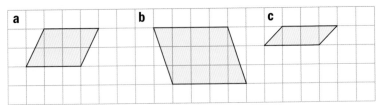

2 Calculate the area of each trapezium.

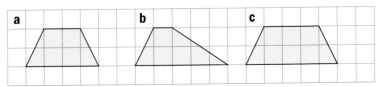

3 Calculate the area of each parallelogram. State the units of your answers.

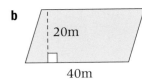 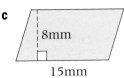 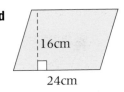

4 Calculate the area of each trapezium. State the units of your answers.

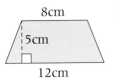 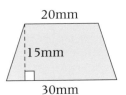 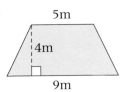 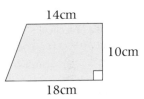

5 The areas of these shapes are given. Calculate the unknown lengths.

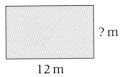
area = 72 m²

area = 196 cm²

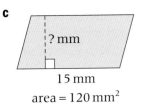
area = 120 mm²

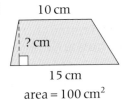
area = 100 cm²

6 a Calculate the area of this shape using the formula for the area of a trapezium.

b Calculate the area by adding the areas of the triangles and the square.

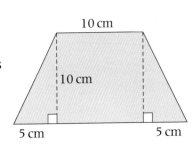

19

Circumference and area of a circle

This spread will show you how to:

● Calculate the circumference and area of a circle

Keywords
Centre
Circle
Circumference
Diameter
Pi (π)
Radius

In a **circle**:
● the **radius** is r
● the **diameter** is d
● the **circumference** is C.

C, d and r are all
measures of length.

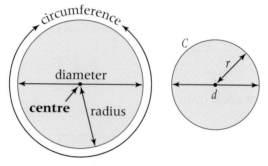

The perimeter of a
circle is called the
circumference.

● Diameter = 2 × radius   ● $C = \pi \times$ diameter $= \pi d = 2\pi r$

$d = 2 \times r$

$\pi = 3.14 \ldots$

Example

Calculate the circumference of this circle.

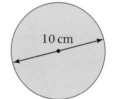

10 cm

$C = \pi \times d$
$\quad = 3.14 \times 10$
$\quad = 31.4 \text{ cm}$ Remember to state the units.

● Area of a circle $= \pi \times$ radius × radius
$\qquad\qquad\quad = \pi \times r \times r \quad \text{or} \quad \pi r^2$

r^2 means $r \times r$

Example

A circular lawn has radius 3 metres.
a Calculate the area of the lawn. State the units of
your answer.
b Calculate the length of edging stones needed to fit
all round the edge of the lawn.
Give your answer to a suitable degree of accuracy.

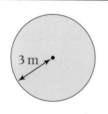

3 m

a Area $= \pi r^2$
$\qquad\quad = 3.14 \times 3 \times 3$
$\qquad\quad = 3.14 \times 9$
$\qquad\quad = 28.26 \text{ m}^2$
b Circumference $= \pi d$
$\qquad\qquad\qquad = 3.14 \times 6$
$\qquad\qquad\qquad = 18.84$
So 19 m of edging stones are needed.

Area is measured
in square units.

Take $\pi = 3.14$ for all questions on this page.

1 Calculate the circumferences of these circles. State the units of your answers.

a
diameter = 10 cm

b
diameter = 8 m

c
diameter = 12 cm

d
diameter = 20 m

e
radius = 2 m

f
radius = 8 cm

g
radius = 1.5 m

h
radius = 3.5 cm

2 Calculate the diameter of a circle, if its circumference is

a 18.84 cm   **b** 15.7 m   **c** 28.26 cm   **d** 47.1 m   **e** 314 cm

3 Calculate the areas of these circles. State the units of your answers.

a
radius = 7 cm

b
radius = 5 m

c
radius = 4 cm

d
radius = 3 m

e
diameter = 20 m

f
diameter = 16 cm

g
diameter = 12 mm

h
diameter = 18 cm

4 A garden pond is circular.
The radius of the pond is 1.5 m.

a Calculate the diameter of the pond.

b Calculate the circumference of the pond.

c Calculate the area of the pond.

Give your answers to a suitable degree of accuracy.

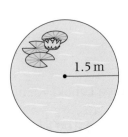
1.5 m

Volume of a cuboid

This spread will show you how to:

● Calculate the volume of cuboids and shapes made from cuboids

Keywords

Cube
Cuboid
Cubic centimetre (cm^3)
Cubic metre (m^3)
Volume

● The **volume** of a 3-D shape is the amount of space it takes up.

You measure volume using **cubes**.

One **cubic centimetre** is 1 cm^3.

One **cubic metre** is 1 m^3.

The ^{3} in cm^3 shows there are 3 dimensions in the cube: length, width and height.

You can find the volume of a **cuboid** by counting cubes.

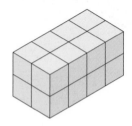 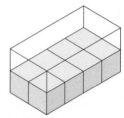 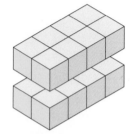

On the bottom layer there are
4 × 2 = 8 cubes.

For 2 layers, there are
2 × 8 = 16 cubes.

● **Volume of cuboid = length × width × height.**

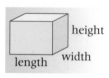

height
length   width

Example

Calculate the volume of each shape. State the units in your answers.

a

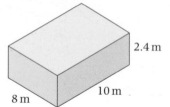

2.4 m

8 m   10 m

b

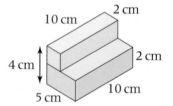

2 cm
10 cm
4 cm   2 cm
5 cm   10 cm

a Volume = length × width × height
= 8 × 10 × 2.4 = 192 m^3

b Volume of yellow cuboid = length × width × height
= 2 × 2 × 10
= 40 cm^3

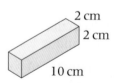

2 cm
2 cm
10 cm

Volume of green cuboid = length × width × height
= 5 × 10 × 2
= 100 cm^3

Total volume = 100 + 40
= 140 cm^3

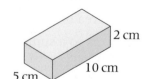

2 cm
5 cm   10 cm

1 Calculate the volume of each cuboid. State the units of each answer.

a

3 cm
4 cm
3 cm

b
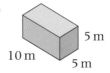
5 m
10 m
5 m

c
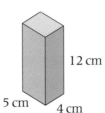
12 cm
5 cm
4 cm

2 How many 1 cm cubes will fit into this box?

1 cm

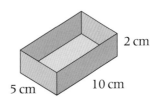
2 cm
5 cm
10 cm

3 Calculate the volume of these cuboids. Give each answer to a suitable degree of accuracy.

a
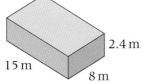
2.4 m
15 m
8 m

b
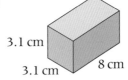
3.1 cm
3.1 cm
8 cm

c
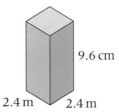
9.6 cm
2.4 m
2.4 m

4 This cuboid has a square base.
The square measures 15 cm by 15 cm.
The volume of the cuboid is 1350 cm³.
Calculate its height, in centimetres.

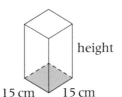
height
15 cm
15 cm

Volume =
15 × 15 × height
so
1350 =
15 × 15 × height

5 Calculate each unknown length. Give your answers to a suitable degree of accuracy.

a
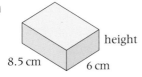
height
8.5 cm
6 cm

Volume = 153 cm³

b
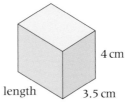
4 cm
length
3.5 cm

Volume = 80 cm³

c
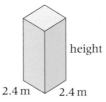
height
2.4 m
2.4 m

Volume = 50 m³

6 Calculate the volume of each shape. State the units of your answers.

a
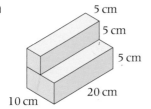
5 cm
5 cm
5 cm
20 cm
10 cm

b
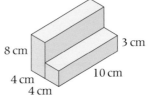
8 cm
3 cm
4 cm
10 cm
4 cm

c
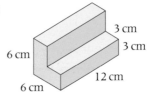
3 cm
3 cm
6 cm
6 cm
12 cm

Key objectives

● Calculate perimeters and areas of shapes made from triangles and rectangles

● Find circumferences of circles and areas enclosed by circles

1 Work out the perimeter of this shape. (3)

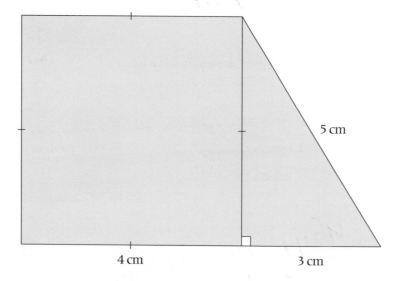

4 cm   3 cm   5 cm

2 A circle has a radius of 6.1 cm.
Work out the area of the circle. (3)

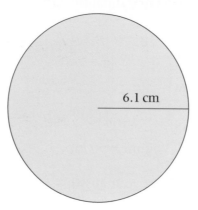

6.1 cm

(Edexcel Ltd., 2003)

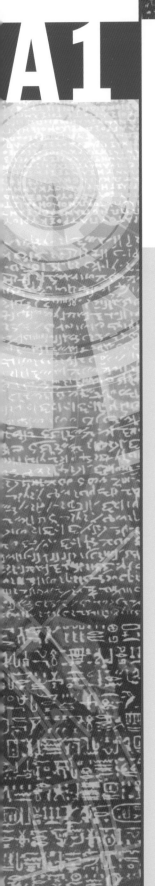

A1

This unit will show you how to

- Use letters to represent unknown numbers in algebraic expressions
- Simplify algebraic expressions by collecting like terms
- Use index notation and simple laws of indices
- Expand single and double brackets within algebraic expressions
- Transform algebraic expressions using the rules of arithmetic
- Factorise an algebraic expression

Before you start ...

You should be able to answer these questions.

Review

1 $3 + 3 + 3 + 3 = 4$ lots of $3 = 4 \times 3 = 12$.

Key stage 3

  a Write these addition sums as multiplications.

    i $2 + 2 + 2$

    ii $5 + 5 + 5 + 5 + 5 + 5$

    iii $10 + 10 + 10 + 10$

    iv $7 + 7 + 7$

  b Work out the answer of the multiplications.

2 a Work out.

Key stage 3

    i $3 + 2 + 4$ **ii** $4 + 2 + 3$ **iii** $2 + 4 + 3$

  b What do you notice?

3 a Work out.

Key stage 3

    i $2 \times 3 \times 5$ **ii** $5 \times 2 \times 3$ **iii** $3 \times 2 \times 5$

  b What do you notice?

4 Follow the order of operations to work out these calculations.

Key stage 3

  a $3 \times 5 - 12 + 2$ **b** $4 + 2 \times 3 - 1$

  c $6 \div 3 + 2$ **d** $3 \times 4 - 4 \div 2$

5 a Write all the factors of

Unit N1

    i 18   **ii** 12   **iii** 24

  b Write all the common factors of 18, 12 and 24.

  c What is the highest common factor of 18, 12 and 24?

Algebraic expressions

This spread will show you how to:

- Use letters to represent unknown numbers in algebraic expressions
- Simplify algebraic expressions by collecting like terms

You can describe everyday situations using algebra.

- In algebra, you use letters to represent unknown numbers.

These boxes hold n pens each.

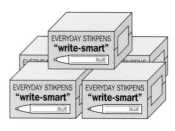

These boxes hold s pens each.

You do not write
the × sign.
$n = 1 \times n$

In 5 boxes there are
$n + n + n + n + n = 5 \times n = 5n$ pens

In 3 boxes there are $3s$ pens.

$5n$ and $3s$ are
terms.

There are $5n + 3s$ pens in total.

$5n + 3s$ is an
expression.

- You can **simplify** an algebraic expression by collecting **like terms**.
  Like terms have exactly the same letters.

Simplify these expressions:

a $4x + 2y - 2x + 3y$ **b** $7p - 3q + 5q - p$ **c** $5c - 2b + 2c - 3b$

a $4x + 2y - 2x + 3y$
$= 4x - 2x + 2y + 3y$
$= 2x + 5y$

b $7p - 3q + 5q - p$
$= 7p - p + 5q - 3q$
$= 6p + 2q$

c $5c - 2b + 2c - 3b$
$= 5c + 2c - 2b - 3b$
$= 7c - 5b$

Rearrange,
keeping terms and
their signs
together.

In a fruit shop,
apples cost 20p each and
oranges cost 15p each.
Write an expression for the cost
of x apples and y oranges.

Cost of x apples: $x \times 20 = 20x$
Cost of y oranges: $y \times 15 = 15y$
Total cost: $20x + 15y$

Write numbers
before letters.

Exercise A1.1

1 Simplify these expressions.

a $b + b + b + b$ **b** $y + y + y - y$ **c** $a - a + a + a + a + a - a$

d $3p + 6p$ **e** $5x - 2x$ **f** $4z - z + 3z$

2 Simplify these expressions.

a $2p + 5q + 3p + q$ **b** $6x + 2y + 3x + 5y$

c $4m + 2n - 2m + 6n$ **d** $5x + 3y - 4x + 2y$

e $7r - 4s + r - 2s$ **f** $2f - 3g + 5g - 6f$

g $3a + 2b + 5c - a + 4b$ **h** $7u - 5v + 3w + 3v - 2u$

i $5x - 3y - 2x + 4z - y + z$ **j** $4r + 6s - 3t + 2r + 5t - s$

3   **a** One guitar has 6 strings. How many strings are there on t guitars?

     b One cookie has 3 peanuts on top. How many peanuts are needed for n cookies?

     c One horse has 4 horseshoes. How many horseshoes are needed for x horses?

4 In one month, Dan sends x texts.

     a Alix sends 4 times as many texts as Dan. How many is this?

     b Kris sends 8 more texts than Alix. How many is this?

5 A factory makes bags.

     a The factory makes m small bags. A small bag has 2 zips. How many zips do they need?

     b The factory makes three times as many large bags as small bags. How many large bags do they make?

     c Each large bag has 4 buttons. How many buttons do they need for the large bags?

6 In a pizza takeaway
- a medium pizza has 6 slices of tomato
- a large pizza has 10 slices of tomato.

How many slices of tomato are needed

     a for c medium pizzas

     b for d large pizzas?

     c Write an expression for the total number of slices of tomato needed for c medium and d large pizzas.

7 Write algebraic expressions for the cost of

     a f teas and g scones

     b j fruit juices and k flapjacks

     c x teas, y milks and z scones

     d p milks, q fruit juices and r flapjacks.

Café price list	
Tea	50p
Fruit juice	80p
Milk	60p
Scone	30p
Flapjack	40p

Indices

This spread will show you how to:

- Use index notation and simple laws of indices

Keywords
Base
Index
Indices
Power
Simplify

- You can use **index** notation to write repeated multiplication.

$5 \times 5 = 5^2$ $m \times m = m^2$ You say 'm squared'
$5 \times 5 \times 5 = 5^3$ $m \times m \times m = m^3$ You say 'm cubed'
$5 \times 5 \times 5 \times 5 = 5^4$ $m \times m \times m \times m = m^4$ You say 'm to the **power** of 4'

5 is the **base**, 4 is the index.

You can simplify expressions with **indices** and numbers.

'index 4' and 'power 4' mean the same.

Indices is the plural of index.

Example

Simplify

a $y \times y \times y \times y \times y$ **b** $4 \times r \times r$
c $3 \times p \times p \times p \times q \times q$ **d** $2 \times s \times s \times 3 \times t \times t \times t$

---

a $y \times y \times y \times y \times y = y^5$ **b** $4 \times r \times r = 4 \times r^2 = 4r^2$

c $3 \times p \times p \times p \times q \times q$ **d** $2 \times s \times s \times 3 \times t \times t \times t$
$\quad = 3 \times p^3 \times q^2$ $\quad = 2 \times s^2 \times 3 \times t^3$
$\quad = 3p^3 q^2$ $\quad = 2 \times 3 \times s^2 \times t^3$
$\qquad\qquad\qquad\qquad\qquad\qquad\qquad = 6s^2 t^3$

y is multiplied by itself 5 times, so index is 5.

Rearrange so the numbers are together.

You can simplify expressions with powers of the same base.

$$n^2 \times n^2$$
$$= n \times n \times n \times n = n^4$$

$$t^5 \div t^2 = \frac{t^5}{t^2} = \frac{{}^1\!\!\not t \times {}^1\!\!\not t \times t \times t \times t}{{}^1\!\!\not t \times {}^1\!\!\not t} = t^3$$

- To multiply powers of the same base, add the indices.
  $x^a \times x^b = x^{(a+b)}$

- To divide powers of the same base, subtract the indices.
  $x^a \div x^b = x^{(a-b)}$

These are the index laws.

Example

Simplify

a $s^2 \times s \times s^3$ **b** $\dfrac{d^2 \times d^4}{d^3}$

---

a $s^2 \times s \times s^3 = s^{(2+1+3)} = s^6$ **b** $\dfrac{d^2 \times d^4}{d^3} = \dfrac{d^6}{d^6} = d^{(6-3)}$
$\qquad\qquad\qquad\qquad\qquad\qquad\qquad\qquad\quad = d^3$

1 Write these in the simplest form.

   a $y \times y \times y \times y$ **b** $m \times m \times m \times m \times m \times m$ **c** $x \times x \times x \times x$ **d** $p \times p$

2 Simplify these.

   a $3 \times t \times t$ $\qquad\qquad\qquad$ **b** $4 \times p \times q \times q$

   c $6 \times v \times v \times w \times w \times w$ $\qquad$ **d** $2 \times r \times r \times r \times r \times s$

3 Simplify these.

   a $2 \times m \times m \times 3 \times n$ $\qquad\qquad$ **b** $4 \times y \times y \times y \times 2 \times z \times z$

   c $3 \times g \times 4 \times h \times h \times h$ $\qquad\quad$ **d** $5 \times x \times 2 \times y \times y \times y \times y$

4 Simplify these.

   a $3m^2 \times 2$ $\qquad$ **b** $3 \times 4p^3$ $\qquad$ **c** $2x \times 3y^2$ $\qquad$ **d** $5r^2 \times 2s^2$

5 Simplify these.

   a $n^2 \times n^3$ $\qquad$ **b** $s^3 \times s^4$ $\qquad$ **c** $p^3 \times p$ $\qquad$ **d** $t \times t^3$

6 Write each of these as a single power in the form x^n.

   a $x^2 \times x^2 \times x^3$ $\qquad$ **b** $x \times x^5 \times x^2$ $\qquad$ **c** $x^3 \times x^2 \times x^4$ $\qquad$ **d** $x^5 \times x \times x$

7 Write each of these as a single power in the form r^n.

   a $r^4 \div r^2$ $\qquad$ **b** $r^5 \div r^4$ $\qquad$ **c** $r^7 \div r^2$ $\qquad$ **d** $r^8 \div r^5$

8 Simplify these.

   a $\dfrac{m^6}{m^2}$ $\qquad$ **b** $\dfrac{x^4}{x^3}$ $\qquad$ **c** $\dfrac{t^7}{t^5}$ $\qquad$ **d** $\dfrac{y^4}{y}$

9 Simplify these.

   a $\dfrac{x^2 \times x^3}{x^4}$ $\qquad$ **b** $\dfrac{m^3 \times m}{m^2}$ $\qquad$ **c** $\dfrac{s^2 \times s^4}{s^3}$ $\qquad$ **d** $\dfrac{v \times v^3 \times v^2}{v^4}$

   e $\dfrac{q^2 \times q^3 \times q^2}{q^4}$ $\qquad$ **f** $\dfrac{t^3 \times t \times t^2}{t^2}$ $\qquad$ **g** $\dfrac{p^4 \times p^2 \times p^2}{p^7}$ $\qquad$ **h** $\dfrac{y^2 \times y^4 \times y}{y^3 \times y^2}$

10 Match each of the pairs.

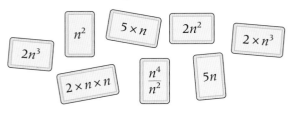

$2n^3$ $\qquad$ n^2 $\qquad$ $5 \times n$ $\qquad$ $2n^2$ $\qquad$ $2 \times n^3$

$2 \times n \times n$ $\qquad$ $\dfrac{n^4}{n^2}$ $\qquad$ $5n$

Brackets in algebra

This spread will show you how to:

- Expand single and double brackets within algebraic expressions

Keywords
Brackets
Expand
Simplify

You can use **brackets** in algebraic equations.

> - You can multiply out brackets.
>   - You multiply each term inside the bracket by the term outside.

$2(x+4) = 2 \times x + 2 \times 4 = 2x + 8$

$2 \times (x+4) = 2(x+4)$
You don't write the ×.

To **simplify** expressions with brackets, expand the brackets and collect like terms.

Example

Expand.

a $2(3x+1)$ **b** $n(n+5)$

a $2(3x+1) = 2 \times 3x + 2 \times 1$
$= 6x + 2$

b $n(n+5) = n \times n + 5 \times n$
$= n^2 + 5n$

Expand means 'multiply out'.

$n \times n = n^2$

Example

Simplify.

a $m(m+2)+m$ **b** $3(x+1)+2(4x+2)$

a $m(m+2)+m = m^2 + 2m + m$
$= m^2 + 3m$

b $3(x+1)+2(4x+2)$

$= 3x + 3 + 8x + 4$
$= 11x + 7$

Like terms have the same power of the same letter. m^2 and m are **not** like terms.

You can **expand** a double bracket by multiplying pairs of terms.

Each term in the first bracket multiplies each term in the second bracket.

$(p+7)\ (p+3) \longrightarrow p^2 + 3p + 7p + 21 \longrightarrow p^2 + 10p + 21$

$p^2 + 10p + 21$ is the product of $(p+7)$ and $(p+3)$.

F... **F**irsts
O ... **O**uters
I ... **I**nners
L ... **L**asts

Example

Expand and simplify.

$(x+3)(x+4)$

$(x+3)(x+4) = x^2 + 4x + 3x + 12$
$= x^2 + 7x + 12$

F: $x \times x = x^2$
O: $x \times 4 = 4x$
I: $3 \times x = 3x$
L: $3 \times 4 = 12$

---

1 Expand the brackets in these expressions.
  a $3(m + 2)$ **b** $4(p + 6)$ **c** $2(x + 4)$ **d** $5(q + 1)$
  e $2(6 + n)$ **f** $3(2 + t)$ **g** $4(3 + s)$ **h** $2(4 + v)$

2 Expand these.
  a $3(2q + 1)$ **b** $2(4m + 2)$ **c** $3(4x + 3)$ **d** $2(3k + 1)$
  e $5(2 + 2n)$ **f** $3(4 + 2p)$ **g** $4(1 + 3y)$ **h** $2(5 + 4z)$

3 At a pick-your-own fruit farm, Lucy picks n apples.

Mary picks 5 more apples than Lucy.
  a Write down, in terms of n, the number of apples Mary picks.

Nat picks 3 times as many apples as Mary.
  b Write down, in terms of n, the number of apples Nat picks.

4 Expand and simplify each of these.
  a $3(p + 3) + 2p$ **b** $2(m + 4) + 5m$ **c** $4(x + 1) - 2x$
  d $2(5 + k) + 3k$ **e** $4(2t + 3) + t - 2$ **f** $3(2r + 1) - 2r + 4$

5 On Monday a shop sells s DVDs.
On Tuesday the shop sells 6 more DVDs than on Monday.
  a Write an expression for the number of DVDs it sells on Tuesday.

On Wednesday the shop sells twice as many DVDs as on Tuesday.
  b Write an expression for the number of DVDs it sells on Wednesday.

On Thursday the shop sells 7 more DVDs than on Wednesday.
  c Write an expression for the number of DVDs it sells on Thursday.

Give your answer in its simplest form.

6 Expand and simplify each of these.
  a $2(n + 3) + 3(n + 2)$ **b** $4(p + 1) + 2(3 + p)$
  c $4(2x + 1) + 2(x + 3)$ **d** $2(3n + 2) + 3(4n + 1)$

7 A small box contains 12 toffees.
Sam buys y small boxes of toffees.
  a Write an expression for the number of toffees Sam buys.

A large box contains 20 toffees.
Sam buys 2 more of the large boxes than the small ones.
  b Write an expression for the number of large boxes of toffees he buys.
  c Find, in terms of y, the total number of toffees in the large boxes
    that Sam buys.
  d Find, in terms of y, the total number of toffees Sam buys.
    Give your answer in its simplest form.

8 Simplify these.
  a $x(4x + 1)$ **b** $m(m^2 + 2)$ **c** $2t(t^2 + 4)$ **d** $3p(p^2 + 1)$

9 Expand and simplify.
  a $(p + 2)(p + 1)$ **b** $(5w + 1)(3w + 9)$ **c** $(2m + 1)(3 - m)$ **d** $(y + 1)^2$

This spread will show you how to:

- Transform algebraic expressions using the rules of arithmetic

You can add, subtract, multiply or divide algebraic terms.

$$3n + 5n + 8n = 16n \qquad 4p - p = 3p \qquad 2 \times 6p = 12p \qquad 8r \div 4 = 2r$$

- To simplify an expression, you follow the same order of operations as in arithmetic.

  Brackets $\Rightarrow$ **I**ndices $\Rightarrow$ **D**ivision or **M**ultiplication $\Rightarrow$ **A**ddition or **S**ubtraction

You can use the acronym BIDMAS to remember the order.

Example

Simplify.

a $4n + 2 \times 5n$ **b** $3r \times 2s$ **c** $4t^2 - 3 \times t^2 + t$

a $4n + 2 \times 5n = 4n + (2 \times 5n)$
$\qquad\qquad\quad = 4n + 10n$
$\qquad\qquad\quad = 14n$

b $3r \times 2s = 3 \times 2 \times r \times s$
$\qquad\qquad = 6rs$

Collect like terms.

c $4t^2 - 3 \times t^2 + t = 4t^2 - (3 \times t^2) + t$
$\qquad\qquad\qquad\quad = 4t^2 - 3t^2 + t$
$\qquad\qquad\qquad\quad = t^2 + t$

To simplify an expression with brackets, expand the brackets first.

$$3(n - 2) = 3 \times n + 3 \times -2 = 3n - 6$$

$3 \times -2 = -6$

When you expand brackets, keep each term with its sign.

$$4(x - 1) - 2(x + 3) = 4 \times x + 4 \times -1 + -2 \times x + -2 \times 3$$
$$\qquad\qquad\qquad\quad = 4x \quad - 4 \qquad - 2x \quad - 6$$
$$\qquad\qquad\qquad\quad = 4x - 2x - 4 - 6$$
$$\qquad\qquad\qquad\quad = 2x - 10$$

Example

Expand and simplify.

a $3(5y - 2)$ **b** $2(3p + 1) - 3(p + 2)$ **c** $2(3m + 1)(2m - 2)$

a $3(5y - 2) = 3 \times 5y + 3 \times -2$
$\qquad\qquad\quad = 15y - 6$

b $2(3p + 1) - 3(p + 2) = 6p + 2 - 3p - 6$
$\qquad\qquad\qquad\qquad\quad = 3p - 4$

c $2(3m + 1)(2m - 2) = 2(6m^2 - 6m + 2m - 2)$
$\qquad\qquad\qquad\qquad\quad = 2(6m^2 - 4m - 2$
$\qquad\qquad\qquad\qquad\quad = 12m^2 - 8m - 4$

In part **c**, multiply the brackets together first and then multiply by the 2 outside the brackets.

1 Simplify these.

   a $3r + 3 \times 2r$ **b** $2m^2 + 2m \times m$ **c** $6x \div 2 + x$

   d $2t \times 4v$ **e** $5m \times 2n$ **f** $3x \times 2y^2$

   g $x^2 + x^2 + x$ **h** $3 \times 3w - 2 \times 4$ **i** $z \times z^2 + 3z + 1$

2 Expand these.

   a $4(2y + 3)$ **b** $2(3x - 2)$ **c** $3(2k - 2)$ **d** $4(1 - n)$

3 Write these expressions in their simplest form.

   a $3k^2 - 2 \times k^2 + k$ **b** $4m + 6m \div 2 + m^2$ **c** $6t - (4 \times -t) + 5$

4 Expand these.

   a $2m(m - 3)$ **b** $4p(2p - 1)$ **c** $r(r^2 + 3)$ **d** $2s(s^2 - 4)$

5 Expand and simplify each of these.

   a $3(r + 2) + 2(r - 1)$ **b** $4(s + 1) - 2(s + 2)$

   c $3(2j + 3) - 2(j + 2)$ **d** $3(4t - 2) + 3(t - 1)$

6 Simplify these.

   a $3(4m + 1)(m - 1)$ **b** $2(3p - 1)(p - 2)$

   c $-5(2q + 3)(q - 3)$ **d** $4(2v - 3)(v - 1)$

7 Jake is n years old.
   Jake's sister is 4 years older than Jake.
   Jake's mother is 3 times older than his sister.
   Jake's father is 4 times older than Jake.
   Jake's uncle is 2 years younger than Jake's father.
   Jake's grandmother is twice as old as Jake's uncle.

   a Copy the table and write each person's age in terms of n.

Jake	Sister	Mother	Father	Uncle	Grandmother
n					

   b Find, in terms of n, how much older Jake's grandmother is than his mother. Give your answer in its simplest form.

A1.5 Factorising

This spread will show you how to:

- Factorise an algebraic expression

Keywords
Common factor
Factor
Factorise

- Factorising is the 'opposite' of expanding brackets.

$$2(x+4) \overset{\text{expand}}{\underset{\text{factorise}}{=}} 2x+8$$

In number...
a factor is a number that exactly divides into another number.

2, 3 and 4 are factors of 12.

In algebra...
a factor is a number or letter that exactly divides into another term.

3 and 2x are factors of 6x.

- To factorise an expression, look for a **common factor** for all the terms.

A common factor divides into all the terms.

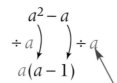

Write the common factor outside the bracket.

Sometimes the common factor is a letter.

a divides into a^2 and a.

Example

a Find the common factors of 12x and 8.
b Factorise: 12x + 8.

a 2 and 4 are common factors of 12x and 8.
b $12x + 8 = 4 \times 3x + 4 \times 2$
$\qquad = 4(3x + 2)$

To factorise completely, use the highest common factor. The highest common factor of 12x and 8 is 4.

Example

Factorise

a $3y - 9$
b $x^2 - 3x$

a $3y - 9 = 3 \times y - 3 \times 3 = 3(y - 3)$
b $x^2 - 3x = x \times x - 3 \times x = x(x - 3)$

You can check your answer by expanding:
$x(x - 3) = x^2 - 3x$

1 Find all the common factors of

   a $2x$ and 6   **b** $4y$ and 12   **c** 10 and $20j$ **d** 6 and $12p$

   e 9 and $6q$ **f** $6t$ and 4   **g** $4x$ and 10   **h** $24t$ and 8

2 Find the highest common factor of

   a $3x$ and 9   **b** $12r$ and 10   **c** $6m$ and 8   **d** 4 and $4z$

3 Find the highest common factor of

   a y^2 and y **b** $4s^2$ and s **c** $7m$ and m^3 **d** $2y^2$ and $2y$

4 Factorise these.

   a $2x + 10$ **b** $3y + 15$ **c** $8p - 4$ **d** $6 + 3m$

   e $5n + 5$ **f** $12 - 6t$ **g** $14 + 4k$ **h** $9z - 3$

5 Factorise these.

   a $w^2 + w$ **b** $z - z^2$ **c** $4y + y^2$ **d** $2m^2 - 3m$

   e $4p^2 + 5p$ **f** $7k - 2k^2$ **g** $3n^3 - 2n$ **h** $5r + 3r^2$

6 The cards show expansions and factorisations.
Match the cards in pairs.

$4(x + 3)$	$4x^2 - 3x$	$3(x - 4)$	$4x + 3x^2$
$3x - 12$	$x(4 + 3x)$	$4x + 12$	$x(4x - 3)$

7 Factorise these.

   a $4y - 12$ **b** $2x^2 + 3x$ **c** $3y^2 - y$ **d** $15 + 5t^2$

   e $3m + 9m^2$ **f** $2r^2 - 2r$ **g** $4v^3 + v$ **h** $3w^2 + 3w$

Check your
answers by
expanding.

8 Debbie, Kate and Bryn factorise $16x^2 + 4x$.
Here are their answers.

Debbie	Kate	Bryn
$16x^2 + 4x = 2(x^2 + 2x)$	$16x^2 + 4x = 4x(4x + 1)$	$16x^2 + 4x = 2x(8x^2 + 2)$

   a Who is correct?

   b Explain where the other two have gone wrong.

A1

Exam review

Key objectives

- Use index notation for simple positive integer powers, and simple instances of index laws
- Understand that the transformation of algebraic expressions obeys and generalises the rules of arithmetic
- Manipulate algebraic expressions by collecting like terms, multiplying a single term over a bracket, taking out common factors

1 Expand the brackets.

  a $2(x + 1)$

  b $x(1 + x)$

  c $x(x - y)$ (3)

2 a Simplify $y + y$ (1)

  b Simplify $p^2 + p^2 + p^2$ (1)

  c Factorise $x^2 - 3x$ (2)

(Edexcel Ltd., 2004)

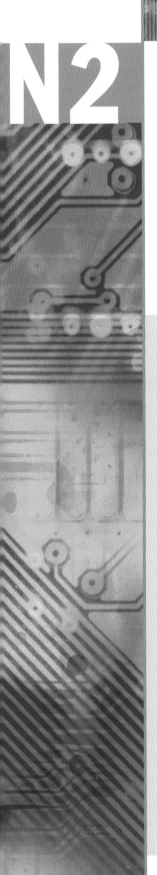

This unit will show you how to

- Round numbers to any number of significant figures
- Use rounding to estimate answers to calculations
- Use suitable degrees of accuracy in calculations
- Recognise the inaccuracy of rounded measurements
- Use a range of mental and written methods for addition, subtraction, multiplication and division
- Understand and use simple divisibility tests
- Use approximation to estimate answers to problems

Before you start ...

You should be able to answer these questions.

Review

1 Round 35 265

   a to the nearest 1000

   b to the nearest 100

   c to the nearest 10.

Key stage 3

2 Calculate.

   a 257 + 178   **b** 375 − 189

Key stage 3

3 Steve sells potatoes.
On Saturday he sells 18.6 kg. On Sunday he sells 13.8 kg.
What weight of potatoes has he sold over the two days?

Key stage 3

4 Calculate.

   a 9 × 8   **b** 42 × 10

   c 72 ÷ 6   **d** 143 ÷ 30

Key stage 3

5 Calculate.

   a 29 × 48   **b** 204 ÷ 12

Key stage 3

This spread will show you how to:

- Round numbers to any number of significant figures
- Use rounding to estimate answers to calculations
- Recognise the inaccuracy of rounded measurements

Keywords
Approximate
Decimal places
Estimate
Rounding
Significant figures

You can round a decimal number to a given accuracy.
To round 718.394 to 2 **decimal places**, look at the **thousandths** digit.

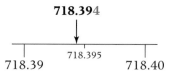

718.394

718.39   718.40
718.395

The **thousandths** digit is **4**, so round down to 718.39.

718.394 ≈ 718.39 (to 2 decimal places).

When **rounding** numbers to a given degree of accuracy, look at the next digit. If it is 5 or more then round up, otherwise round down.

To round 54.76 to 2 **significant figures**, look at the 3rd significant figure.

Tens	Units	•	tenths	hundredths
5	4	•	7	6

The **3rd significant** figure is **7**, so the number is rounded up to 55.

54.76 ≈ 55 (to 2 significant figures).

The first **non-zero** digit in the number is called the **1st significant figure** – it has the highest value in the number.

- You can **estimate** the answer to a calculation by rounding the numbers.

Example

Estimate the answer to $\dfrac{6.23 \times 9.89}{18.7}$.

You can round each of the numbers to 1 significant figure.

$$\frac{6.23 \times 9.89}{18.7} \approx \frac{6 \times 10}{20} = \frac{60}{20} = 3$$

- When a measurement is written down, it is always written to a given degree of accuracy. The real measurement can be anywhere within ± half a unit.

Example

A man walks 23 km (to the nearest km). Write the maximum and minimum distance he could have walked.

Because the real measurement has been rounded, it can lie anywhere between 22.5 km (minimum) and 23.5 km (maximum).

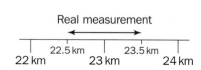

Real measurement

22.5 km   23.5 km
22 km   23 km   24 km

1 Round each of these numbers to the

  i nearest 10   **ii** nearest 100   **iii** nearest 1000.

  a 3487   **b** 3389   **c** 14 853 m   **d** £57 792

  e 92 638 kg   **f** £86 193   **g** 3438.9   **h** 74 899.36

2 Round each of these numbers to the nearest whole number.

  a 3.738   **b** 28.77   **c** 468.63   **d** 369.29

  e 19.93   **f** 26.9992   **g** 100.501   **h** 0.001

3 Round each of these numbers to the nearest

  i 3 dp   **ii** 2 dp   **iii** 1 dp.

  a 3.4472   **b** 8.9482   **c** 0.1284   **d** 28.3872

  e 17.9989   **f** 9.9999   **g** 0.003 987 **h** 2785.5555

4 Round each of these numbers to the nearest

  i 3 sf   **ii** 2 sf   **iii** 1 sf.

  a 8.3728   **b** 18.82   **c** 35.84   **d** 278.72

  e 1.3949   **f** 3894.79   **g** 0.008 372 **h** 2399.9

  i 8.9858   **j** 14.0306   **k** 1403.06   **l** 140 306

5 Write a suitable estimate for each of these calculations. In each case, clearly show how you estimated your answer.

  a 4.98×6.12 **b** $17.89 + 21.91$ **c** $\dfrac{5.799 \times 3.1}{8.86}$

  d $34.8183 - 9.8$ **e** $\dfrac{32.91 \times 4.8}{3.1}$ **f** $\{9.8^2 + (9.2 - 0.438)\}^2$

6 For each of these measurements (given to a specified degree of accuracy), write

  i the minimum value it could be **ii** the maximum value it could be.

  a 67 cm (nearest whole number) **b** 34.7 litres (1 decimal place)

  c 8.36 kg (2 decimal places)   **d** 0.387 mm (3 decimal places)

7 The length of a car is 2.6 m correct to 1 decimal place.

  a Write the maximum value that the length could be.

  b Write the minimum value that the length could be.

This spread will show you how to:

- Use a range of mental and written methods for addition, subtraction, multiplication and division

Keywords

Compensation
Complement
Mental methods
Partitioning

There are lots of **mental methods** to help work out additions and subtractions of whole numbers. You could:

- Use **partitioning** to split the numbers you are adding or subtracting into parts.
- Use **compensation** when the number you are adding or subtracting is nearly a whole number, a multiple of 10 or a multiple of 100.

Example

Calculate   **a** $19.5 - 7.2$ **b** $5.8 + 4.8$

a $19.5 - 7.2 = 19.5 - 7 - 0.2$
$\qquad\qquad\quad = 12.5 - 0.2$
$\qquad\qquad\quad = 12.3$

Split smaller number into parts.
Subtract the units from the highest number.
Subtract the tenths.

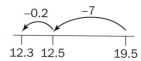

b $5.8 + 4.8 = 5.8 + 5 - 0.2$
$\qquad\qquad\quad = 10.8 - 0.2$
$\qquad\qquad\quad = 10.6$

Round 4.8 to the nearest whole number, 5.
Rewrite **add 4.8** as **add 5 − 0.2**.
Add the 5 to the highest number.
Subtract 0.2.

For most calculations, there is more than one way to work it out. Use the method that you are most comfortable with.

You could count up from the smallest number to the largest number.

Example

Hetti runs in a 3500 m race. She has already covered 1792 m. How far does she have left to run?

$3500 \text{ m} - 1792 \text{ m}$

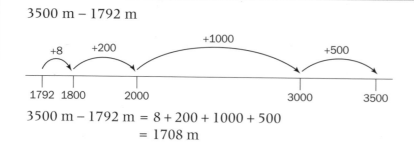

$3500 \text{ m} - 1792 \text{ m} = 8 + 200 + 1000 + 500$
$\qquad\qquad\qquad\qquad\quad = 1708 \text{ m}$

1 Write the answer to each of these calculations.

   a $150 + 120$ **b** $170 - 90$ **c** $160 + 170$ **d** $130 - 90$

   e $1900 + 1900$ **f** $210 - 140$ **g** $320 - 110$ **h** $510 - 120$

2 Find the missing number in each of these calculations.

   a $37 + ? = 100$ **b** $? + 0.4 = 1$ **c** $0.31 + ? = 1$ **d** $7.3 + ? = 10$

3 Use a mental method for each of these calculations. Write the method you have used.

   a $257 + 98$ **b** $448 + 112$ **c** $427 + 523$ **d** $256 + 552$

   e $354 + 213$ **f** $561 + 328$ **g** $16.2 - 1.9$ **h** $5.8 + 14.9$

4 Copy and complete this number addition square.

+	2.9	4.8	3.9	2.5	5.9	?
3.1						
?		11.3				12.2
8.2						
?		9.7				
7.1						
9.6						

5 Use a mental method of calculation to solve each of these problems.

   a Charlie has to travel 435 km. After 2 hours he has travelled 187 km. How much further does he have to travel?

   b Emma has to write an assignment of at least 500 words. After 15 minutes she has written 237 words. How many more words does she need to write to complete her assignment?

   c In a test, Alex scores 93 marks, Sophie scores 75 marks and Louise scores 97 marks. How many marks did the girls score altogether?

   d Luke downloads 355 minutes of music from the internet. By accident he deletes 186 minutes. How many minutes of music does he have left?

6 Copy and complete each of these addition pyramids.

a
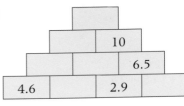

b
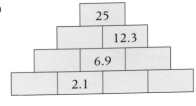

Each number is the sum of the two numbers beneath it.

This spread will show you how to:

● Use a range of mental and written methods for addition, subtraction, multiplication and division

Keywords

Addition
Decimals
Subtraction
Written method

When numbers are too difficult to add or subtract in your head, use a **written method**.
The standard written method for **addition** is based on partitioning.

Example

Hera the baby gorilla weighs 21.62 kg, and Horace her brother weighs 46.34 kg. Henna, the mother, weighs 186.7 kg.
What is the combined weight of the gorillas?

$21.62 + 46.34 + 186.7 \approx 20 + 50 + 190$ (rounding to the nearest 10)
$\approx 260 \text{ kg}$

You should always estimate the answer first.

Set out the calculation in columns, making sure you line up the decimal points.

	Hundreds	Tens	Units	•	tenths	hundredths
		2	1	•	6	2
		4	6	•	3	4
+	1	8	6	•	7	
	2	5	4	•	6	6

The combined weight = 254.66 kg.

There is an informal written method for **subtraction**.

Example

A crate is packed full of tins. The total mass of the tins and the crate is 72.6 kg. When the tins are removed the crate weighs 18.73 kg.
What is the mass of the tins?

Estimate: $72.6 - 18.73 \approx 73 - 19$ (rounding each number to the nearest 1)
$\approx 54 \text{ kg}$

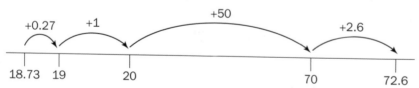

$72.6 \text{ kg} - 18.73 \text{ kg} = 0.27 + 1 + 50 + 2.6$
$= 53.87 \text{ kg}$

	Tens	Units	•	tenths	hundredths
		0	•	2	7
		1	•		
	5	0	•		
		2	•	6	
+	5	3	•	8	7

This is a standard method for subtraction:

$$^6\cancel{7}\,^1\cancel{2}\,^{15}\cancel{.}\cancel{6}\,^1\cancel{0}$$
$$-\ 1\ 8\ .\ 7\ 3$$
$$\overline{\ \ 5\ 3\ .\ 8\ 7}$$

Count up from 18.73 to 19.
Count up from 19 to 20.
Count up from 20 to 70.
Count up from 70 to 72.6.
Add together $0.27 + 1 + 50 + 2.6$.

1 Use a mental or written method to work out these calculations.

   a 23.4 + 13.4   **b** 24.6 + 53.7   **c** 19.7 + 7.4   **d** 27.8 + 14.3

2 Use a mental or written method to work out these calculations.

   a 9.6 − 3.4   **b** 16.7 − 9.6   **c** 16.3 − 7.8   **d** 61.7 − 33.8

3 Use a written method to work out these additions.

   a 4.32 + 6.4   **b** 16.32 + 3.4   **c** 4.5 + 13.61   **d** 73.2 + 68.79

4 Use a written method to work out these subtractions.

   a 16.3 − 8.25   **b** 12.6 − 7.87   **c** 67.3 − 28.56   **d** 47.38 − 28.7

5 Use a written method for each of these calculations.

   a 25.3 + 8.76   **b** 38.1 + 6.61   **c** 8.31 − 4.8   **d** 15.8 + 8.79

   e 25.46 − 7.48   **f** 47.39 − 18.5

6 Calculate these using a mental or written method.

   a 12.3 + 2.7 + 7.08   **b** 38.76 + 16.9 − 8.32

   c 61.3 + 14.85 + 7.02

7 Use a mental or written method to solve each of these problems.

   a Lindsey sells cheese. On Monday she sells 28.6 kg; on Tuesday she sells 33.38 kg. How much cheese has she sold?

   b Keir earns £298.17 a week. He pays £76.37 each week in tax. How much money does he have left after paying his tax?

   c Jess needs three pieces of wood to build a wooden frame. The lengths are 2.32 m, 1.8 m and 1.75 m. What is the total length of wood she will need to buy?

   d A box full of bottles weighs 34.6 kg. It is taken to the recycling centre. The bottles are thrown into the bottle bank. The box now weighs 3.87 kg. How much did the bottles weigh?

   e Lucce is making a Tuscan bean casserole for 8 people. Here is his recipe:

Kidney beans	1.6 kg
Red onions	0.375 kg
Celery	0.15 kg
French beans	0.2 kg
Tomatoes	1.2 kg

What is the total weight of the ingredients?

This spread will show you how to:

- Use a range of mental and written methods for addition, subtraction, multiplication and division

Keywords

Factor
Multiple
Mental method
Partitioning

To work out multiplications and divisions in your head, you can use **partitioning** to split the numbers into parts.

Example

Calculate **a** 8.2×11 **b** $368 \div 16$

a $11 = 10 + 1$

$$8.2 \times 11 = (8.2 \times 10) + (8.2 \times 1)$$
$$= 82 + 8.2$$
$$= 90.2$$

b $368 = 320 + 48$

$$368 \div 16 = (320 \div 16) + (48 \div 16)$$
$$= 20 + 3$$
$$= 23$$

You split one of the two numbers up to make the calculation easier.

You can re-write a number as a product of two of its **factors**.

Example

Calculate **a** 5.6×20 **b** $156 \div 6$

a $5.6 \times \mathbf{20} = 5.6 \times \mathbf{2} \times \mathbf{10}$

$$5.6 \times 2 = 11.2$$
$$11.2 \times 10 = 112$$
$$5.6 \times 20 = 112$$

b $156 \div \mathbf{6} = 156 \div \mathbf{2} \div \mathbf{3}$

$$156 \div 3 = 52$$
$$52 \div 2 = 26$$
$$156 \div 6 = 26$$

Here are some other methods you can use:

You can use compensation when the number you are multiplying by is nearly a multiple of 10.

$$14.2 \times 19 = (14.2 \times 20) - (14.2 \times 1)$$
$$= 284 - 14.2$$
$$= 269.8$$

You can double one of the numbers and halve the other.

$$12 \times 6.5 = 6 \times 13$$
$$= 78$$

You can double both of the numbers before you divide.

$$18 \div 1.5 = 36 \div 3$$
$$= 12$$

Example

Alan needs to stack 168 tins of peas. Each tray holds 12 tins of peas.
The 12 tins on each tray weighs 11 kg.
What is the weight of the tins Alan has to stack?

This problem can be broken down into two parts.

i Find the number of trays needed for 168 tins.

$$168 \div 12$$
$$168 \div 4 = 42$$
$$42 \div 3 = 14$$

Alan needs to stack 14 trays.

ii Find the total weight of the trays.

$$14 \times 11 \text{ kg} = (14 \times 10) + (14 \times 1)$$
$$= 140 + 14$$
$$= 154 \text{ kg}$$

The 168 tins weigh 154 kg.

Exercise N2.4

1 Calculate these.

   a 8×7　　**b** $72 \div 10$　　**c** 2×4.7　　**d** $480 \div 2$

   e 9×8　　**f** $6.75 \div 10$　　**g** $930 \div 2$　　**h** 7×9

2 Calculate each of these without using a calculator.

   a 4.6×100　　**b** $170 \div 100$　　**c** 12.7×10　　**d** $0.82 \div 100$

3 Use an appropriate **mental method** to calculate these.

   a 14×6　　**b** 14×9　　**c** $105 \div 5$　　**d** $78 \div 3$

   e 17×11　　**f** 31×9　　**g** $192 \div 6$　　**h** 29×6

   i 13×14　　**j** 29×21　　**k** 31×29　　**l** 15×99

4 Use the mental method of partitioning to calculate these. Show the method you have used.

   a 1.6×11　　**b** 21×8　　**c** 7.2×11　　**d** 31×2.8

   e 18×7　　**f** 12×6.4　　**g** $618 \div 3$　　**h** $316 \div 4$

5 Use the mental method of compensation to calculate each of these. Show the method you have used.

   a 17×9　　**b** 23×9　　**c** 2.3×11　　**d** 11×8.9

   e 4.2×11　　**f** 21×5.3　　**g** 12.7×9　　**h** 23.1×31

6 Use the mental method of factors to calculate each of these. Show the method you have used.

   a 4.3×20　　**b** $132 \div 6$　　**c** 142×4　　**d** 27×8

   e $192 \div 6$　　**f** 237×4　　**g** 3.2×30　　**h** $420 \div 15$

7 Use the mental method of halving and doubling (multiplication) or doubling (division) to calculate each of these. Show the method you have used.

   a 4×61　　**b** 16×2.25　　**c** 16×8　　**d** $36 \div 1.5$

   e $63 \div 4.5$　　**f** 3.4×4.5　　**g** 4.2×2.5　　**h** 2.44×5

8 Use an appropriate mental method to calculate each of these.

   a 22×2.1　　**b** 2.3×20　　**c** 13×1.4　　**d** 8×7.5

   e $7.5 \div 1.25$　　**f** 75×29　　**g** $4.5 \div 1.5$　　**h** $4.5 \div 0.15$

9 Use an appropriate mental method to solve each of these problems.

   a The average weight of a piglet is 7.5 kg. A pig has a litter of 12 piglets. What is the total weight of the 12 piglets?

   b Four friends win £124 on the lottery. They share their winnings equally. How much money does each friend receive?

This spread will show you how to:

- Understand and use simple divisibility tests
- Use approximation to estimate answers to problems

Keywords

Dividend
Divisor
Estimate
Grid method
Standard
  method
Whole number

You can use different written methods to multiply numbers together.

Example

Simone buys 16 packets of biscuits.
Each packet costs £1.28. How much does this cost in total?

Estimate:

$16 \times 1.28 \approx 20 \times 1$ (rounding 16 to the nearest 10 and 1.28 to the nearest whole number)
$\approx £20$

You rewrite the calculation 16×1.28 as $16 \times 128 \div 100$.

Grid method

×	100	20	8
10	$10 \times 100 = 1000$	$10 \times 20 = 200$	$10 \times 8 = 80$
6	$6 \times 100 = 600$	$6 \times 20 = 120$	$6 \times 8 = 48$

$16 \times 128 = 1000 + 200 + 80 + 600 + 120 + 48$
$= 2048$

Answer: Simone spends $16 \times £1.28 = 16 \times 128 \div 100$
$= 2048 \div 100$
$= £20.48$

Standard method

Write the calculation in columns:

```
                    128
                  × 16
        10 × 128   1280
         6 × 128  + 768
                  ──────
                   2048
```

Standard 'chunking' method

This method involves subtracting multiples of the **divisor** from the **dividend** until you cannot subtract any more.

Example

A box will hold 16 glasses. Howard needs to pack 752 glasses into boxes.
Calculate the number of boxes he will need.

Estimate: $752 \div 16 \approx 800 \div 20$ (rounding 752 up to the next multiple of 100
$= 40$ boxes and 16 to the next multiple of 10)

```
   16)752
     −640    16 × 40
      ────
      112
     −112    16 × 7
      ────
        0
```

$752 \div 16 = 47$

Howard will need 47 boxes.

1 Use an appropriate method of calculation to work out each of these.

   a 27×8 **b** 7×84 **c** 9×327 **d** 13×28

   e 26×28 **f** 25×35 **g** 14×115 **h** 24×162

   i 38×272 **j** 22×211 **k** 40×133 **l** 29×318

2 Use an appropriate method of calculation to work out each of these.
   Where appropriate leave your answer in remainder form.

   a $156 \div 6$ **b** $184 \div 8$ **c** $165 \div 5$ **d** $266 \div 7$

   e $333 \div 9$ **f** $544 \div 8$ **g** $125 \div 8$ **h** $325 \div 7$

3 Use an appropriate method of calculation to work out each of these.

   a 16×2.4 **b** 4.7×23 **c** 6.4×23 **d** 13×9.3

   e 48×3.2 **f** 7.3×89

4 Use an appropriate method of calculation to work out each of these.

   a 13×1.54 **b** 16×1.73 **c** 17×1.93 **d** 25×1.38

   e 87×1.63 **f** 38×1.62 **g** 34×2.45 **h** 54×9.48

5 Use an appropriate method of calculation to work out each of these.

   a 13.9×23 **b** 45×15.3 **c** 82×14.7 **d** 23.7×34

   e 46.1×73 **f** 38.7×43

6 **a** Skye buys 18 packets of rice. Each packet costs £1.17. How much
   does this cost in total?

   b 1 litre of petrol costs 81.9 pence. On a journey Kai uses 45 litres of
   petrol. What is the total cost of the petrol for the journey?

   c Laura buys 27 CDs. Each CD costs £7.49. How much is this in
   total?

   d Kieron runs 32 laps of a track. Each lap takes him 73.2 seconds.
   What is his total time to run 32 laps?

   e Kimberley buys 48 troll dolls. Each doll costs £1.67. What is the
   total cost of the troll dolls?

7 Use an appropriate method of calculation to work out each of these.

   a $192 \div 16$ **b** $234 \div 13$ **c** $342 \div 18$ **d** $483 \div 21$

   e $899 \div 31$ **f** $987 \div 47$

8 Use an appropriate method of calculation to work out each of these.

   a $26.6 \div 7$ **b** $35.4 \div 6$ **c** $67.2 \div 8$ **d** $74.4 \div 6$

   e $118.8 \div 9$ **f** $123.2 \div 8$ **g** $109.6 \div 8$ **h** $248.4 \div 9$

Exam review

Key objectives

- Round to a given number of significant figures
- Estimate answers to problems involving decimals
- Develop a range of strategies for mental calculation
- Understand where to position the decimal point
- Recognise limitations on the accuracy of data and measurements

1 Work these out, rounding your answers correct to two significant figures.

   a 5.635 − 2.91   **b** 9.5 + 10.56

   c 13.976 − 2.5   **d** 23.47 + 5.023   (4)

2 Nick takes 26 boxes out of his van.
The weight of each box is 32.9 kg.
Work out the **total** weight of the 26 boxes.   (3)

(Edexcel Ltd., 2004)

A2

This unit will show you how to

- Set up simple equations from written problems
- Solve simple equations using inverse operations
- Solve two-step problems using inverse operations
- Solve simple equations using the balance method
- Solve simple one-sided and two-sided inequalities, representing the solution on a number line

Before you start ...

You should be able to answer these questions.

Review

1 Copy and complete.

Unit N1

a $4 + \square = 12$ **b** $\square - 5 = 6$

c $18 - \square = 11$ **d** $13 + \square = 19$

2 Copy and complete.

Unit N1

a $3 \times \square = 21$ **b** $\square \times 4 = 24$

c $\square \div 3 = 5$ **d** $14 \div \square = 7$

3 Insert > or < to make these statements true.

Key stage 3

a $2 \square 5$ **b** $8 \square 3$

c $42 \square 40$ **d** $12 \square 15$

4 Work out the perimeter of this rectangle.

Unit S1

5 cm

3 cm 3 cm

5 cm

5 Work out.

Unit N1

a $4x \div 4$ **b** $3m \div 3$

c $6n \div 2$ **d** $8p \div 4$

Solving equations using function machines

This spread will show you how to:

Keywords

Equation
Function machine
Inverse operation

- Set up simple equations from written problems
- Solve simple equations using inverse operations

You can solve simple 'think of a number' problems mentally.

I think of a number,
I add 7 and my answer is 27.
What is my number?

In your head, you subtract the 7 that was added.

You can write the problem as an **equation**, using x for the unknown number: $x + 7 = 27$

You can solve the equation to find x, using a **function machine**.

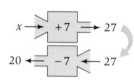

$$x \rightarrow +7 \rightarrow 27$$
$$20 \leftarrow -7 \leftarrow 27$$

−7 'undoes' the +7.
−7 is the **inverse operation** of +7.

- To solve an equation you can
  - write it as a function machine
  - work backwards through the function machine, using the inverse operation.

Example

Complete these function machines.

a $\quad 4 \rightarrow \boxed{\times 7} \rightarrow \blacksquare$

b $\quad 16 \rightarrow \boxed{\div \blacksquare} \rightarrow 2$

c $\quad \blacksquare \rightarrow \boxed{-5} \rightarrow 9$

a $\quad 4 \rightarrow \boxed{\times 7} \rightarrow 28$

b $\quad 16 \rightarrow \boxed{\div 8} \rightarrow 2$

c $\quad 14 \rightarrow \boxed{-5} \rightarrow 9$

In part **c**, work backwards using the inverse:
$9 + 5 = 14$

You can write equations with division and multiplication using function machines.

Example

Write each equation as a function machine.
Then solve it using inverse operations.

a $\quad y - 6 = 15$ 　　　 b $\quad 4x = 12$ 　　　 c $\quad \dfrac{z}{3} = 5$

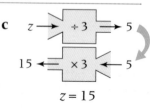

a $\quad y \rightarrow \boxed{-6} \rightarrow 15$
$\quad 21 \leftarrow \boxed{+6} \leftarrow 15$
$\quad y = 21$
Check: $21 - 6 = 15$ ✓

b $\quad x \rightarrow \boxed{\times 4} \rightarrow 12$
$\quad 3 \leftarrow \boxed{\div 4} \leftarrow 12$
$\quad x = 3$
Check: $3 \times 4 = 12$ ✓

c $\quad z \rightarrow \boxed{\div 3} \rightarrow 5$
$\quad 15 \leftarrow \boxed{\times 3} \leftarrow 5$
$\quad z = 15$
Check: $15 \div 3 = 5$ ✓

$\dfrac{z}{3}$ means $z \div 3$.

1 For each 'think of a number' problem

  i find the number

  ii explain how you worked out the answer.

  a I double a number: the answer is 28.

  b I add 7 to a number: the answer is 33.

  c I subtract 12 from a number: the answer is 9.

  d I divide a number by 6: the answer is 7.

2 Copy and complete these function machines.

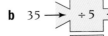

3 Draw the inverse function machine for each machine in question **2**.

4 Write each equation as a function machine.
Then solve it using inverse operations.

  a $a + 9 = 23$ **b** $b - 8 = 17$ **c** $c + 18 = 34$

  d $d - 15 = 41$ **e** $3x = 24$ **f** $\dfrac{f}{5} = 8$

  g $6g = 48$ **h** $\dfrac{h}{7} = 28$ **i** $i - 17 = 14$

  j $j + 28 = 53$ **k** $5k = 95$ **l** $\dfrac{m}{8} = 7$

5 Solve these equations.

  a $c + 13 = 21$ **b** $d - 6 = 35$ **c** $7f = 63$

  d $\dfrac{g}{4} = 6$ **e** $5h = 100$ **f** $\dfrac{i}{7} = 6$

  g $6j = 54$ **h** $k - 7 = 15$ **i** $l + 9 = 24$

  j $8m = 48$ **k** $\dfrac{n}{4} = 12$ **l** $8q = 56$

  m $4r = 128$ **n** $\dfrac{u}{18} = 4$

> Use x for the
> unknown number.

6 Write each 'think of a number' problem as an equation.
Solve the equation to find the number.

  a I think of a number and subtract 12. The answer is 11.

  b I think of a number and divide by 5. The answer is 8.

Solving two-step equations

This spread will show you how to:
- Solve simple equations using inverse operations
- Solve two-step problems using inverse operations

Keywords
Inverse
  operations
Two-step
  problem

This 'think of a number' problem has two steps:

I think of a number, multiply by 4 and add 5. The answer is 13.

Step 1: add 4
Step 2: multiply by 5

For a **two-step problem**, use two function machines:

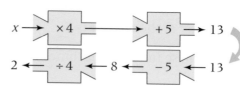

You can write this two-step problem as an equation:

$x \times 4 + 5 = 13$ or $4x + 5 = 13$

In algebra:
- leave out the $\times$
- write numbers before letters.

Example

Use inverse function machines to work out the value of n.

a $n \rightarrow \boxed{\times 3} \rightarrow \boxed{-9} \rightarrow 12$

b $n \rightarrow \boxed{\div 4} \rightarrow \boxed{+5} \rightarrow 6$

a $n \rightarrow \boxed{\times 3} \rightarrow \boxed{-9} \rightarrow 12$
$7 \leftarrow \boxed{\div 3} \leftarrow \boxed{+9} \leftarrow 12$

b $n \rightarrow \boxed{\div 4} \rightarrow \boxed{+5} \rightarrow 6$
$4 \leftarrow \boxed{\times 4} \leftarrow \boxed{-5} \leftarrow 6$

In part **a** the inverse functions are:
$12 + \mathbf{9} = 21$
$21 \div \mathbf{3} = 7$

Example

Copy and complete the table for this two-step function.

	× 6	− 2
1		
2		
x		
		46

	× 6	− 2
1	6	4
2	12	10
x	6x	6x − 2
8	48	46

You can solve an equation using **inverse operations**.

Example

Solve these equations.

a $3m + 5 = 17$ **b** $\dfrac{n}{2} - 4 = 16$

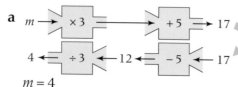

a $m \rightarrow \boxed{\times 3} \rightarrow \boxed{+5} \rightarrow 17$
$4 \leftarrow \boxed{\div 3} \leftarrow 12 \leftarrow \boxed{-5} \leftarrow 17$

$m = 4$
Check: $3 \times 4 + 5 = 12 + 5 = 17$ ✓

b $n \rightarrow \boxed{\div 2} \rightarrow \boxed{-4} \rightarrow 16$
$40 \leftarrow \boxed{\times 2} \leftarrow \boxed{+4} \leftarrow 16$

$n = 40$
Check: $40 \div 2 - 4 = 20 - 4 = 16$ ✓

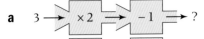

1 Copy and complete these two-step function machines.

a $3 \rightarrow \boxed{\times 2} \rightarrow \boxed{-1} \rightarrow ?$ **b** $6 \rightarrow \boxed{\times 4} \rightarrow \boxed{+8} \rightarrow ?$

c $18 \rightarrow \boxed{\div 3} \rightarrow \boxed{+4} \rightarrow ?$ **d** $28 \rightarrow \boxed{\div 4} \rightarrow \boxed{-6} \rightarrow ?$

e $12 \rightarrow \boxed{\div 2} \rightarrow \boxed{} \rightarrow 11$ **f** $5 \rightarrow \boxed{} \rightarrow \boxed{-3} \rightarrow 22$

2 Use inverse function machines to solve each of these.

a $a \rightarrow \boxed{\times 4} \rightarrow \boxed{-5} \rightarrow 19$ **b** $b \rightarrow \boxed{\times 3} \rightarrow \boxed{+8} \rightarrow 35$

c $e \rightarrow \boxed{\div 4} \rightarrow \boxed{-5} \rightarrow 2$ **d** $f \rightarrow \boxed{\div 3} \rightarrow \boxed{+11} \rightarrow 17$

e $g \rightarrow \boxed{\div 5} \rightarrow \boxed{+3} \rightarrow 9$ **f** $h \rightarrow \boxed{\div 8} \rightarrow \boxed{-3} \rightarrow -1$

3 Copy and complete the tables for these two-step functions.

a

	×4	+3
1		
2		
x		
		43

b

	÷3	−1
12		
9		
x		
		7

c

	×5	−3
1		
2		
x		
		52

4 Solve these equations.

a $3a - 5 = 25$ **b** $2b + 9 = 27$ **c** $6e + 11 = 23$ **d** $\dfrac{f}{5} + 3 = 6$

e $\dfrac{g}{7} - 8 = 2$ **f** $\dfrac{i}{6} + 4 = 9$ **g** $\dfrac{j}{5} - 8 = 4$ **h** $3k - 20 = -5$

i $8m - 5 = 7$ **j** $3p - 8 = -14$

5 Write these functions as equations.

a $x \rightarrow \boxed{\times 3} \rightarrow \boxed{-1} \rightarrow 11$ **b** $n \rightarrow \boxed{\times 4} \rightarrow \boxed{+7} \rightarrow 27$

c $q \rightarrow \boxed{\times 5} \rightarrow \boxed{+3} \rightarrow 33$ **d** $r \rightarrow \boxed{\div 3} \rightarrow \boxed{+15} \rightarrow 22$

6 For each of these 'think of a number' problems

i write an equation   **ii** solve your equation to find the number.

a I double a number and add 7. The answer is 15.

b I multiply a number by 4 and subtract 5. The answer is 13.

c I divide a number by 5 and add 3. The answer is 11.

This spread will show you how to:

- Solve simple equations using the balance method

Keywords

Inverse
operation

You can solve simple equations using the balance method.
You change both sides in the same way.

$$5x + 12 = 32$$
$$5x + 12 - 12 = 32 - 12$$
$$5x = 20$$
$$5x \div 5 = 20 \div 5$$
$$x = 4$$

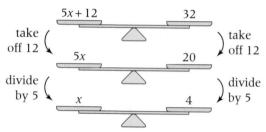

take off 12 ⟵ ⟶ take off 12

Subtract 12 from both sides.

divide by 5 ⟵ ⟶ divide by 5

Divide both sides by 5.

You can use **inverse operations** to transform the equation.

$$3x - 10 = 11$$
$$3x - 10 + 10 = 11 + 10$$
$$3x = 21$$
$$3x \div 3 = 21 \div 3$$
$$x = 7$$

+10 is the inverse of −10.

÷3 is the inverse of ×3.

Example

Solve these equations using the balance method.

a $\dfrac{t}{3} - 5 = -3$

b $18 - 4m = 6$

a $\dfrac{t}{3} - 5 = -3$

$\dfrac{t}{3} - 5 + 5 = -3 + 5$

$\dfrac{t}{3} = 2$

$\dfrac{t}{3} \times 3 = 2 \times 3$

$t = 6$

b $18 - 4m = 6$

$18 - 4m + 4m = 6 + 4m$

$18 = 6 + 4m$

$18 - 6 = 6 - 6 + 4m$

$12 = 4m$

$3 = m$

$m = 3$

To avoid having −4m, add 4m to both sides of the equation.

Example

The perimeter of this rectangle is 24 cm.

a Write an equation for the perimeter of the rectangle.
b Hence find x, the length of the rectangle.

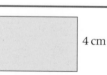

4 cm

x cm

a Perimeter $= 4 + x + 4 + x = 24$
$2x + 8 = 24$

b $2x + 8 = 24$
$2x = 16$ Subtract 8 from both sides.
$x = 8$ cm

1 Solve these equations using the balance method.

  a $3x + 9 = 24$ **b** $5 + 7x = 40$ **c** $4x - 8 = 24$ **d** $5x - 17 = 13$

  e $2x + 7 = 18$ **f** $\dfrac{x}{10} + 6 = 11$ **g** $\dfrac{y}{3} - 2 = 4$ **h** $\dfrac{z}{4} - 4 = 60$

  i $15 - 4y = 3$ **j** $22 - 6p = 10$

2 Solve these equations using the method you prefer.

  a $5m - 6 = 29$ **b** $18 + 2p = 4$ **c** $10 - 3n = 4$ **d** $14 = 6q - 16$

  e $7 = 29 + 2r$ **f** $4k - 36 = -12$ **g** $-11 = 6m - 41$ **h** $\dfrac{a}{2} + 2 = 6$

3 One of these equations has a different solution to the other two. Which is it?

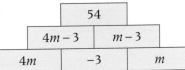

$\dfrac{m}{2} + 12 = 16$ $6p + 12 = 16$ $\dfrac{n}{4} + 11 = 13$

4 In each wall, add two bricks to find the number on the brick above. Write and solve equations to find the unknown letter in each wall.

  a

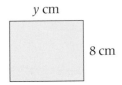

  b

54

  5 The perimeter of this rectangle is 36 cm.

y cm

8 cm

  a Write an equation for the perimeter in terms of y.

  b Solve your equation to find y, the width of the rectangle.

6 Find the missing side length for each shape.

  a

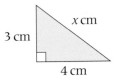

x cm

3 cm

4 cm

Perimeter = 12 cm

  b

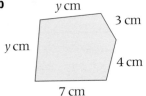

y cm

3 cm

y cm

4 cm

7 cm

Perimeter = 26 cm

  c

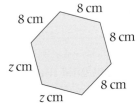

8 cm

8 cm

8 cm

z cm

z cm

8 cm

Perimeter = 48 cm

What do you notice about shape **c**?

This spread will show you how to:

- Solve simple one-sided and two-sided inequalities, representing the solution on a number line

Keywords
Greater than
Inequality
Less than
Solution set

- In an **equation**, the left-hand side equals the right-hand side.
  - In an **inequality**, the left-hand and right-hand sides are not necessarily equal.
  - An inequality usually has a range of values.

You use one of these signs to show the relationship between the two sides of an inequality:

<	less than	>	greater than
⩽	less than or equal to	⩾	greater than or equal to

You can show inequalities on a number line.

$x < 2$	x is less than 2	
$x > 2$	x is greater than 2	
$y \leqslant 4$	y is less than or equal to 4	
$y \geqslant 4$	y is greater than or equal to 4	

The open circle shows that 2 is not included.

The filled-in circle shows that 4 is included.

Example

a Show the inequality $x > -1$ on a number line.
b If $x < 4$, what can you say about $2x$?

a

$x > -1$

b If $x < 4$, then $2x$ must be less than $2 \times 4 = 8$.
So $2x < 8$.

Values greater than −1 are in the **solution set**.

Inequalities can have more than one term, for example $3x + 4 < 19$.
You can solve an inequality to find a set of values for x.
You can use the balance method, as for solving an equation, by treating the inequality sign like an equals sign.

Example

a Solve the inequality $3x + 4 < 19$
b Show the solution set on a number line.

a Using the balance method:
$$3x + 4 < 19$$
$$3x + 4 - 4 < 19 - 4$$
$$3x < 15$$
$$x < 5$$

b

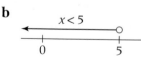

$x < 5$

The solution set is $x < 5$.

1 Show these inequalities on a number line.

a $x < 1$ **b** $x \geqslant 1$ **c** $x \geqslant 5$ **d** $x < -2$

e $x < 1.5$ **f** $x > -4$ **g** $x \leqslant 3$ **h** $x \leqslant -1.5$

2 **a** If $x > 5$, what can you say about   **i** $2x$ **ii** $4x$?

    b If $y \leqslant 6$, write an inequality for   **i** $3y$ **ii** $5y$.

    c If $x \geqslant -4$, write an inequality for $5x$.

    d If $m < -3$, write an inequality for $6m$.

3 Solve these inequalities and show the solution sets on number lines.

    a $2x \leqslant 4$ **b** $2x < 10$ **c** $3x > -6$ **d** $4x \geqslant -16$

4 Copy and complete these.

    a If $3x + 2 > 11$ then $3x > \square$ and $x > \square$

    b If $7x - 4 > 31$ then $7x > \square$ and $x > \square$

    c If $2x + 9 \leqslant 11$ then $2x \leqslant \square$ and $x \leqslant \square$

    d If $5x - 3 \geqslant 12$ then $5x \geqslant \square$ and $x \geqslant \square$

5 Solve each of these inequalities.
Show each solution on a number line.

    a $x + 7 \leqslant 12$ **b** $x - 2 \geqslant 4$ **c** $3x + 5 \geqslant 11$ **d** $2x - 5 < 3$

    e $5x + 1 \geqslant -4$ **f** $6x - 2 \leqslant 16$ **g** $3x + 2 > 11$ **h** $2x - 9 \leqslant -5$

6 Solve these inequalities.

    a $5x - 4 \geqslant 11$ **b** $4x + 7 > 15$ **c** $3x + 5 \geqslant 5$ **d** $4x + 7 > 3$

    e $5x + 6 \geqslant -4$ **f** $3x - 8 \leqslant 4$ **g** $4x + 20 \geqslant 10$ **h** $2x + 23 < 8$

7 Match each inequality to a number line.

a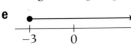
(number line: 0 to 3, filled dot at 3, arrow left)

i $x < -3$

b
(number line: −2, 0, open circle at −2, arrow right)

ii $x \leqslant 3$

c
(number line: −8, −4, 0, open circle at −4, arrow left)

iii $x - 1 \leqslant -3$

d
(number line: −8, −3, 0, open circle at −3, arrow left)

iv $x \geqslant -3$

e
(number line: −3, 0, filled dot at −3, arrow right)

v $x - 1 > -3$

f
(number line: −6, −2, 0, filled dot at −2, arrow left)

vi $x + 2 < -2$

This spread will show you how to:

- Solve simple one-sided and two-sided inequalities, representing the solution on a number line

Keywords

Greater than
Inequality
Integer
Less than
Solution set

You can read inequalities in two directions.

If $x > 5$, then $5 < x$ If $y \leqslant -2$, then $-2 \geqslant y$

You can use two-sided inequalities to show upper and lower limits.

$2 < x < 5$ means that x is greater than 2 and less than 5.

On a number line:

$x > 2$ and $x < 5$.

You can combine two inequalities to show a range of values:

$y > 3$ and $y < 10$
combine to give $3 < y < 10$

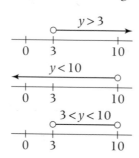

Example

Split each two-sided inequality into two single inequalities.

a $-3 < x \leqslant 1$ **b** $8 > y \geqslant 2$

---

a $x > -3$, $x \leqslant 1$ **b** $y < 8$, $y \geqslant 2$

- You can solve two-sided inequalities to find the solution set.
  - You can give the **integer** values in the solution set.

An integer is a whole number such as -1, 4, 10.

Example

If $-4 < 2n \leqslant 6$
     n is an integer.

a   Show all the possible values of n on a number line.
b   Write all the possible values of n.

---

a $-4 < 2n$, so $2n > -4$ $2n \leqslant 6$
           $n > -2$ $n \leqslant 3$

Divide both sides by 2 to get n on its own.

The solution is $-2 < n \leqslant 3$:

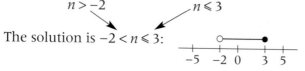

-2 is not included.
3 is included.

b   The possible integer values of n are -1, 0, 1, 2, 3.

1 If $7 < x$ (7 is less than x) then you can say x is greater than 7 or $x > 7$.
Write each of these in another way.

a $5 > x$ **b** $6 \leqslant y$ **c** $4 \geqslant y$ **d** $9 < r$

e $15 \geqslant w$ **f** $2 < s$ **g** $-12 > u$ **h** $-4 \leqslant v$

2 Split each two-sided inequality into two single inequalities.

a $1 < x < 5$ **b** $-1 < x < -5$ **c** $-2 < x < 4$
d $-6 \leqslant x \leqslant -1$ **e** $2 < x < 7$ **f** $2 \geqslant x \geqslant -1$

3 Write the inequalities shown by these number lines.

a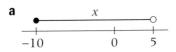

b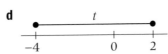

c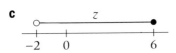

d

4 Show these inequalities on number lines like this.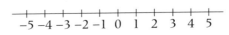

a $-3 \leqslant x < 2$ **b** $4 \geqslant n > -1$ **c** $1 < y \leqslant 3$ **d** $-4 \leqslant m < 0$

5 For each of the inequalities in question 4, list the integer values.

6 If x can take the possible integer values $-1, 0, 1, 2, 3$, which of these could be true?

a $x > -2$ **b** $-1 \leqslant x \leqslant 3$ **c** $-2 < x < 4$

d $-1 \leqslant x < 3$ **e** $-2 < x \leqslant 3$

7 n is an integer.

$-4 \leqslant n < 5$

a Show all the possible values of n on a number line.

b Write all the possible values of n.

> Using a number line may be helpful.

8 $2 \leqslant 2x < 10$
x is an integer.
Write all the possible values of x.

9 In these inequalities, y is an integer.
For each inequality, write all the possible values of y.

a $-6 < 2y \leqslant 4$

b $-3 \leqslant 3y < 15$

c $3 < 2y \leqslant 10$

Key objectives

- Set up simple equations
- Solve simple equations by using inverse operations or by transforming both sides in the same way
- Solve simple linear unequalities in one variable, and represent the solution set on a number line

1 a Solve the inequality:

$$3x - 2 \leqslant 5x + 4.$$ (2)

b Represent the solution set of this inequality on a number line:

$$-6 < 2x \leqslant 4$$ (2)

2 a Solve:

$$20y - 16 = 18y - 9$$ (3)

b Solve:

$$\frac{40 - x}{3} = 4 + x$$ (3)

(Edexcel Ltd., 2004)

This unit will show you how to

- Recognise the difference between primary and secondary data
- Design and use data-collection sheets for discrete and grouped data
- Understand and use frequency tables
- Collect primary and secondary data using a variety of methods
- Use efficient methods of random sampling
- Discuss how data relates to a problem, identifying and minimising possible sources of bias
- Design and use two-way tables

Before you start ...

You should be able to answer these questions.

1 Put these numbers in order of size, smallest first.

   a 56, 47, 48, 55, 65, 44, 61, 59

   b 1.7, 2.5, 0.8, 2.1, 1.5, 0.5

   c 31.2, 32.1, 23.1, 13.2, 13.1, 21.3

2 Calculate.

   a 36 + 45

   b 82 + 97

   c 36 + 45 + 24

   d 138 + 67

   e 325 + 116

   f 91 − 17

   g 148 − 13

   h 256 − 79

   i 345 − 126

   j 125 − 84

3 This table shows the average sunrise and sunset times for six months of the year.

	Sunrise	Sunset
January	08.22	17.00
March	07.25	18.17
May	07.09	22.03
July	06.20	23.04
September	07.48	20.27
November	08.01	17.08

At what average time does the sun

   a rise in September

   b set in March?

Review

Unit N1

Key stage 3

Unit N1

This spread will show you how to:

- Recognise the difference between primary and secondary data
- Design and use data-collection sheets for discrete and grouped data
- Understand and use frequency tables

Keywords

Data
Data-collection
  sheet
Frequency table
Primary data
Secondary data
Tally chart

Before this headline could be written, information, or **data**, was collected.

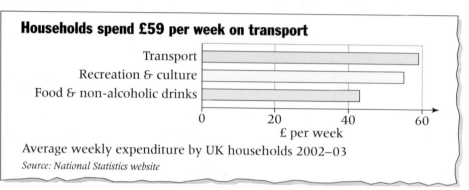

Households spend £59 per week on transport

Average weekly expenditure by UK households 2002–03
Source: National Statistics website

- **Primary data** is data you collect yourself.
  You count the scores when rolling a dice.

- **Secondary data** is data someone else has already collected.
  This includes information from newspapers or the internet.

- **You can collect data using a data-collection sheet.**
  This one is a **tally chart**.

Coin face	Tally	Frequency
Head	⨫ ⨫ III	13
Tail	⨫ ⨫ II	12

⨫ = 5

The coin was spun
13 + 12 = 25 times.

Data can also be shown using a **frequency table**.

Example

The number of televisions in each house in my street is shown in the frequency table.

Number of TVs	Number of houses
0	1
1	5
2	12
3	9
4	1

a Calculate the number of houses in my street.

b Calculate the total number of televisions in my street.

The numbers in the table are

0, 1, 1, 1, 1, 1, 2, 2, 2, 2, 2, 2, 2, 2,
2, 2, 2, 2, 3, 3, 3, 3, 3, 3, 3, 3, 3, 4

a 1 + 5 + 12 + 9 + 1 = 28 houses

b 0 + 5 + 24 + 27 + 4 = 60 televisions

TVs	Houses	TVs × Houses
0	1	0 × 1 = 0
1	5	1 × 5 = 5
2	12	2 × 12 = 24
3	9	3 × 9 = 27
4	1	4 × 1 = 4

Exercise D1.1

1 **a** Copy and complete the tally chart to find the frequency of the vowels a, e, i, o, u in this sentence.

  b Which vowel occurs the most often?

  c Which vowel occurs the least often?

  d Calculate the total number of vowels in the sentence.

  e Find a paragraph of writing in a newspaper and complete a similar tally chart.

Vowel	Tally	Frequency
a		
e		
i		
o		
u		

2 Rainfall, measured in millimetres, is recorded daily for the month of April.

```
4 2 1 0 0 1 2 2 3 5
7 8 5 3 3 2 0 0 0 1
2 3 2 4 6 7 8 8 1 2
```

  a Copy and complete the tally chart to show this information.

  b State the number of completely dry days in April.

  c Calculate the total amount of rain to fall throughout April. State the units of your answer.

Rainfall (mm)	Tally	Number of days
0		
1		
2		
3		
4		
5		
6		
7		
8		

3 Nails can be bought in bags.
There are approximately 20 nails in each bag.
The numbers of nails in 40 bags are recorded.

```
19  20  19  21  20  20  20  21
22  19  19  19  21  20  20  21
19  21  21  22  20  19  20  21
20  20  21  21  20  20  22  21
19  19  20  20  21  20  20  20
```

NAILS

Approximately 20 nails in this bag

  a Copy and complete the tally chart to show this information.

  b Calculate the total number of nails in all 40 bags.

Number of nails	Tally	Number of bags
19		
20		
21		
22		

4 Sophie did a survey to find the number of CDs owned by the students in her class. The results are shown in the frequency table.

  a Calculate the number of students in Sophie's class.

  b Calculate the total number of CDs owned by the whole class.

Number of CDs	Number of students
0	1
1	8
2	6
3	8
4	2
5	3

Observation, controlled experiment and sampling

This spread will show you how to:

- Collect primary and secondary data using a variety of methods
- Use efficient methods of random sampling
- Discuss how data relates to a problem, identifying and minimising possible sources of bias

Keywords

Biased
Data logging
Observation
Random sample

- You can collect data by **observation**.

  To find the average daily rainfall, you would have to measure the rainfall every day for a period of time.

- You can collect data by **controlled experiment**.

  To see if a Head or a Tail occurs more often, you would have to spin a coin a number of times.

- You can collect data by **data logging**.

  For example, your heart rate can be measured when exercising.

You will need a **data-collection sheet**, whichever method you use.

> An observation usually involves watching.

> An experiment usually involves setting up a test.

> Data is usually collected automatically when data logging.

Example

Design a suitable data-collection sheet to find the number of cars in households in your class.

Covers all possibilities {

Number of cars	Tally	Frequency
0		
1		
2		
3		
4 or more		

Sometimes it is impossible to collect data from all the population and so a **random sample** is used.

- In a random sample, each person or item must be equally likely to be chosen.

The sample must not be **biased**.
The sample is biased if each person or item is not equally likely to be chosen.

Example

Describe a method to choose a random sample of 30 students for a year group of 120 students.

- Number each student from 1 to 120.
- Put a different number on 120 pieces of paper.
- Place the pieces of paper in a bag.
- Pick out 30 numbers from the bag.

> Taking every 4th student from an alphabetical or form list is biased. Why is this so?

1 Decide whether these data collections are an observation, a controlled experiment, or data logging.

   a Spinning a spinner

   b The types of drink bought from a vending machine at break

   c Choosing a colour from a given set of colours

   d Automatically measuring the temperature of ice as it is heated

   e Measuring the 'bounce' of different rubber balls dropped from the same height

   f The make of vehicles passing the school gates

   g The number of passes a player makes during a game

   h Automatically measuring the number of vehicles travelling on a road

   i The usage of the slide, the swing and the roundabout in a playground

   j Automatically measuring pulse rate on a jogging machine.

A spinner is an instrument for creating random outcomes, usually in probability experiments.

2 The number of occupants in passing cars are counted.
The results are

```
1  2  1  4  3  1  2  1  5  4
1  1  1  2  1  3  1  4  1  1
1  2  1  1  1  2  1  1  4  2
2  2  1  2  1  3  2  1  2  1
```

   a Is this data collection an observation, a controlled experiment or data logging?

   b Construct a data-collection sheet to show this data.

   c Calculate the total number of cars that passed.

   d Calculate the total number of occupants of the cars that passed.

DID YOU KNOW?

In 2008 the UK's first carpool lane will open on the M1. Lone drivers will be banned, encouraging drivers to share their cars and ease congestion.

3 A dice, numbered 1 to 6, is rolled and the scores recorded.

   a Is this data collection an observation, a controlled experiment or data logging?

   b Construct a suitable data-collection sheet.
The scores are

```
1  5  6  2  1  4  2  1  2  5  6  1  3  2  2
2  1  2  1  2  2  1  6  5  4  3  2  1  1  1
5  5  6  1  2  2  1  4  3  3  2  2  1  4  6
```

   c Complete your data-collection sheet with the data.

   d Which score occurred the most often?

   e Calculate the total number of rolls of the dice.

   f Do you think the dice is biased? Explain your answer.

   g How could you improve the reliability of your answer?

Surveys and questionnaires

This spread will show you how to:

- Collect primary and secondary data using a variety of methods

Keywords

Data-collection
  sheet
Hypothesis
Questionnaire
Survey

Surveys are used to find people's opinions or to test a **hypothesis**.

- You can collect data by using a survey with
  - a **data-collection sheet**
  - a **questionnaire**.

This data-collection sheet allows you to ask one question and collects all the data on one sheet.

A hypothesis is a predictive statement, for example 'boys are taller than girls'.

Do you smoke?	Tally	Frequency
Yes	ЖЖ ЖЖ I	
No	ЖЖ	

A questionnaire gives you more data, but you need one questionnaire for each person in your survey.

You must be careful what questions you ask in a survey.

Male ☐   Female ☐
Age group: Under 20 ☐
             20 or over ☐
Do you smoke? Yes ☐
                No ☐

Never ask a leading question, such as: The speed of cars today, it's very bad, isn't it?	• Avoid giving your opinion. What do you think of the speed of cars today? Too slow ☐ About right ☐ Too fast ☐
Never ask a vague question, such as: Do you eat cereal?	• Ask for factual responses. Did you eat cereal for breakfast today?
Never ask a question that gives too many responses, such as: What do you like to eat?	• Limit the choice of responses. Meat ☐ Fish ☐ Vegetables ☐
Never ask a complicated, wordy question.	• Ask simple, straightforward questions.
Don't forget to allow for all possible responses.	• Use 'Don't know' or 'Other'.
Never use 'occasionally', 'regularly' or 'sometimes' as they mean different things to different people.	• Ask for numerical responses. 1–10 ☐ 11–20 ☐ 21–30 ☐

Example

Give two reasons why the response section of this questionnaire is unsatisfactory.

How much money are you carrying?
£0.01–£1 ☐   £1–£2 ☐   Over £2 ☐

- No response is possible for £0.
- £1 is in two categories.

1 Lauren wants to find out how often the students in her class eat 'Take-away' food.

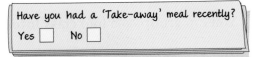

Which 'Take-away' meals do you like?

a One of the questions in her questionnaire is shown. Write one criticism of this question.

b Another question is shown. Write one criticism of this question.

Have you had a 'Take-away' meal recently?

Yes ☐   No ☐

2 **a** Devise a question that could be used to give this frequency table.

b Calculate the number of people that completed this survey.

Fruit	Number of people
Apple	43
Banana	35
Pear	13
Other	9

3 Ross intends to survey shoppers about their shopping habits.

a One of the questions in his questionnaire is shown. Write two criticisms of the response section.

How old are you?

Under 20 ☐   20–30 ☐   30–40 ☐

b Another question is shown. Write one criticism of the question and one criticism of the response section.

Do you shop often?

Seldom ☐   Rarely ☐   Sometimes ☐

c Ross is going to use the questionnaire outside one shop. Write one criticism of his plan.

d Rewrite the questions in parts **a** and **b**.

4 **a** Devise a question that could produce this data-collection sheet.

b Calculate the total number of people that completed the survey.

c Write one criticism of the choice of categories for the channel.

Channel	Tally	Frequency
BBC1	||||| ||	7
BBC2	|||	3
ITV	|||||		6
Channel 4	||	2
Five			1
Other	||||| |||||		11

5 One question in a questionnaire about reading habits is 'Do you read a newspaper regularly?'

a Write one criticism of this question.

b Rewrite the question, including a response section.

c Another question is:

Write two criticisms of the response section.

When was the last time you bought a book?

1 year ago ☐   2 years ago ☐   3 or more years ago ☐

Grouped data

This spread will show you how to:

- Design and use data-collection sheets for discrete and grouped data

Keywords

Class intervals
Continuous
Discrete
Group
Grouped
  frequency table

Some surveys produce data with many different values.

- You can **group** data into **class intervals** to avoid too many categories.

Example

The exam marks of class 10A are shown:

35	47	63	25	31	8	19	55	47	14
24	36	56	61	15	43	22	50	66	10
36	45	18	20	53	31	40	60	44	47

Complete the **grouped frequency table**.

Mark	Tally	Frequency
1–20		
21–40		
41–60		
61–80		

➡

Mark	Tally	Frequency
1–20	JHT II	7
21–40	JHT IIII	9
41–60	JHT JHT I	11
61–80	III	3

JHT = 5

Check that the frequencies add to 30.

- **Discrete** data can only take exact values (usually collected by counting), for example the number of students in each class in a school.

- **Continuous** data can take any value (collected by measuring), for example the heights of the students in your class.
  Continuous data cannot be measured exactly.

- You can write class intervals for discrete data like this:

People
1–10
11–20
21–30

11–20 means between 11 and 20 including 11 and 20.

- You can write class intervals for continuous data like this:

Weight (w)
$50 \leqslant w < 55$
$55 \leqslant w < 60$
$60 \leqslant w < 65$

The first interval is between 50 and 55, including 50 but not including 55.

1 Decide whether this data is discrete or continuous.

a The number of taxis waiting at a station   **b** The number of drinks in a machine

c The heights of people   **d** The number of magazines in a shop

e The weights of animals   **f** The number of people in an office

g The handspans of people   **h** The speed of cars

i Dress sizes   **j** Shoe sizes.

2 a Copy and complete the frequency table using these test marks.

Test mark	Tally	Frequency
1–5		
6–10		
11–15		
16–20		
21–25		

```
 8  14  21   4  15  22  25  24  15  11
10  17  24  20  13  16  12   9   3  14
20  10  16  15   7  23  23  14  15  16
 8   2   9  19  12  10  10  20  13  13
15  17  11  14  19  20  23  23  24   5
```

b Calculate the number of people who took the test.

3 a Copy and complete the frequency table using these weights of people, given to the nearest kilogram.

Weight (kg)	Tally	Number of people
$45 \leqslant w < 50$		
$50 \leqslant w < 55$		
$55 \leqslant w < 60$		
$60 \leqslant w < 65$		
$65 \leqslant w < 70$		
$70 \leqslant w < 75$		

```
48  63  73  55  59  61  70  63  58  67
46  45  57  58  63  71  60  47  49  51
53  61  68  65  70  60  52  59  50  49
48  47  63  61  58  71  53  51  60  70
```

b Calculate the number of people who were weighed.

4 Every student in Emma's class threw a ball as far as possible. The lengths of the throws, to the nearest metre, are shown.

```
 8  15  18  11  10  20  24  11  12
21  22   9   7  12  14  18   6  19
20  22  21  17  13  15  20
```

a Draw and complete a frequency table, using class intervals $0 \leqslant l < 5$, $5 \leqslant l < 10$, $10 \leqslant l < 15$, ...

b How many students are in Emma's class?

5 The masses of parcels, in kilograms, are shown.

```
1.8  1.9  2.3  2.0  0.7  1.9  3.4  1.8
2.1  1.2  3.2  3.1  1.5  1.7  2.9  2.7
3.7  0.9  2.5  3.3  0.2  2.7  2.8  3.5
1.9  1.8  0.3  0.8  2.5  1.7  0.5  1.0
0.5  2.4  3.0  3.6  1.3  3.3  3.2  1.9
```

a Draw and complete a frequency table, using class intervals $0 < m \leqslant 1.0$, $1.0 < m \leqslant 2.0$, ...

b Which class interval has the greatest number of parcels?

c Calculate the total number of parcels that were weighed.

This spread will show you how to:

- Design and use two-way tables

Keywords

Column
Frequency table
Row
Two-way table

- You can organise data in a table, such as a **frequency table**, using **rows** and **columns**.

Method of travel	Number of students
Car	14
Bus	11
Walk	5

11 students travelled by bus.

- A **two-way table** shows more detail and links two types of information, for example, method of travel and gender.

	Boys	Girls
Car	4	10
Bus	6	5
Walk	2	3

5 girls travelled by bus.

Example

Design a data-collection sheet, in the form of a two-way table, that could be used to survey the audience at a pantomime.
The survey must distinguish between children and adults.

	Child	Adult
Male		
Female		

or

	Male	Female
Child		
Adult		

Example

Katie and Marcus counted their music collection.
Complete the two-way table.

Type	Katie	Marcus	Totals
CD	6		
MP3		10	
Totals	15		28

Calculate the missing values
$15 - 6 = 9$
$9 + 10 = 19$
$28 - 19 = 9$
$9 - 6 = 3$
$3 + 10 = 13$

Type	Katie	Marcus	Totals
CD	6	3	9
MP3	9	10	19
Totals	15	13	28

Check: $15 + 13 = 28$

1 The two-way table shows the numbers of cars and vans that are crushed or saved for spare parts.

	Crushed	Spare parts
Cars	15	24
Vans	7	12

a State the number of

   i cars that are crushed

   ii vans that are saved for spare parts.

b Calculate the total number of

   i cars

   ii crushed vehicles.

c Calculate the total number of vehicles shown in the table.

2 A class of 32 students play either football ⚽ or badminton 🏸.
There are 15 girls in the class, with 5 boys and 8 girls playing badminton.

a Copy and complete the two-way table.

	⚽	🏸
Boys		
Girls		

b How many boys play football?

3 One hundred mobile phones are surveyed for colour (either black or silver) and for the payment method (either pay as you go or contract).

a Devise a two-way table that would show this information.

b Choose four suitable numbers for your table.

4 A vending machine only sells tea and coffee.
Janice is carrying out a survey about the use of sugar in drinks.
Devise a two-way table that Janice could use to show this information.

5 A car salesman sells vehicles that are either saloons or hatchbacks and are bought part-exchange or cash.
Devise a suitable two-way table to summarise his sales.

D1

Exam review

Key objectives

- Collect data from a variety of suitable sources, including experiments and surveys, and primary and secondary sources
- Design an experiment or survey
- Design and use two-way tables
- Discuss how data relate to a problem, identify possible sources of bias and plan to minimise it

1 Samantha asked her fellow classmates what their favourite season was and recorded the results in a two-way table. Copy and complete her table:

	Spring	Summer	Autumn	Winter	Total
Girls	3		4	1	
Boys	2	4		3	
Total		11	12		32

(4)

2 The manager of a school canteen has made some changes. She wants to find out what students think of these changes. She uses this question on a questionnaire:

> What do you think of the changes in the canteen?
>
> Excellent ☐   Very good ☐   Good ☐

a Write down what is wrong about this question. (1)

This is another question on the questionnaire:

> How much money do you normally spend in the canteen?
>
> A lot ☐   Not much ☐

b i Write down one thing that is wrong with this question. (1)

ii Design a better question for the canteen manager to use. (2)

You should include some response boxes.

(Edexcel Ltd., 2004)

This unit will show you how to

- Use fraction notation to describe parts of a shape
- Compare, order and simplify fractions, converting between mixed numbers and improper fractions
- Add, subtract, multiply and divide with fractions
- Recognise and use a unit fraction as a multiplicative inverse
- Recognise the equivalence of fractions, decimals and percentages, ordering them and converting between forms using a range of methods
- Express a number as a percentage of a whole

Before you start ...

You should be able to answer these questions.

	Review

1 Here are the results of a survey for a class about their favourite colours.
What fraction of the class chose blue?
Give your answer in its simplest form.

Key stage 3

Colour	Frequency
Red	8
Blue	10
Green	7
Black	5
Total	30

2 Copy and complete these equivalent fractions.

Key stage 3

a $\frac{2}{3} = \frac{x}{15}$ **b** $\frac{45}{60} = \frac{3}{y}$

3 Calculate $12 \times \frac{1}{4}$.

Key stage 3

4 Copy and complete.

Key stage 3

$$10\% = \frac{1}{10} = ?$$ $$25\% = ? = 0.25$$
$$50\% = ? = ?$$ $$? = ? = 0.23$$

5 Put these decimals in order from smallest to largest.

Unit N1

0.75   0.8   0.7   0.875

This spread will show you how to:

- Compare, order and simplify fractions, converting between mixed numbers and improper fractions

Keywords
Denominator
Equal
Equivalent
Fraction
Improper fraction
Mixed number
Numerator

This sandwich is divided into 12 parts. Adam takes $\frac{3}{12}$ of the whole sandwich.

Adam's portion is also $\frac{1}{4}$ of the whole sandwich. $\frac{3}{12}$ and $\frac{1}{4}$ are **equivalent** fractions.

$$\frac{1}{4} \xrightarrow[\times 3]{\times 3} \frac{3}{12}$$

- You can find equivalent fractions by multiplying or dividing the numerator and denominator by the same number.

- You can simplify a fraction by dividing the numerator and denominator by a common factor.

This process is called cancelling down.

Example

Write each of these fractions in its simplest form.

a $\frac{18}{30}$ **b** $\frac{64}{80}$ **c** $\frac{13}{27}$

a $\frac{18}{30} \xrightarrow[\div 6]{\div 6} \frac{3}{5}$

$\frac{18}{30} = \frac{3}{5}$

b $\frac{64}{80} \xrightarrow[\div 4]{\div 4} \frac{16}{20} \xrightarrow[\div 4]{\div 4} \frac{4}{5}$

$\frac{64}{80} = \frac{4}{5}$

c Has no common factors. It cannot be simplified.

- You can compare and order fractions by writing them as equivalent fractions with the same denominator.

Example

Which is bigger: $\frac{3}{7}$ or $\frac{4}{9}$?

You need an equivalent fraction for both $\frac{3}{7}$ and $\frac{4}{9}$.

$$\frac{3}{7} \xrightarrow[\times 9]{\times 9} \frac{27}{63} \qquad \frac{4}{9} \xrightarrow[\times 7]{\times 7} \frac{28}{63}$$

$\frac{27}{63} < \frac{28}{63}$ so $\frac{3}{7} < \frac{4}{9}$

The common denominator of these equivalent fractions will be $7 \times 9 = 63$.

Fractions can be used to describe numbers which are bigger than 1 as **mixed numbers** like $1\frac{2}{3}$ and **improper fractions** like $\frac{5}{3}$.

Example

a Change $\frac{13}{8}$ into a mixed number.   **b** Change $1\frac{3}{5}$ into an improper fraction.

a $\frac{13}{8} = \frac{8}{8} + \frac{5}{8}$

$\quad = 1 + \frac{5}{8} = 1\frac{5}{8}$

b $1\frac{3}{5} = 1 + \frac{3}{5}$

$\quad = \frac{5}{5} + \frac{3}{5} = \frac{8}{5}$

1 **i** Write the fraction of each of these shapes that is shaded.

ii Write your fraction in its simplest form.

a **b**

c  **d**

2 Cancel down each of these fractions into its simplest form.

a $\frac{4}{12}$ **b** $\frac{21}{28}$ **c** $\frac{24}{40}$ **d** $\frac{28}{63}$ **e** $\frac{45}{72}$ **f** $\frac{42}{126}$ **g** $\frac{64}{144}$ **h** $\frac{23}{93}$

3 Change each of these fractions to an improper fraction.

a $1\frac{1}{2}$ **b** $3\frac{2}{3}$ **c** $4\frac{3}{8}$ **d** $2\frac{2}{9}$ **e** $5\frac{6}{7}$ **f** $7\frac{4}{5}$ **g** $8\frac{8}{11}$ **h** $12\frac{4}{7}$ **i** $12\frac{7}{13}$

4 Change each of these fractions to a mixed number.

a $\frac{5}{4}$ **b** $\frac{8}{5}$ **c** $\frac{11}{7}$ **d** $\frac{9}{4}$ **e** $\frac{11}{5}$ **f** $\frac{20}{7}$ **g** $\frac{23}{5}$ **h** $\frac{28}{9}$ **i** $\frac{67}{8}$

5 Find the missing number in each of these pairs of equivalent fractions.

a $\frac{2}{3} = \frac{?}{12}$ **b** $\frac{3}{4} = \frac{?}{36}$ **c** $\frac{5}{7} = \frac{40}{?}$ **d** $\frac{7}{8} = \frac{?}{64}$

e $\frac{12}{30} = \frac{?}{5}$ **f** $\frac{6}{7} = \frac{?}{105}$ **g** $\frac{5}{4} = \frac{?}{68}$ **h** $\frac{?}{10} = \frac{154}{220}$

6 **a** Here are two fractions, $\frac{1}{3}$ and $\frac{2}{5}$.

Explain which is the larger fraction.

Use the grids to help with your explanation.

b Write these fractions in order of size.

Start with the smallest fraction.

$\frac{7}{18}$ $\frac{4}{9}$ $\frac{1}{3}$

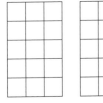

7 For each pair of fractions, write which is the larger fraction.
Show your working.

a $\frac{3}{8}$ and $\frac{2}{5}$ **b** $\frac{3}{5}$ and $\frac{2}{3}$ **c** $\frac{4}{7}$ and $\frac{2}{5}$

d $\frac{5}{6}$ and $\frac{7}{9}$ **e** $\frac{5}{9}$ and $\frac{4}{7}$ **f** $\frac{7}{5}$ and $\frac{10}{7}$

Convert each of the fractions to an equivalent fraction with the same denominator.

8 Put these fractions in order from smallest to largest.
Show your working.

a $\frac{2}{5}, \frac{3}{15}$ and $\frac{1}{3}$ **b** $\frac{4}{7}, \frac{15}{28}, \frac{1}{2}$ **c** $\frac{4}{7}, \frac{5}{8}$ and $\frac{9}{14}$

This spread will show you how to:

- Add, subtract, multiply and divide with fractions

Keywords

Common
denominator
Equivalent
Fraction

It is easy to add or subtract **fractions** when they have the same denominator.

 + =

$\frac{3}{8}$ + $\frac{1}{8}$ = $\frac{4}{8}$

- You can add or subtract fractions with different denominators by first writing them as **equivalent** fractions with the same denominator.

Calculate   **a** $\frac{3}{5} + \frac{1}{3}$ **b** $1\frac{3}{4} - \frac{5}{7}$ **c** $1\frac{7}{10} + 2\frac{3}{5}$

a $\frac{3}{5} + \frac{1}{3}$

$\frac{3}{5} + \frac{1}{3} = \frac{9}{15} + \frac{5}{15}$

$= \frac{9 + 5}{15}$

$= \frac{14}{15}$

$\frac{3}{5} \xrightarrow{\times 3} = \frac{9}{15} \xleftarrow{\times 3}$ $\frac{1}{3} \xrightarrow{\times 5} = \frac{5}{15} \xleftarrow{\times 5}$

The lowest **common denominator** is the lowest common multiple of 5 and 3, which is 15.

b $1\frac{3}{4} - \frac{5}{7}$

Change the mixed number to an improper fraction:

$1\frac{3}{4} = \frac{7}{4}$

$1\frac{3}{4} - \frac{5}{7} = \frac{7}{4} - \frac{5}{7}$

$= \frac{49}{28} - \frac{20}{28}$

$= \frac{49 - 20}{28}$

$= \frac{29}{28}$

$= 1\frac{1}{28}$

$\frac{7}{4} \xrightarrow{\times 7} = \frac{49}{28} \xleftarrow{\times 7}$ $\frac{5}{7} \xrightarrow{\times 4} = \frac{20}{28} \xleftarrow{\times 4}$

The lowest common denominator is the lowest common multiple of 4 and 7, which is 28.

c $1\frac{7}{10} + 2\frac{3}{5}$

Change the mixed numbers to improper fractions:

$1\frac{7}{10} = \frac{17}{10}$ $2\frac{3}{5} = \frac{13}{5}$

$1\frac{7}{10} + 2\frac{3}{5} = \frac{17}{10} + \frac{13}{5}$

$= \frac{17}{10} + \frac{26}{10}$

$= \frac{17 + 26}{10}$

$= \frac{43}{10}$

$= 4\frac{3}{10}$

$\frac{13}{5} \xrightarrow{\times 2} = \frac{26}{10} \xleftarrow{\times 2}$

The lowest common denominator is the lowest common multiple of 5 and 10, which is 10.

An alternative method is to write:

$1 + \frac{7}{10} + 2 + \frac{3}{5}$

$= 3 + \frac{7}{10} + \frac{3}{5}$

$= ...$

1 Work out these.

a $\frac{1}{3} + \frac{1}{3}$ **b** $\frac{3}{8} + \frac{2}{8}$ **c** $\frac{8}{11} - \frac{3}{11}$ **d** $\frac{8}{17} + \frac{5}{17}$

e $\frac{14}{23} - \frac{11}{23}$ **f** $\frac{5}{27} + \frac{8}{27}$

2 Work out each of these, leaving your answer in its simplest form.

a $\frac{2}{3} + \frac{1}{3}$ **b** $\frac{8}{9} - \frac{2}{9}$ **c** $\frac{8}{11} + \frac{5}{11}$ **d** $\frac{15}{13} - \frac{8}{13}$

e $\frac{14}{9} + \frac{1}{9}$ **f** $\frac{17}{12} - \frac{9}{12}$ **g** $1\frac{2}{3} + \frac{2}{3}$ **h** $4\frac{2}{7} - \frac{5}{7}$

3 Work out these.

a $\frac{1}{3} + \frac{1}{2}$ **b** $\frac{1}{4} + \frac{3}{5}$ **c** $\frac{3}{5} - \frac{1}{3}$ **d** $\frac{4}{5} - \frac{2}{7}$

e $\frac{5}{8} + \frac{1}{3}$ **f** $\frac{4}{9} + \frac{2}{5}$ **g** $\frac{7}{9} - \frac{2}{11}$ **h** $\frac{7}{15} + \frac{3}{7}$

> Write both fractions as equivalent fractions with the same denominator.

4 Work out each of these, leaving your answer in its simplest form as appropriate.

a $\frac{2}{5} - \frac{1}{15}$ **b** $\frac{1}{2} - \frac{1}{3}$ **c** $\frac{2}{5} + \frac{7}{20}$ **d** $\frac{1}{2} - \frac{1}{6}$

5 Work out each of these, leaving your answer in its simplest form.

a $\frac{4}{5} + \frac{2}{3}$ **b** $1\frac{1}{2} + \frac{3}{5}$ **c** $1\frac{1}{3} + 1\frac{1}{4}$ **d** $1\frac{2}{7} + \frac{3}{5}$

e $2\frac{2}{5} - \frac{1}{3}$ **f** $3\frac{3}{8} - 1\frac{1}{2}$ **g** $4\frac{1}{3} - 2\frac{3}{4}$ **h** $3\frac{4}{7} - 2\frac{8}{9}$

6 Work out each of these, leaving your answer in its simplest form.

a Pete walked $3\frac{2}{3}$ miles before lunch and then a further $2\frac{1}{4}$ miles after lunch. How far did he walk altogether?

b A bag weighs $2\frac{3}{16}$ lb when it is full. When empty the bag weighs $\frac{3}{8}$ lb. What is the weight of the contents of the bag?

c Henry and Paula are eating peanuts. Henry has a full bag weighing $1\frac{3}{16}$ kg. Paula has a bag that weighs $\frac{4}{5}$ kg. What is the total mass of their two bags of peanuts?

d Simon spent $\frac{2}{3}$ of his pocket money on a computer game. He spent $\frac{1}{5}$ of his pocket money on a ticket to the cinema. Work out the fraction of his pocket money that he had left.

e Calculate the perimeter of each of these swimming pools.

i $2\frac{2}{7}$ feet

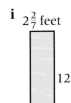

$12\frac{3}{8}$ feet

ii $22\frac{4}{9}$ feet

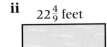

$8\frac{3}{5}$ feet

iii $4\frac{5}{6}$ m

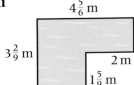

$3\frac{2}{9}$ m   2 m

$1\frac{5}{9}$ m

This spread will show you how to:

- Add, subtract, multiply and divide with fractions
- Recognise and use a unit fraction as a multiplicative inverse

Keywords

Equivalent
Integer
Fraction
Multiplicative
  inverse
Unit fraction

A unit fraction has numerator 1:
$\frac{1}{2}, \frac{1}{3}, \frac{1}{4}, \dots$

You can multiply a **unit fraction** by an integer using a number line.

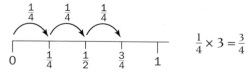

$\frac{1}{4} \times 3 = \frac{3}{4}$

Multiplying by $\frac{1}{4}$ is the same as dividing by 4.

$$3 \times \frac{1}{4} = \frac{3}{4} \quad \Longleftrightarrow \quad 3 \div 4 = \frac{3}{4}$$

● **You can multiply any fraction by an integer using unit fractions.**

$$4 \times \frac{3}{8} = 4 \times 3 \times \frac{1}{8} = \frac{12}{8} = 1\frac{4}{8} = 1\frac{1}{2}$$

You can divide an integer by a unit fraction.

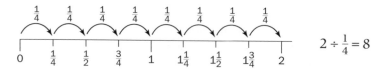

$2 \div \frac{1}{4} = 8$

● **You can divide an integer by any fraction using unit fractions.**

$$4 \div \frac{2}{3} = 4 \div 2 \div \frac{1}{3} = 2 \div \frac{1}{3} = 2 \times 3 = 6$$

Think how many $\frac{1}{4}$s are there in 2 wholes?

1	2	5	6
3	4	7	8

● **You can multiply a fraction by another fraction by multiplying the numerators together and multiplying the denominators together.**

$$\frac{3}{5} \times \frac{5}{8} = \frac{3 \times 5}{5 \times 8} = \frac{15}{40} = \frac{3}{8}$$

You can use the relationship between multiplication and division.

$\div \frac{2}{3}$ Dividing by $\frac{2}{3}$ is the same as multiplying by $\frac{3}{2}$. $\times \frac{3}{2}$

4 ⟶ 6   4 ⟵ 6

$\times \frac{2}{3}$ Multiplying by $\frac{2}{3}$ is the same as dividing by $\frac{3}{2}$. $\div \frac{3}{2}$

$\times \frac{3}{2}$ is the **multiplicative inverse** of $\div \frac{3}{2}$.

Calculate

a $4 \div \frac{3}{5}$ **b** $\frac{3}{8} \div \frac{5}{6}$ **c** $2\frac{2}{5} \div 1\frac{1}{4}$

a $4 \div \frac{3}{5} = 4 \times \frac{5}{3}$

$\quad = \frac{20}{3}$

$\quad = 6\frac{2}{3}$

b $\frac{3}{8} \div \frac{5}{6} = \frac{3}{8} \times \frac{6}{5}$

$\quad = \frac{3 \times 6}{8 \times 5}$

$\quad = \frac{18}{40}$

$\quad = \frac{9}{20}$

c $2\frac{2}{5} \div 1\frac{1}{4} = \frac{12}{5} \div \frac{5}{4}$

$\quad = \frac{12}{5} \times \frac{4}{5}$

$\quad = \frac{12 \times 4}{5 \times 5}$

$\quad = \frac{48}{25} = 1\frac{23}{25}$

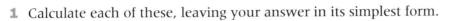

1 Calculate each of these, leaving your answer in its simplest form.

a $3 \times \frac{1}{2}$ b $6 \times \frac{1}{3}$ c $10 \times \frac{1}{3}$

d $15 \times \frac{1}{7}$ e $\frac{1}{10} \times 25$ f $\frac{1}{3} \times 13$

2 Calculate each of these, leaving your answer in its simplest form.

a $3 \times \frac{2}{3}$ b $6 \times \frac{2}{3}$ c $5 \times \frac{2}{3}$ d $2 \times \frac{7}{24}$

e $4 \times \frac{3}{20}$ f $\frac{4}{5} \times 20$ g $\frac{3}{5} \times 10$ h $\frac{11}{8} \times 17$

3 Calculate each of these, leaving your answer in its simplest form.

a $4 \div \frac{1}{2}$ b $2 \div \frac{1}{5}$ c $2 \div \frac{1}{7}$

d $10 \div \frac{1}{2}$ e $12 \div \frac{1}{4}$ f $22 \div \frac{1}{10}$

4 Calculate each of these, leaving your answer in its simplest form.

a What is the total weight of 7 boxes that each weigh $\frac{2}{5}$ kg?

b What is the total length of 5 pieces of wood that are each $\frac{3}{7}$ of a metre long?

5 Calculate each of these, leaving your answer in its simplest form.

a $4 \div \frac{2}{3}$ b $7 \div \frac{2}{5}$ c $2 \div \frac{5}{6}$ d $12 \div \frac{6}{7}$

e $20 \div \frac{5}{12}$ f $5 \div \frac{7}{9}$ g $3 \div 1\frac{1}{2}$ h $3 \div 1\frac{2}{5}$

6 Calculate each of these, leaving your answer in its simplest form.

a $\frac{2}{5} \times \frac{3}{4}$ b $\frac{3}{5} \times \frac{3}{4}$ c $\frac{5}{7} \times \frac{3}{4}$ d $\frac{4}{7} \times \frac{3}{5}$

e $\frac{5}{6} \times \frac{4}{5}$ f $\frac{3}{8} \times \frac{7}{9}$ g $\frac{3}{5} \times \frac{10}{9}$ h $\frac{15}{16} \times \frac{12}{5}$

i $\left(\frac{3}{7}\right)^2$ j $1\frac{3}{4} \times \frac{2}{7}$ k $3\frac{2}{3} \times \frac{7}{11}$ l $1\frac{3}{8} \times 1\frac{2}{5}$

7 Calculate each of these, leaving your answer in its simplest form.

a $4 \div \frac{2}{5}$ b $\frac{2}{3} \div \frac{4}{5}$ c $\frac{4}{5} \div \frac{3}{4}$ d $\frac{4}{7} \div \frac{2}{3}$

e $\frac{3}{7} \div \frac{4}{9}$ f $\frac{3}{5} \div \frac{1}{2}$ g $\frac{3}{4} \div 3$ h $\frac{4}{7} \div 5$

i $\frac{4}{11} \div 5$ j $\frac{7}{4} \div \frac{2}{3}$ k $\frac{7}{4} \div \frac{3}{2}$ l $\frac{9}{5} \div \frac{5}{3}$

m $1\frac{1}{2} \div \frac{3}{4}$ n $2\frac{1}{4} \div \frac{2}{3}$ o $2\frac{2}{5} \div \frac{9}{7}$

8 Calculate each of these, leaving your answer in its simplest form.

a A plank of wood is $4\frac{3}{5}$ metres long. How many pieces of wood of length $1\frac{1}{4}$ metres can be cut from the piece of wood?

b A paint pot can hold $2\frac{3}{4}$ litres of paint. Hector buys $11\frac{1}{5}$ litres of emulsion paint. How many times can Hector fill the paint pot with emulsion paint?

This spread will show you how to:

● Recognise the equivalence of fractions, decimals and percentages, ordering them and converting between forms using a range of methods

● Percentages, fractions and decimals are all ways of writing the same thing.

$$40\% = \frac{4}{10} = \frac{2}{5} = 0.4$$

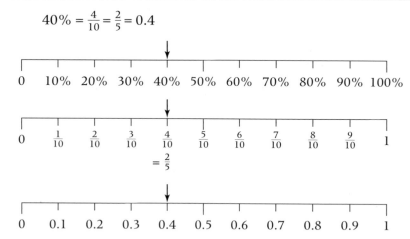

Some useful **equivalents** to remember:

$10\% = \frac{10}{100} = \frac{1}{10} = 0.1$
$20\% = \frac{20}{100} = \frac{1}{5} = 0.2$
$25\% = \frac{25}{100} = \frac{1}{4} = 0.25$
$50\% = \frac{50}{100} = \frac{1}{2} = 0.5$
$75\% = \frac{75}{100} = \frac{3}{4} = 0.75$

● You can write a terminating decimal as a fraction.

$$3.42 = 3 \text{ units} + \frac{4}{10} + \frac{2}{100}$$
$$= 3 \text{ units} + \frac{42}{100}$$
$$= 3\frac{42}{100}$$
$$= 3\frac{21}{50}$$

A terminating decimal ends after a definite number of digits.

$\frac{4}{10} + \frac{2}{100}$ is the same as $\frac{40}{100} + \frac{2}{100} = \frac{42}{100}$

● You can convert a fraction into a decimal ...

... using equivalent fractions

$$\overset{\times 2}{\frac{3}{5}} = \frac{6}{10}$$
$$\underset{\times 2}{}$$

$$\overset{\times 5}{\frac{7}{40}} = \overset{\div 2}{\frac{35}{200}} = \frac{17.5}{100}$$
$$\underset{\times 5}{} \quad \underset{\div 2}{}$$

... using division

$$\frac{7}{40} = 7 \div 40 = 0.175$$

$$\frac{3}{5} = \frac{6}{10} = 0.6$$

$$\frac{7}{40} = \frac{17.5}{100} = 0.175$$

You can convert between percentages and fractions.

$$30\% = \frac{30}{100} = \frac{3}{10}$$

$$145\% = \frac{145}{100} = \frac{29}{20} = 1\frac{9}{20}$$

To cancel down a fraction, divide the numerator and denominator by a common factor.

You can convert between percentages and decimals.

$$32 \div 100$$
$$32\% = \frac{32}{100} = 0.32$$

$$5.4 \div 100$$
$$5.4\% = \frac{5.4}{100} = 0.054$$

1 Write each of these decimals as a fraction in its simplest form.

  a 0.3   **b** 0.6   **c** 0.64   **d** 0.45

  e 0.375   **f** 1.08   **g** 3.2375   **h** 3.0625

2 Change these fractions to decimals without using a calculator.

  a $\frac{3}{10}$ **b** $\frac{11}{25}$ **c** $\frac{26}{25}$ **d** $\frac{124}{200}$ **e** $\frac{27}{60}$ **f** $\frac{39}{75}$ **g** $\frac{42}{150}$ **h** $3\frac{21}{60}$

3 Change these fractions into decimals using an appropriate method.
Give your answers to 2 decimal places where necessary.

  a $\frac{22}{50}$ **b** $\frac{2}{3}$ **c** $\frac{27}{20}$ **d** $\frac{11}{15}$ **e** $\frac{8}{7}$ **f** $1\frac{2}{5}$ **g** $2\frac{11}{66}$ **h** $\frac{11}{13}$

4 Write each of these percentages as a fraction in its simplest form.

  a 40%   **b** 90%   **c** 35%   **d** 65%

  e 1%   **f** 362%   **g** 15.25%   **h** 2.125%

5 Write each of these fractions as a percentage without using a
calculator.

  a $\frac{27}{50}$ **b** $\frac{2}{5}$ **c** $\frac{17}{20}$ **d** $\frac{13}{25}$ **e** $\frac{2}{3}$ **f** $\frac{48}{200}$ **g** $1\frac{3}{15}$ **h** $\frac{33}{75}$

6 Write these percentages as decimals.

  a 37%   **b** 7%   **c** 189%   **d** 45%

  e 145%   **f** 0.8%   **g** 250%   **h** 123.2%

7 Write these decimals as percentages.

  a 0.72   **b** 0.2   **c** 1.25   **d** 0.03

  e 1.02   **f** 0.0325   **g** 0.333 ... **h** 1.372

8 Write these fractions as percentages. Give your answers to 1 decimal
place as appropriate.

  a $\frac{48}{70}$ **b** $\frac{16}{25}$ **c** $\frac{17}{19}$ **d** $1\frac{11}{12}$ **e** $\frac{5}{19}$

> Try converting the
> fraction into a
> decimal first!

9 **Investigation**
All fractions can be turned into a decimal by dividing the numerator
by the denominator. Some produce recurring decimals.

  For example $\frac{1}{3} = 1 \div 3 = 0.333\ 333\ 333\ ...$

  a Convert each of the fractions less than 1 with a denominator of
  seven into a decimal using your calculator. Write down all the
  decimal places in your answer.

  For example $\frac{1}{7} = 1 \div 7 = 0.142\ 857\ 142\ ...$
  $\frac{2}{7} = 2 \div 7 = ...$

  b Write what you notice about each of your answers.

  c Repeat for all the fractions less than one with a denominator of 13.

This spread will show you how to:

- Recognise the equivalence of fractions, decimals and percentages, ordering them and converting between forms using a range of methods
- Express a number as a percentage of a whole

Keywords
Decimal
Equivalent
Fraction
Order
Percentage

You can convert between **fractions**, **decimals** and **percentages** using a range of mental and written methods.

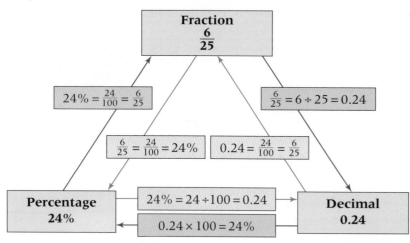

$$24\% = \frac{24}{100} = \frac{6}{25}$$

$$\frac{6}{25} = 6 \div 25 = 0.24$$

$$\frac{6}{25} = \frac{24}{100} = 24\%$$

$$0.24 = \frac{24}{100} = \frac{6}{25}$$

Fraction $\frac{6}{25}$

Percentage 24%

$$24\% = 24 \div 100 = 0.24$$

$$0.24 \times 100 = 24\%$$

Decimal 0.24

You can write something as a percentage by first finding the fraction.

Example

a What percentage of this shape is shaded?

b In a class there are 40 students. 24 of them are boys. What percentage of the class are boys?

a There are 16 equal parts.
7 of the parts are shaded.
The fraction shaded is $\frac{7}{16}$.

% shaded $= \frac{7}{16} = 0.4375 = 43.75\%$

b There are 40 students in the class.
24 of the students are boys.
The fraction of boys is $\frac{24}{40}$.

% of boys $= \frac{24}{40} = \frac{12}{20} = \frac{60}{100} = 60\%$

● You can **order** fractions, decimals and percentages by converting them into decimals.

Example

Write these numbers in order of size. Start with the smallest number.

0.8   70% $\frac{7}{8}$ $\frac{3}{4}$

$70\% = \frac{70}{100} = 0.7$ $\frac{7}{8} = \frac{35}{40} = \frac{175}{200} = \frac{875}{1000} = 0.875$ $\frac{3}{4} = 0.75$

Place the decimals in order: 0.7   0.75   0.8   0.875
                                70% $\frac{3}{4}$ 0.8 $\frac{7}{8}$

Rewrite $\frac{7}{8}$ as an equivalent fraction with a denominator of 1000.

1 Copy and complete this table.

Fraction	Decimal	Percentage
$\frac{3}{8}$		
	0.28	
		15%
	0.375	
$\frac{4}{5}$		
		17.5%

2 For each pair of fractions, write which is the larger fraction.
   Show your working.

   a $\frac{5}{8}$ and $\frac{3}{5}$ **b** $\frac{4}{5}$ and $\frac{2}{3}$ **c** $\frac{5}{7}$ and $\frac{3}{5}$ **d** $\frac{3}{8}$ and $\frac{4}{11}$

   e $\frac{10}{7}$ and $\frac{16}{11}$ **f** $\frac{14}{9}$ and $\frac{17}{11}$ **g** $1\frac{2}{7}$ and $1\frac{7}{23}$ **h** $2\frac{7}{12}$ and $2\frac{8}{11}$

   > Convert each of the fractions into a decimal.

3 Copy each pair of fractions, decimals and percentages and insert '>'
   or '<' in between them. Show your working out clearly for each
   question.

   a $\frac{3}{5}$ 0.7   **b** $\frac{7}{15}$ $\frac{30}{65}$ **c** $\frac{5}{9}$ $\frac{7}{13}$ **d** $2\frac{2}{3}$ 265%

4 Put these fractions, decimals and percentages in order from smallest
   to largest. Show your working.

   a 47%, $\frac{12}{25}$ and 0.49   **b** $\frac{4}{5}$, 78% and 0.81

   c $\frac{5}{8}$, 66% and $\frac{7}{12}$ **d** $\frac{5}{16}$, 0.3, 29% and $\frac{7}{22}$

5 In each of these questions express the answer first as a fraction, then
   convert the fraction to a percentage using an appropriate method.

   a In a class there are 28 students. 19 of the students are right-
   handed. What percentage of the class are right-handed?

   b In a survey of 80 people, 55 said they would prefer school to be
   compulsory until the age of 18. What percentage of the 80 people
   preferred school to be compulsory until the age of 18?

   c In a football squad of 24 players, 5 of the players are goalkeepers.
   What percentage of the football squad are not goalkeepers?

   d In a mixed packet of 54 biscuits, 36 of the biscuits are covered in
   chocolate. What percentage of the biscuits in the packet are not
   covered in chocolate?

6 **a** Jo scores 68% in his French exam and gets $\frac{37}{54}$ in his German exam.
   In which subject did he do the best? Explain your answer.

   b In a school survey 23% of the students said they did not like eating
   meat. In Sarah's class $\frac{7}{31}$ students said they did not like eating meat.
   How do the results of Sarah's class compare with the rest of the
   school?

Exam review

Key objectives

- Order fractions by rewriting them with a common denominator
- Convert simple fractions of a whole to percentages of a whole and vice versa
- Multiply and divide a given fraction by an integer, by a unit fraction and by a general fraction

1 Work out the following, giving your answers in their simplest form:

a $\frac{3}{4} - \frac{2}{5}$

b $\frac{5}{8} + \frac{1}{3}$

c $\frac{5}{4} \times 3$

d $5 \div \frac{2}{3}$ (4)

2 **a** Write these five fractions in order of size.

Start with the smallest fraction. (2)

$$\frac{3}{4} \qquad \frac{1}{2} \qquad \frac{3}{8} \qquad \frac{2}{3} \qquad \frac{1}{6}$$

b Write these numbers in order of size.

Start with the smallest number. (2)

$$65\% \qquad \frac{3}{4} \qquad 0.72 \qquad \frac{2}{3} \qquad \frac{3}{5}$$

(Edexcel Ltd., 2004)

This unit will show you how to

- Recall and use properties of lines and angles
- Recall the geometric properties of triangles
- Explain why the angle sum of any quadrilateral is 360°
- Calculate and use interior and exterior angles of polygons
- Use parallel lines, alternate angles and corresponding angles

Before you start ...

You should be able to answer these questions.

1 Evaluate.

   a 180 – 107   **b** 180 – 38

   c 360 – 183   **d** 360 – 217

   e 360 – 197

2 Evaluate.

   a 180 ÷ 2   **b** 360 ÷ 3

   c 360 ÷ 4

3 Use a protractor to measure these angles.

   a

   b

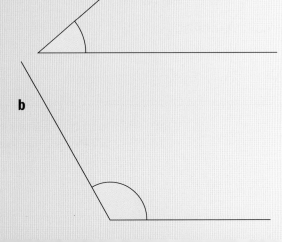

Review

Key stage 3

Key stage 3

Key stage 3

Angle properties

This spread will show you how to:

- Recall and use properties of lines and angles
- Recall the geometric properties of triangles

Keywords

Angle
Degree (°)
Straight line
Triangle
Vertically
opposite

You should know these facts:

There are 360° at a point.

There are 180° on a straight line.

Vertically opposite angles are equal.

Example

Calculate the values of x, y and z. Give a reason for each of your answers.

a

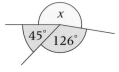

b

c

a $126° + 45° = 171°$
$360° - 171° = 189°$
$x = 189°$

(angles at a point add to 360°)

b $54° + 90° = 144°$
$180° - 144° = 36°$
$y = 36°$

(angles on a straight line add
to 180°)

c $z = 85°$

(vertically opposite angles
are equal)

You should know the names of these triangles:

Right-angled

One 90° angle,
marked ∟

Equilateral

3 equal angles
3 equal sides

Isosceles

2 equal angles
2 equal sides

Scalene

No equal angles
No equal sides

A triangle is a 2-D
shape with 3 sides
and 3 angles.

- **The angles in a triangle add to 180°.**

Draw any triangle,
tear off the corners,

and put them
together to make
a straight line.

Example

Calculate the value of p.
Give a reason for your answer.

$180° - 38° = 142°$ (angles in a △ add to 180°)
$142° ÷ 2 = 71°$ (two equal angles in an isosceles △)
$p = 71°$

1 Calculate the size of the unknown angles in each diagram.
Give a reason for each answer.

The diagrams are not drawn to scale.

a

b
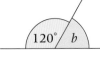

c
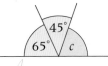

d
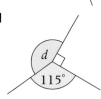

e
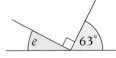

f
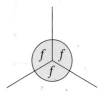

2 Calculate the size of the angles marked by letters in each diagram.

a

b
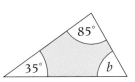

c
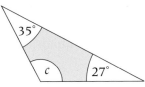

d
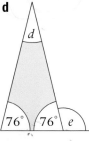

e
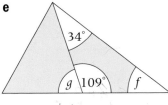

3 Find the unknown angle and state the type of triangle.

a

b

c

4 Calculate the size of the angles marked with letters in each diagram.

a

b
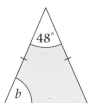

c
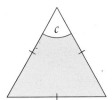

Angles in quadrilaterals

This spread will show you how to:

● Explain why the angle sum of any quadrilateral is 360°

Keywords
Angle
Degree (°)
Diagonal
Point
Quadrilateral
Triangle

● A quadrilateral is a 2-D shape with 4 sides and 4 angles.

You should know the names of these quadrilaterals:

The equal angles are coloured the same.

Square 　　Rectangle 　　Rhombus 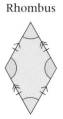　　Parallelogram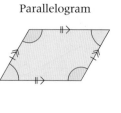

Trapezium 　　Isosceles trapezium 　　Kite 　　Arrowhead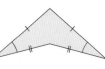

You can draw a diagonal in a quadrilateral to form two triangles.
2 × 180° = 360°

The angles in each triangle add to 180°.

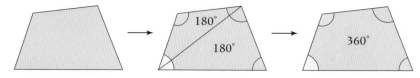

● The angles in a quadrilateral add to 360°.

Example

Calculate the values of *x*, *y* and *z*. Give a reason for each of your answers.

a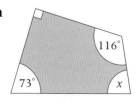

b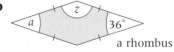
a rhombus

a 90° + 116° + 73° = 279°
　　360° − 279° = 81°
　　　　　x = 81°　(angles in a quadrilateral add to 360°)

b 　　　　*a* = 36°　(opposite angles of a rhombus are equal)
　　36° + 36° = 72°
　　360° − 72° = 288°　(opposite angles of a rhombus are equal and angles in a quadrilateral add to 360°)
　　288° ÷ 2 = 144°
　　　　　z = 144°

1 Calculate the size of the unknown angles in each diagram.

The diagrams are not drawn to scale.

a

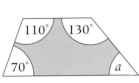

b

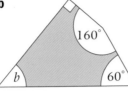

c

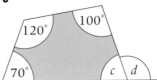

d

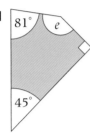

e

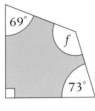

2 Find the unknown angles in each quadrilateral and state the type of quadrilateral.

a

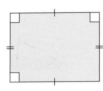

b

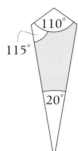

c

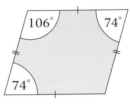

d

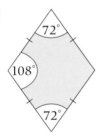

e

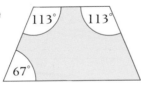

3 Calculate the value of x for each quadrilateral.

a

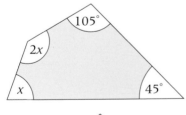

b

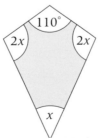

c

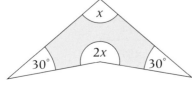

89

Interior angles of a polygon

This spread will show you how to:

● Calculate and use interior and exterior angles of polygons

Keywords
Diagonal
Exterior
Interior
Polygon
Regular
Vertices

A **polygon** is a 2-D shape with three or more straight sides.

● A **regular** shape has equal sides and equal angles.

You should know the names of these polygons:

Sides	Name	Sides	Name
3	triangle	7	heptagon
4	quadrilateral	8	octagon
5	pentagon	9	nonagon
6	hexagon	10	decagon

A regular hexagon has 6 equal sides and 6 equal angles.

● The angles inside a shape are called **interior** angles.

● The interior angles in a triangle add to 180°.

'interior' means inside.

You can split a polygon into triangles by drawing diagonals from the same vertices.

A **diagonal** joins two vertices, but is not a side.

Example

Calculate the sum of the interior angles for a pentagon.

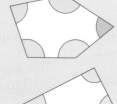

Draw in the two diagonals.
Three triangles formed: 3 × 180° = 540°
Sum of interior angles =
Sum of all angles in each triangle = 540°

Example

Calculate the value of x in this regular hexagon.

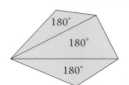

4 triangles
4 × 180° = 720°
Sum of interior angles = 720°
There are 6 interior angles, so:
One interior angle, x = 720° ÷ 6 = 120°

1 **a** Calculate the value of one interior angle of an equilateral triangle.

Two equilateral triangles are placed together to form a rhombus.

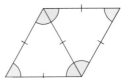

b Calculate the value of each interior angle of this rhombus.

c Calculate the sum of the interior angles of a rhombus.

2 Draw these polygons. Draw diagonals from **one** vertex.
(The quadrilateral is done for you.)
Copy and complete this table of results.

Number of sides	Number of triangles	Sum of the interior angles
3	1	180°
4	2	
5		
6		
7		
8		
9		
10		

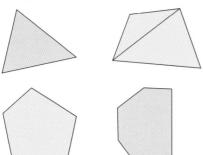

3 **a** Calculate the sum of the interior angles for a regular octagon.

b Calculate the value of one interior angle of a regular octagon.

c Copy and complete this table for regular polygons.

Number of sides	Name	Number of triangles	Sum of the interior angles	One interior angle
3	Equilateral triangle	1	180°	60°
4	Square	2	360°	90°
5				
6				
7				
8	Regular octagon			
9				
10				

Exterior angles of a polygon

This spread will show you how to:

● Calculate and use interior and exterior angles of polygons

Keywords
Exterior
Interior
Polygon
Regular

The angles inside a shape are called interior angles.

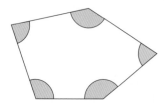

Interior = inside

You find the exterior angles of a polygon by extending each side of the shape in the same direction.

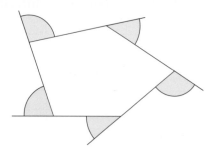

Exterior = outside

● The exterior angles of any polygon add to 360°.

Interior angle + exterior angle = 180°
(angles on a straight line add to 180°)

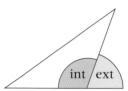

Example

Calculate the values of *x* and *y* in this regular hexagon.

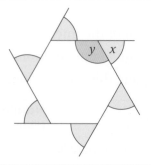

The six exterior angles add to 360°.

$$x = 360° \div 6 = 60°$$

$180° - 60° = 120°$ (angles on a straight line add to 180°)
$$y = 120°$$

1 **a** State the total of the exterior angles of this regular octagon.

 b Calculate the value of one of the exterior angles.

 c Copy and complete this table of results for regular polygons.

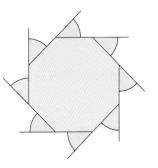

Number of sides	Name	Sum of exterior angles	One exterior angle
3	Equilateral triangle		
4	Square		
5			
6			
7			
8	Regular octagon		
9			
10			

2 The interior angle of a regular polygon is 162°.

 a Calculate the value of an exterior angle.

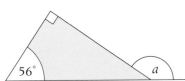

 b State the sum of the exterior angles of the polygon.

 c Calculate the number of exterior angles in the polygon.

 d State the number of sides of the regular polygon.

3 A regular polygon has 15 sides.

 a Calculate the value of an exterior angle.

 b Calculate the value of an interior angle.

4 Calculate the size of the angles marked with letters in these polygons.

a

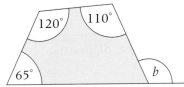

b

5 An interior angle of a regular polygon is three times the exterior angle.

 a Calculate the value of each exterior angle.

 b Calculate the value of each interior angle.

 c Give the name of the regular polygon.

Angles in parallel lines

This spread will show you how to:

● Use parallel lines, alternate angles and corresponding angles

Keywords

Alternate
Corresponding
Parallel
Vertically
  opposite

When two lines cross, four angles are formed.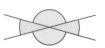

● **Vertically opposite** angles are equal.

When a line crosses two **parallel** lines, eight angles are formed.

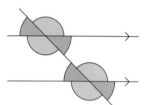

The four red **acute** angles are equal.

The four purple **obtuse** angles are equal.

Acute + obtuse = 180°

Parallel lines are
always the same
distance apart.

An acute angle is
less than 90°.
An obtuse angle is
more than 90° but
less than 180°.

● **Alternate** angles are equal.

They are called Z angles.

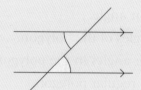

The Z shape can
take several forms.

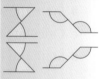

● **Corresponding** angles are equal.

They are called F angles.

The F shape can
take several forms.

Example

Find the unknown angles in these diagrams.
Give reasons for your answers.

a 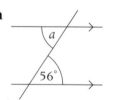 **b** 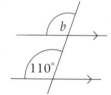 **c**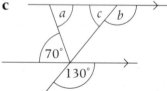

a $a = 56°$
  (alternate angles)

b $b = 110°$
  (corresponding angles)

c $a = 70°$ (alternate angles)
  $b = 130°$ (corresponding angles)
  $c = 180° - 130°$
    $= 50°$ (angles on straight line add to 180°)

1 Calculate the size of the angles marked by a letter in each diagram. Give a reason for each answer.

The diagrams are not drawn to scale.

a

b

c

d
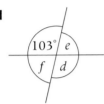

e

2 Find the value of each angle marked with a letter. Give a reason for each answer.

a **b** **c**
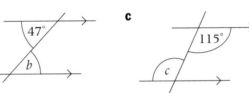

d
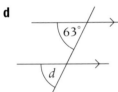

e
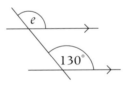

f
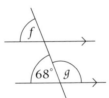

g
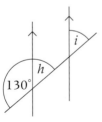

h
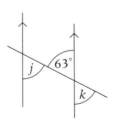

i
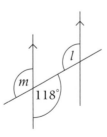

3 Find the value of each angle marked with a letter. Give a reason.

a
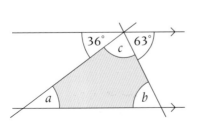

b
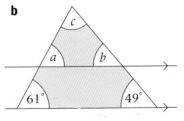

c
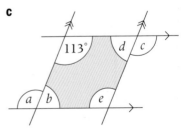

Key objectives

- Use parallel lines, alternate angles and corresponding angles
- Calculate and use the sums of the interior and exterior angles of polygons

1 Work out the size of the largest missing angle.

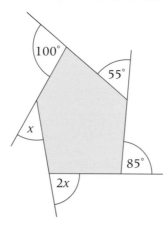

(4)

2

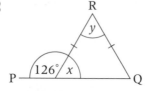

PQ is a straight line.

a Work out the size of the angle marked $x°$. (1)

b i Work out the size of the angle marked $y°$. (3)

ii Give reasons for your answer.

(Edexcel Ltd., 2003)

A3

This unit will show you how to

- Generate and describe sequences using a term-to-term rule
- Understand the difference between increasing and decreasing sequences
- Generate and describe sequences using a position-to-term rule
- Describe and find the general term of a linear sequence
- Explain how the formula for the general term of a linear expression works

Before you start ...

You should be able to answer these questions.

Review

1 Work out the difference between

    a 5 and 8   **a** 3 and 9

    c 6 and 11   **d** −4 and +2

Unit N1

2 Find the difference between

    a 10 and 7   **b** 9 and 5

    c 12 and 7   **d** 3 and −1

Unit N1

3 Write down the first six multiples of

    a 4   **b** 3

    c 5   **d** 6

Unit N1

4 Copy and complete

    a $2 \times 7 = ?$ **b** $4 \times ? = 36$

    c $8 \times ? = 24$ **d** $3 \times ? = 21$

Unit N2

5 Work out.

    a 2^2 **b** 4^2

    c 5^2 **d** 3^2

    e 6^2 **f** 9^2

Unit N2

Term-to-term rules

This spread will show you how to:

● Generate and describe sequences using a term-to-term rule

Keywords
Common
  difference
Decreasing
Increasing
Linear
Rule
Sequence
Term

You can describe a **sequence** by giving the first **term** and the term-to-term **rule**.

The rule tells you how to work out each term from the one before.

Example

Write the first five terms in the sequence with first term 4 and term-to-term rule 'add 3'.

4, 7, 10, 13, 16

Start with 4; add 3
each time.

● In an **increasing** sequence, the terms are getting larger.   For example 5, 9, 13, 17, 21, ...
● In a **decreasing** sequence, the terms are getting smaller.   For example 12, 10, 8, 6, 4, ...

You can work out the term-to-term rule for a sequence and use it to find more terms.

Example

For each sequence, work out the two missing terms.
Describe the sequence in words.

a 19, 9, −1, −11, ...   **b** 2, ___, 14, ___, 26, 32

a 19, 9, −1, −11, ___, ___
   The first term is 19 and the terms decrease by 10 each time.
   The next two terms are −21 and −31.
b From 26 to 32 is an increase of 6.
   The sequence is 2, 8, 14, 20, 26, 32.
   The first term is 2 and the terms increase by 6 each time.

A **linear** sequence increases or decreases in equal-sized steps.
The size of the 'step' is called the **common difference**.

For example: 7,   3,   −1,   −5,   −11   Common difference = 4
                    −4   −4   −4   −4

In some sequences, the 'steps' from one term to another are not equal.

Example

Describe how this sequence is increasing: 3, 4, 7, 12, 19, ...
Work out the next two terms in the sequence.

3,   4,   7,   12,   19, ...
   +1   +3   +5   +7

To find the next
term, +9:
19 + 9 = 28
To find the one
after, +11:
28 + 11 = 39

The first difference is 1 and the difference increases by 2 each time.
The next two terms are 28 and 39.

1 Write out the first five terms of these sequences.

1st term	Rule
6	Increase by 4 each time
26	Increase by 5 each time
10	Decrease by 3 each time
−6	Increase by 2 each time
−23	Increase by 7 each time

2 Write down the first five terms in each of these sequences.

a Even numbers

b Odd numbers larger than 16

c Multiples of 4

d Multiples of 6 greater than 20

e Two more than the 5 times table

f Square numbers

g One more than square numbers

h Powers of 2.

3 Write out the first five terms of these sequences.

a 2nd term 7, increases by 3 each time.

b 2nd term 19, decreases by 6 each time.

c 3rd term 12, increases by 4 each time.

d 3rd term 14, decreases by 8 each time.

e 5th term is 8, increases by 6 each time.

4 For each sequence

i work out the two missing terms

ii describe the sequence.

a 3, 10, 17, 24, ___, ___

b −7, 1, 9, 17, ___, ___

c −19, −16, −13, −10, ___, ___

d 7, ___, 15, 19, 23, ___

e 3, ___, ___, 27, 35, 43

f 16, 11, 6, ___, ___, −9

g ___, −8, −5, −2, ___, 4

h ___, 6, ___, −8, −15

5 For each sequence

i write the terms in order from smallest to largest

ii describe the sequence.

a 8, 3, 5, 12, 2

b 25, 18, 27, 22, 28

c −3, 0, −6, 4, −5

d 20, 8, 6, 15, 11

e −21, −9, −23, −17, −24

f −1, 5, −15, −7, 3

6 Challenge

In each set of numbers there are two sequences mixed together.
Write out each pair of sequences.

a 1, 3, 4, 5, 7, 7, 9, 10, 11, 13   **b** 2, 4, 7, 8, 11, 15, 16, 19, 23, 32

The general term

This spread will show you how to:

● Generate and describe sequences using a position-to-term rule

Keywords

General term
*n*th term
Position-to-term

● A **position-to-term** rule links a term with its position in the sequence.

For example, the 4 times table: 4, 8, 12, 16, 20, 24, ... can be written as

1st term = T(1)	2nd term = T(2)	3rd term = T(3)	4th term = T(4)	5th term = T(5)	6th term = T(6)
4	8	12	16	20	24

$T(1) = 1 \times 4$
$T(2) = 2 \times 4$
$T(3) = 3 \times 4$
$T(10) = 10 \times 4$

The **general term** or ***n*th term** of the 4 times table is $T(n) = n \times 4$ or $4n$.

You can generate a sequence from the general term.

Example

Find the first three terms and the 10th term of the sequence with general term $3n + 2$.

1st term $3 \times 1 + 2 \rightarrow 5$
2nd $\quad 3 \times 2 + 2 \rightarrow 8$
3rd $\quad 3 \times 3 + 2 \rightarrow 11$
10th $\quad 3 \times 10 + 2 \rightarrow 32$

To find a term, substitute its position number for *n*.

Example

The *n*th term of a sequence is $n^2 - 8$.
Copy and complete the table of results.

Term number	Term
1	
2	
3	
4	
10	
n	$n^2 - 8$

Term number	Term
1	$1^2 - 8 = \quad 1 - 8 = -7$
2	$2^2 - 8 = \quad 4 - 8 = -4$
3	$3^2 - 8 = \quad 9 - 8 = 1$
4	$4^2 - 8 = \quad 16 - 8 = 8$
10	$10^2 - 8 = 100 - 8 = 17$
n	$n^2 - 8$

Squared comes
first then
subtract 8.

1 Find the first three terms and the 10th term of these sequences.

   a $5n + 1$ **b** $3n + 8$ **c** $8n - 4$ **d** $6n - 8$

   e $24 - 2n$ **f** $15 - 5n$ **g** $7n - 20$ **h** $4n - 6$

2 Copy and complete the table of results for each sequence.

   a $3n + 8$

Term number	Term
1	11
2	
3	
5	
10	
n	$3n + 8$

   b $6n - 15$

Term number	Term
1	−9
2	
3	
5	
10	
n	$6n - 15$

3 Write the first five terms of the sequences with nth term

   a $n^2 + 4$ **b** $n^2 - 2$ **c** $2n^2$ **d** $12 - n^2$

4 Find the 2nd, 5th and 10th terms of the sequences with nth term

   a $n^2 + 8$ **b** $n^2 - 6$ **c** $2n^2 + 7$

5 The general term of a sequence is given by $4n + 1$.

   a Find the first three terms.

   b Copy and complete:
   Each term is _____ more than a multiple of _____

   c Is 222 in the sequence? Explain.

6 The general term of a sequence is $2n^2 + 1$.

   a Find the first three terms.

   b Manjit worked out that the 5th term was 101. Explain why he was wrong.

7 The general term of the sequence of square numbers is n^2.

   a Write the first five terms of this sequence.

   b Work out the differences between consecutive terms.

   c Copy and complete this table.

1st square number	1	1
2nd square number	4	$1 + 3$
3rd square number	9	$1 + 3 + 5$
4th square number		
5th square number		
6th square number		

   d What square number is equal to
   $1 + 3 + 5 + 6 + 7 + 9 + 11 + 13 + 15 + 17 + 19$?
   Do not work out the addition!

This spread will show you how to:

● Describe and find the general term of a linear sequence

Keywords
Arithmetic
   sequence
Coefficient
Common
   difference
Linear

In some *n*th terms, the **coefficient** of *n* is negative.
For example, $5 - 3n$. The coefficient of *n* is -3.

Example

Write the first five terms of the sequence whose *n*th term is $5 - 3n$.

1st term: $5 - 3 \times 1 = 2$
2nd term: $5 - 3 \times 2 = -1$
3rd term: $5 - 3 \times 3 = -4$
4th term: $5 - 3 \times 4 = -7$
5th term: $5 - 3 \times 5 = -10$

The coefficient of *n*
is the number that
n is multiplied by.
In this example,
the coefficient of *n*
is -3.

● For a **linear** sequence, the **common difference** tells you the multiple of *n* in the general form.

Here are some linear sequences you have met before.

Name of sequence	General term	Sequence	Common difference
Multiples of 2	$2n$	2, 4, 6, 8, 10, …	$+2$
Multiples of 3	$3n$	3, 6, 9, 12, 15, …	$+3$
Multiples of 4	$4n$	4, 8, 12, 16, 20, …	$+4$
Multiples of 5	$5n$	5, 10, 15, 20, 25, …	$+5$
Multiples of -3	$-3n$	$-3, -6, -9, -12, -15, …$	-3

Another name for a
linear sequence is
an **arithmetic
sequence**.

● To find the general term of a linear sequence.
   ● work out the common difference
   ● write the common difference as the coefficient of *n*
   ● compare the terms in the sequence to the multiples of *n*

Example

Find the general term of the sequence
5, 8, 11, 14, 17 …

The common difference is $+3$.
The *n*th term contains the term $3n$.
Compare the sequence to the multiples of 3:

$3n$	3	6	9	12	15
Term	5	8	11	14	17

Each term is 2 more than a multiple of 3.
The general term is $3n + 2$.

Check:
$n = 1 \rightarrow 3 + 2 = 5$
$n = 2 \rightarrow 6 + 2 = 8$
$n = 3 \rightarrow 9 + 2 = 11$
…

1 Write the first five terms for the sequence with nth term

    a $10 - 2n$ **b** $2 - n$ **c** $18 - 4n$ **d** $20 - 7n$

    e $16 - 3n$ **f** $6 - 5n$ **g** $-2n - 5$ **h** $30 - 5n$

    i $8 - 3n$ **j** $14 - 10n$ **k** $6 - n^2$ **l** $2n^2 - 10$

2 **a** Find the common difference for the series 5, 9, 13, 17, 21, ...

    b Copy and complete:
    The nth term contains the term $\square n$.

    c Copy and complete this table to show the sequence and the multiples of n.

Sequence					
$\square n$					

    d Compare the terms in the sequence to the multiples of n and write the general term for the sequence.

3 Follow the steps in question 2 to find the general terms for these sequences.

    a 11, 17, 23, 29, 35, ...   **b** 1, 10, 19, 28, 37, ...

    c 15, 22, 29, 36, 43, ...   **d** $-10, -6, -2, 2, 6, ...$

    e 20, 17, 14, 11, 8, ...   **f** 15, 11, 7, 3, -1, ...

    g 16, 8, 0, -8, -16, ...   **h** 31, 23, 15, 7, -1, ...

4 Find the nth term for each of these arithmetic sequences.

    a 7, 11, 15, 19, 23, ...   **b** $-6, -2, 2, 6, 10, ...$

    c 32, 23, 14, 5, -4, ...   **d** 15, 9, 3, -3, 9, ...

5 Copy and complete these tables for linear sequences.

a

Term number	Term
1	7
2	10
3	
4	16
5	19
n	

b

Term number	Term
1	-4
2	2
3	8
4	
5	20
10	
n	

This spread will show you how to:

● Explain how the formula for the general term of a linear expression works

Keywords
Common
 difference
*n*th term
Pattern

You can find the **nth term** for a sequence of **patterns**.

Here is a pattern made of pencils: The next pattern in the sequence is:

3 pencils

5 pencils

Examiner's tip:
The techniques described here are useful in many coursework assignments.

You add 2 pencils each time.

The *n*th term is an expression for the number of pencils in the *n*th pattern.
To find the *n*th term, write the numbers of pencils in a table.

Pattern number	1	2	3	4	5
Number of pencils	3	5	7	9	11

You can work out the number of pencils in pattern 5 by continuing the number sequence.

The number sequence 3, 5, 7, 9, 11 has **common difference** 2.
So the *n*th term contains the term $2n$.

2n	2	4	6	8	10
Sequence	3	5	7	9	11

Each term is 1 more than a multiple of 2.
The *n*th term is $2n + 1$.

Here are some patterns made up of dots.

○ ○   ○ ○ ○   ○ ○ ○ ○
○ ○ ○   ○ ○ ○ ○   ○ ○ ○ ○ ○

Pattern   Pattern   Pattern
number 1   number 2   number 3

Pattern number	1	2	3	4	5
Number of dots	5	7			

a Draw the next pattern in the sequence.
b Copy and complete the table for the first five terms.
c How many dots will there be in pattern number 10?

a ○ ○ ○ ○ ○ ○
   ○ ○ ○ ○ ○ ○

Pattern
number 4

b

Pattern number	1	2	3	4	5
Number of dots	5	7	9	11	13

Each time you add 2 dots – one to each row

c The number sequence continues:

Pattern number	6	7	8	9	10
Number of dots	15	17	19	21	23

There will be 23 dots in the 10th pattern.

1 Here is a sequence of patterns made from squares.

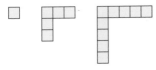

Pattern   Pattern   Pattern
number 1   number 2   number 3

Pattern number	1	2	3	4	5
Number of squares					

  a Draw the next pattern in the sequence.

  b Copy and complete the table for the first five terms.

  c How many squares will there be in pattern number 10?

2 Here are some patterns made from crosses.

```
× × ×    × × × × ×    × × × × × × ×
×   ×    ×       ×    ×           ×
×   ×    ×       ×    ×           ×
× × ×    × × × × ×    × × × × × × ×
```

Pattern number	1	2	3	4	5
Number of crosses					

  a Draw the next pattern in the sequence.

  b Copy and complete the table for the first five terms.

  c Describe in words how the sequence grows.

  d Work out the common difference for the number sequence.

  e Find the nth term for the number sequence.

3 Here is a sequence of patterns of squares.

  a Write the number of squares in the next two patterns.
     Explain how you worked them out.

  b Find, in terms of n, an expression for the number of dots in the
     nth pattern.

  c Find the number of dots in the 50th pattern.

4 Repeat question **3** for these sequences of patterns.

  a

  b

This spread will show you how to:

● Explain how the formula for the general term of a linear expression works

Keywords
Justify

A farmer uses hurdles to build pens for his sheep.
For the first pen he needs four hurdles.

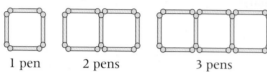

1 pen   2 pens   3 pens

To make each new pen, he adds three more hurdles.
The sequence for the number of hurdles is

4, 7, 10, 13, 16, ...

Common difference = 3

nth term = $3n + 1$

n	1	2	3	4	5
$3n$	3	6	9	12	15
Sequence	4	7	10	13	16

You can **justify** the nth term by looking at the pattern it comes from.

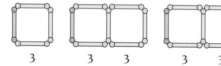

3   3   3   3   3   3

Justify means
explain why it is
correct.

The nth pattern will have n lots of three hurdles (or $3n$), plus the one on the left-hand side.

Here is a sequence of patterns of dots.

a Write the number of dots in the first five patterns.
b Find, in terms of n, an expression
  for the number of dots in the nth pattern.
c Justify your expression in n by comparing it with the dot patterns.

a 5, 7, 9, 11, 13
b Common difference = 2
  Number of dots in nth
  pattern is $2n + 3$.

n	1	2	3	4	5
$2n$	2	4	6	8	10
Sequence	5	7	9	11	13

Each term is 3
more than a
multiple of 2.

c The nth pattern will have
  $2 \times n$ dots, arranged with n
  above and n below the
  horizontal row, plus the
  horizontal row of three dots.

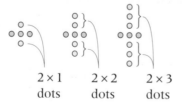

2×1 2×2 2×3
dots   dots   dots

Look for what
changes (the $2n$
term) and what
stays the same (the
$+3$ term).

1 Here is a sequence of patterns of dots.

   a Write the number of dots in the first five patterns.

   b Find, in terms of n, an expression for the number of dots in the nth pattern.

   c Justify your expression in n by comparing it with the dot patterns.

2 Kim is designing bead patterns for different-sized cushions. Here are her patterns for the first three sizes.

   a Write the numbers of beads in the patterns for the first five sizes.

   b Find, in terms of n, an expression for the number of beads for the nth size pattern.

   c Justify your expression in n by comparing it with the bead patterns.

Size 1   Size 2   Size 3

3 Jas is building a house of cards.

   a How many cards does he add each time?

   b Write down the number of cards for the first five stages.

   c Find, in terms of n, an expression for the number of cards in the nth stage.

   d Justify your expression in n by comparing it with the diagrams.

   e There are 52 cards in a pack. If Jas continues his pattern, can he use them all? Explain your answer.

Stage 1   Stage 2   Stage 3

4 Dave is building a fence from vertical and horizontal posts.
The fence grows like this:

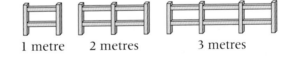

1 metre   2 metres   3 metres

   a Describe in words how the fence grows.

   b How many posts will he need for 5 metres of fence?

   c Find an expression in n for the number of posts for an n metre fence.

   d Justify your expression in n by comparing it with the fence diagrams.

   e Dave's garden is 26 metres long. How many posts will he need?

5 A car hire company charges.

> Small car = £20 per day + £50   Medium car = £25 per day + £60
> Large car = £30 per day + £70

   a Copy and complete this table of charges for 1 to 7 days.

   b How would you work out the charge for

      i large car for 10 days
      ii medium car for 14 days
      iii small car for n days?

		Number of days						
		1	2	3	4	5	6	7
Type of car	Small							
	Medium							
	Large							

A3

Exam review

Key objectives

- Generate terms of a sequence using term-to-term and position-to-term definitions of the sequence
- Use linear expressions to describe the nth term of an arithmetic sequence, justifying its form by reference to the activity or context from which it was generated

1 Here are some terms of a sequence:
3rd term is 5, 4th term is 7, 5th term is 9, 6th term is 11.

  a Find the formula for the nth term, T_n.   (2)

  b Hence find the 1st and 2nd term of the sequence.   (2)

2 Here are some patterns made with sticks.

The graph shows the number of sticks m used in pattern number n:

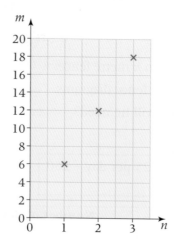

Write down a formula for m in terms of n.   (2)

(Edexcel Ltd., 2003)

D2

This unit will show you how to

- Draw and produce relevant diagrams and charts to display data
- Recognise the difference between discrete and continuous data, using appropriate diagrams and charts
- Draw and use frequency diagrams for continuous data
- Draw and use stem-and-leaf diagrams
- Draw and use line graphs for time series, recognising data trends
- Draw and use scatter graphs, and compare two data sets
- Understand correlation and use lines of best fit

Before you start ...

You should be able to answer these questions.

Review

1 Calculate the value of the angle *x*.

a

b

Unit S2

2 Calculate.

a 360 ÷ 3	**b** 360 ÷ 8	**c** 360 ÷ 6
d 360 ÷ 5	**e** 360 ÷ 60	**f** 360 ÷ 18
g 360 ÷ 12	**h** 360 ÷ 20	**i** 360 ÷ 36

Key stage 3

3 Match the axis with its direction.

a *x*-axis   **b** *y*-axis

i vertical   **ii** horizontal

Key stage 3

4 Put these numbers in order of size, smallest first.

a 746, 751, 665, 714, 661, 756, 741.

b 1.8, 0.9, 1.5, 2.1, 2.2, 0.5.

c 45.9, 44.6, 49.5, 46.4, 45.6.

Unit N2

5 Give the coordinates of

a point A

b point B

Key stage 3

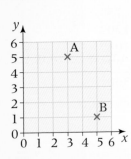

Diagrams and charts

This spread will show you how to:

● Draw and produce relevant diagrams and charts to display data

Keywords

Bar chart
Bar-line chart
Category
Pictogram
Pie chart
Sector

You can use a variety of diagrams and charts to display data.

Pictograms use symbols to represent the size of each category.

Karl's films

Western	
Horror	
Adventure	

 represents 2 films

Bar charts use bars to represent frequencies.

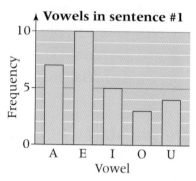

Notice the gaps between the bars.

Bar-line charts use vertical lines to represent numerical data.

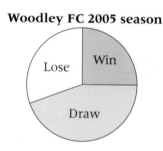

Pie charts use sectors of a circle to represent the size of each category.

Woodley FC 2005 season

The size of the **sector** is proportional to the frequency.

Example

240 people are asked to name their favourite fruit. The results are shown.

Fruit	Apple	Banana	Orange	Other
Number of people	50	80	72	38

Draw a pie chart to illustrate the information.

Calculate the angle for one person:

$360° ÷ 240 = 1.5°$

Calculate the angles for each category:

Apple	$50 × 1.5° =$	$75°$
Banana	$80 × 1.5° =$	$120°$
Orange	$72 × 1.5° =$	$108°$
Other	$38 × 1.5° =$	$57°$
Add to check:		$360°$

Measure, colour and label the sectors.

Favourite fruits

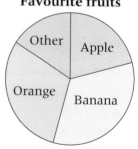

Check by adding the angles of the sectors.

1 The pictogram shows the results for the 'Best Live Band' survey.

U2	
Queen	
Oasis	
Rolling Stones	
Radiohead	

represents 100 votes

The votes were as follows

U2	Queen	Oasis	Rolling Stones	Radiohead
500	350	300	250	150

a Calculate the total number of votes made.

b Copy and complete the pictogram.

2 A football team plays 36 matches in the season. The results are

Win	Draw	Lose
15	8	?

a Calculate the number of matches that were lost.

b Calculate the angle one match represents in a pie chart.

c Calculate the angle of each category in the pie chart.

d Draw a pie chart to show the information.

3 The weather record for 60 days is shown in the frequency table.

a Calculate the angle one day represents in a pie chart.

b Calculate the angle of each category in the pie chart.

c Draw a pie chart to show the data.

Weather	Number of days
Sunny	15
Cloudy	18
Rainy	14
Snowy	3
Windy	10

4 A fishing catch consisted of 480 fish. The frequency table shows the amount of each type.

a Calculate each angle of a pie chart to illustrate this information.

b Draw the pie chart.

Fish	Frequency
Cod	120
Plaice	100
Haddock	96
Sardines	116
Mackerel	48

This spread will show you how to:

● Recognise the difference between discrete and continuous data, using appropriate diagrams and charts

Keywords
Bar chart
Continuous
Discrete
Frequency
  polygon
Grouped
Histogram

● **Discrete** data can only take exact values (usually collected by counting).

● **Continuous** data can take any value (collected by measuring).

You must be careful if the data is **grouped**.

You can use a **bar chart** to display grouped discrete data.

You can use a **histogram** to display grouped continuous data.

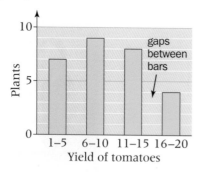

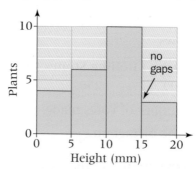

● You can use a **frequency polygon** to display grouped **continuous** data.

Frequency polygons use straight lines drawn from the top centre of each bar.

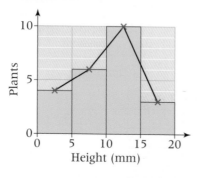

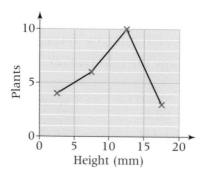

Plot the points at the mid-points of the class intervals.

The times taken, in seconds, to run 100 m are shown in the table.

Time (seconds)	Number of people
$0 < t \leqslant 10$	0
$10 < t \leqslant 20$	4
$20 < t \leqslant 30$	6
$30 < t \leqslant 40$	3

Draw a frequency diagram to illustrate this information.

Either the histogram or the frequency polygon answers this question.

Don't draw both diagrams.

1 a Copy and complete the frequency table using these heights of people.

Height (cm)	Tally	Number of people
$130 < h \leqslant 140$		
$140 < h \leqslant 150$		
$150 < h \leqslant 160$		
$160 < h \leqslant 170$		
$170 < h \leqslant 180$		

153 134 155 142 140 163 150 135
170 156 171 161 141 153 144 163
140 160 172 157 136 160 134 154
176 154 173 179 160 152 170 148
151 165 138 143 147 144 156 139

b Copy and complete the histogram on graph paper.

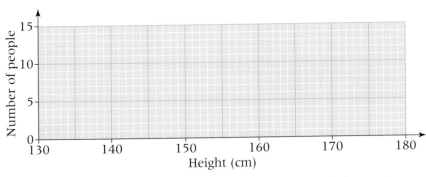

c Draw a frequency polygon on the same axes and graph paper.

2 The depth, in millimetres, of a reservoir is measured daily throughout April.

Draw a histogram to show the depths.

Depth (mm)	Number of days
$0 < d \leqslant 5$	1
$5 < d \leqslant 10$	5
$10 < d \leqslant 15$	14
$15 < d \leqslant 20$	8
$20 < d \leqslant 25$	2

3 The exam marks of 40 students are shown in the frequency table.

Draw a bar chart to show the exam marks.

Exam mark (%)	Number of students
1 to 20	4
21 to 40	9
41 to 60	13
61 to 80	11
81 to 100	3

4 The times taken for 50 runners of the London Marathon are shown in the frequency table.

a Draw a histogram to show the times.

b Draw the frequency polygon on the same diagram.

Time (hours)	Number of runners
$0 < t \leqslant 1$	0
$1 < t \leqslant 2$	1
$2 < t \leqslant 3$	23
$3 < t \leqslant 4$	18
$4 < t \leqslant 5$	8

Stem-and-leaf diagrams

This spread will show you how to:

● Draw and use stem-and-leaf diagrams

Keywords
Ordered
Stem-and-leaf
   diagram

● You can use a **stem-and-leaf diagram** to display numerical data.

A stem-and-leaf diagram shows
● the shape of the distribution
● each individual value of the data.

This stem-and-leaf diagram is **ordered**, as the data is in numerical order.

130	5
120	0 6 9
110	2 2 6 8
100	3 7

stem   leaf

This means 135.

This means 120.

Key: | 110 | 2 | means 112

Always give a key.

Example

The weights, in kilograms, of 10 parcels are shown:

4.2   3.7   3.5   2.8   1.5
0.9   2.4   1.4   1.0   2.4

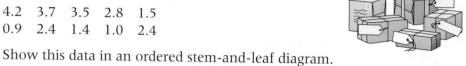

Show this data in an ordered stem-and-leaf diagram.

First choose the stem.
Go up in ones.

0.0	
1.0	
2.0	
3.0	
4.0	

You can order the data before you draw the diagram if you want.

Then write in the leaves.

0.0	9
1.0	5 4 0
2.0	8 4 4
3.0	7 5
4.0	2

↓ order

Finally, order the leaves.

0.0	9
1.0	0 4 5
2.0	4 4 8
3.0	5 7
4.0	2

Key: | 1.0 | 5 | means 1.5 kg

Examiner's tip:
The key is essential to gain full marks.

1 The times, in seconds, for a sample of 30 students to guess
2 minutes are

112	110	108	131	125	130
120	121	117	135	116	110
140	108	142	126	125	136
119	126	137	108	144	119
120	134	117	111	121	138

Copy and complete the ordered stem-and-leaf diagram.

100	
110	
120	
130	
140	

Key:

| 120 | 3 | means 123 seconds

2 The times taken, in seconds, for 25 athletes to run 400 metres are
given.

44.3	44.4	43.3	43.2	44.0
45.2	45.0	44.5	45.6	43.9
46.5	46.3	46.0	46.5	44.7
46.9	44.1	43.8	45.0	46.9
43.0	46.1	45.1	43.8	45.9

Draw an ordered stem-and-leaf diagram, using stems of 43.0, 44.0,
45.0 and 46.0. Remember to give the key.

3 a Use the temperatures in °C to draw an ordered stem-and-leaf
diagram. Choose suitable stems.

	°C	°F		°C	°F		°C	°F
Athens	20	68	**Hong Kong**	32	90	**Paris**	26	79
Berlin	31	88	**London**	19	66	**Perth**	27	81
Brussels	25	77	**Los Angeles**	20	68	**Rome**	26	79
Cairo	34	93	**Malaga**	23	73	**Sydney**	19	66
Cape Town	17	63	**Malta**	26	79	**Tel Aviv**	28	82
Corfu	26	79	**Miami**	29	84	**Tenerife**	23	73
Dublin	14	57	**Moscow**	22	72	**Tokyo**	23	73
Edinburgh	14	57	**Nairobi**	20	68	**Toronto**	19	66
Faro	24	75	**New York**	21	70	**Vancouver**	22	72
Guernsey	14	57	**Oslo**	10	50	**Vienna**	29	84

b Use the temperatures in °F to draw another ordered stem-and-leaf
diagram.

Time series graphs

This spread will show you how to:

- Draw and use line graphs for time series, recognising data trends

You can use a **line graph** to show how data changes as time passes.

The data can be discrete or continuous.

The temperature of a liquid is measured every minute.

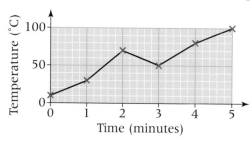

Time is always the **horizontal** axis.

This is an example of a time **series graph**.

- A time series graph shows
  - how the data changes over time, or the **trend**
  - each individual value of the data.

Time could be seconds, minutes, hours, days, weeks, months or years.

Example

The table shows the average monthly rainfall, in centimetres, in Sheffield over the last 30 years.

Month	Jan	Feb	Mar	Apr	May	Jun	Jul	Aug	Sep	Oct	Nov	Dec
Rainfall (cm)	8.7	6.3	6.8	6.3	5.6	6.7	5.1	6.4	6.4	7.4	7.8	9.2

Draw a line graph to show this information.

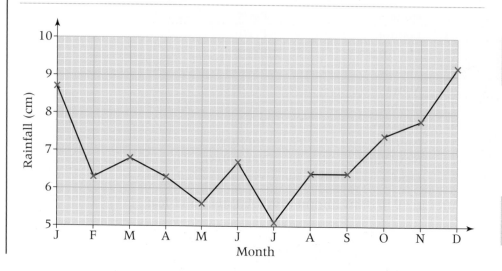

Each division on the vertical axis is 0.2 cm.

The vertical scale doesn't have to start at zero.

1 The numbers of DVDs rented from a shop during a week are shown.

Sunday	Monday	Tuesday	Wednesday	Thursday	Friday	Saturday
18	9	7	11	15	35	36

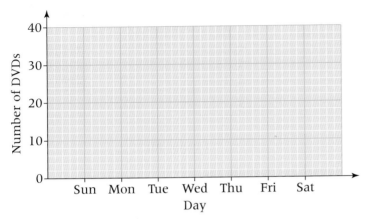

Copy and complete the line graph, choosing a suitable vertical scale.

2 Every year on his birthday, Peter's weight, in kilograms, is measured.

Age	2	3	4	5	6	7	8	9	10	11	12	13
Weight (kg)	14	16	18	20	22	25	28	31	34	38.5	40	45

Draw a line graph to show the weights.

3 The hours of sunshine each month are shown in the table.

Jan	Feb	Mar	Apr	May	Jun	Jul	Aug	Sep	Oct	Nov	Dec
43	57	105	131	185	176	194	183	131	87	53	35

Draw a line graph to show the hours of sunshine.

4 The daily viewing figures, in millions, for a reality TV show are shown.

Day	Sat	Sun	Mon	Tue	Wed	Thu	Fri
Viewers (in millions)	3.2	3.8	4.3	4.5	3.1	5.2	7.1

Draw a line graph to show the viewing figures.

5 The men's world record times for running 100 m are shown.

Draw a line graph to show the world record times.

Year	Athlete	Time (sec)
1968	Jim Hines (USA)	9.95
1983	Calvin Smith (USA)	9.93
1988	Carl Lewis (USA)	9.92
1991	Leroy Burrell (USA)	9.90
1991	Carl Lewis (USA)	9.86
1994	Leroy Burrell (USA)	9.85
1996	Donovan Bailey (Can)	9.84
1999	Maurice Greene (USA)	9.79
2002	Tim Montgomery (USA)	9.78
2005	Asafa Powell (Jam)	9.77

Ben Johnson's world records of 9.83 secs in 1987 and 9.79 secs in 1988 were both annulled after he tested positive for drugs at the Seoul Olympics.

Be careful with the horizontal axis (don't miss out the 1970s!)

This spread will show you how to:

- Draw and use scatter graphs, and compare two data sets
- Understand correlation and use lines of best fit

Keywords

Correlation
Line of best fit
Relationship
Scatter graph
Variables

You can use a **scatter graph** to compare two sets of data, for example, height and weight.

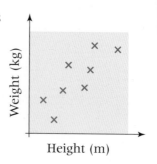

The data can be discrete or continuous.

- The data is collected in pairs and plotted as coordinates.
- If the points lie roughly in a straight line, there is a **relationship** or **correlation** between the two **variables**.

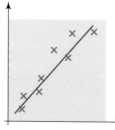

Positive correlation

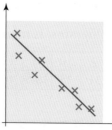

Negative correlation

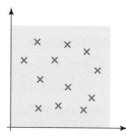

No correlation

Plotted points are not joined on a scatter diagram.

The straight line is the **line of best fit**.

Example

The exam results (%) for Paper 1 and Paper 2 for 10 students are shown.

| Paper 1 | 56 | 72 | 50 | 24 | 44 | 80 | 68 | 48 | 60 | 36 |
| Paper 2 | 44 | 64 | 40 | 20 | 36 | 64 | 56 | 36 | 50 | 24 |

a Draw a scatter graph and line of best fit.

b Describe the relationship between the Paper 1 results and Paper 2 results.

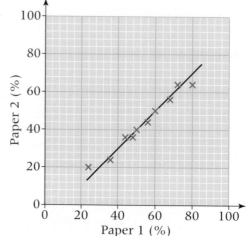

a Plot the exam marks as coordinates. The line of best fit should be close to all the points, with approximately the same number of crosses on either side of the line.

b Students who did well on Paper 1 did well on Paper 2. Students who did not do well on Paper 1 did not do well on Paper 2 either.

The line of best fit does not have to pass through (0, 0).

1 Describe the type of correlation for each scatter graph.

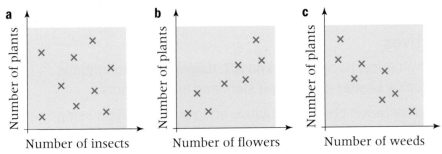

a Number of plants / Number of insects

b Number of plants / Number of flowers

c Number of plants / Number of weeds

2 The table shows the amount of water used to water plants and the daily maximum temperature.

Water (litres)	25	26	31	24	45	40	5	13	18	28
Maximum temperature (°C)	24	21	25	19	30	28	15	18	20	27

a Copy and complete the scatter graph for this information.

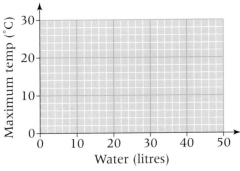

b State the type of correlation shown in the scatter graph.

c Copy and complete these sentences:

   i As the temperatures increases, the amount of water used _____.

   ii As the temperature decreases, the amount of water used _____.

3 The times taken, in minutes, to run a mile and the shoe sizes of ten athletes are shown in the table.

Shoe size	10	$7\frac{1}{2}$	5	9	6	$8\frac{1}{2}$	$7\frac{1}{2}$	$6\frac{1}{2}$	8	7
Time (mins)	9	8	8	7	5	13	15	12	5	6

a Draw a scatter graph to show this information.

   Use 2 cm to represent 1 shoe size on the horizontal axis.
   Use 2 cm to represent 5 minutes on the vertical axis.

b State the type of correlation shown in the scatter graph.

c Describe, in words, any relationship that the graph shows.

Key objectives

- Draw and produce, using paper and ICT, diagrams for continuous data, including scatter graphs and stem-and-leaf diagrams
- Distinguish between positive, negative and zero correlation using lines of best fit

1 The table shows the exam results (%) for Paper 1 and Paper 2 for ten students.

Paper 1	55	82	30	35	70	49	64	72	80	59
Paper 2	46	70	45	30	73	50	63	60	76	60

a Copy and complete the scatter graph to show the results in the table. (1)

b Draw a line of best fit for the data and use this to describe the relationship between the results of the two exams.

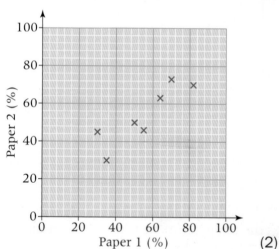

(2)

2 Here are the times, in minutes, taken to change some tyres:

    5   10   15   12   8   7   20   35   24   15
    20   33   15   25   10   8   10   20   16   10

Draw a stem-and-leaf diagram to show these times. (3)

(Edexcel Ltd., 2003)

A4

This unit will show you how to

- Write an equation to represent a function
- Write the input and output values of a function as coordinate pairs
- Plot straight line graphs of functions
- Understand the equation forms of horizontal and vertical graphs
- Understand the equation form of a general straight line graph
- Understand that parallel lines have the same gradient

Before you start ...

You should be able to answer these questions.

Review

1 Write the outputs for these function machines.

a

input   output

-2
0
1 $\rightarrow$ $+5$ $\Rightarrow$
3

b

input   output

-2
0
1 $\rightarrow$ $\times 3$ $\Rightarrow$
3

Unit N1

2 Work out the value of each expression when $x = 4$.

   a $x + 5$ **b** $x - 6$ **c** $3x$ **d** $\frac{x}{2}$

Unit A2

3 Plot these coordinates on a copy of this grid.

  a $(3, 4)$
  b $(1, 3)$
  c $(-1, 2)$
  d $(4, -5)$
  e $(-3, -4)$
  f $(-3, 2)$

Key stage 3

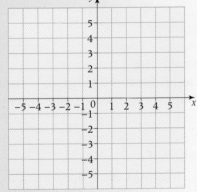

4 If $x + y = 10$

  a Find the value of x when $y = 6$.
  b Find the value of y when $x = 2$.

Unit A2

5 Solve these equations.

  a $3x + 2 = 11$ **b** $4x - 1 = 7$

Unit A2

A4.1 Functions

This spread will show you how to:

- Write an equation to represent a function
- Write the input and output values of a function as coordinate pairs

Keywords
Equation
Function
Maps

- A **function** is a rule that **maps** one number to another number.

You can draw a function machine and work out the outputs for different inputs.

Draw a function machine for the function $x \rightarrow 4x + 7$.
Work out the outputs for the inputs $-2, -1, 0, 1, 2$.

Input, x		Output, y
-2		-1
-1		3
$0 \rightarrow$	$4x+7$ $\Rightarrow$	7
1		11
2		15

Substitute the input value for x in the function machine.

- You can write an **equation** to represent a function.

For the function $x \rightarrow \boxed{4x+7} \Rightarrow$ the equation is $y = 4x + 7$.

Each input value x gives an output value y.

The function links the two variables x and y.

- You can write the input and output values as **coordinate pairs** (x, y).

This function machine is for the function $x \rightarrow 2x - 9$.

Input $x \rightarrow \boxed{2x-9} \Rightarrow$ Output

a Write an equation to represent the function.
b Work out the output values, y, for input values of x from -3 to $+3$.
c Write the inputs and outputs as coordinate pairs.

x-values from -3 to $+3$ are:
$-3, -2, -1, 0, 1, 2, 3$.

a $y = 2x - 9$

b

Input		Output	**c**
-3		-15	$(-3, -15)$
-2		-13	$(-2, -13)$
-1		-11	$(-1, -11)$
$0 \rightarrow$	$2x-9$ $\Rightarrow$	-9	$(0, -9)$
1		-7	$(1, -7)$
2		-5	$(2, -5)$
3		-3	$(3, -3)$

1 Find the outputs for the inputs given in these function machines:

a
0
1
2
3
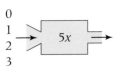

b 1
2
3
4
5
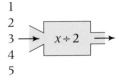

c −2
−1
0
1
2
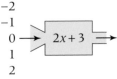

d −3
−2
−1
0
1
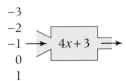

e −8
−7
−6
−5
−4
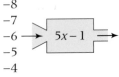

f −2
0
2
4
6
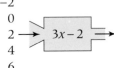

2 For each function
  i draw a function machine
  ii work out the outputs for the inputs −2, −1, 0, 1, 2.
  The first one is started for you.

  a $x \rightarrow 3x + 2$ −2
                              −1
                              0 → 3x + 2
                              1
                              2

  b $x \rightarrow 5x + 2$ **c** $x \rightarrow 2x - 3$
  d $x \rightarrow 4x + 7$ **e** $x \rightarrow \frac{1}{2}x + 3$
  f $x \rightarrow 3x - 11$ **g** $x \rightarrow \frac{1}{2}x - 2$

3 **a** Draw the function machine for $x \rightarrow 2x + 6$.
  b Write an equation to represent the function.
  c Work out the output values, y, for values of x from −3 to +3.
  d Write the inputs and outputs as coordinate pairs.

4 Repeat question **3** for the function $x \rightarrow \frac{1}{2}x - 1$.

5 Match each equation to a function machine and a set of coordinate pairs.

  a $y = x + 3$ (i) → 2x + 1   (1) (−2, −2), (−1, 1), (0, 4), (1, 7), (2, 10)

  b $y = 2x + 1$ (ii) → x + 3   (2) (−2, −9), (−1, −7), (0, −5), (1, −3), (2, −1)

  c $y = 3x + 4$ (iii) → 4x − 1   (3) (−2, 1), (−1, 2), (0, 3), (1, 4), (2, 5)

  d $y = 4x - 1$ (iv) → 2x − 5   (4) (−2, −9), (−1, −5), (0, −1), (1, 3), (2, 7)

  e $y = 2x - 5$ (v) → 3x + 4   (5) (−2, −3), (−1, −1), (0, 1), (1, 3), (2, 5)

123

Drawing linear graphs

This spread will show you how to:

- Plot straight line graphs of functions

You can write the inputs and outputs of a function as **coordinate pairs**.

For example, $y = 2x + 3$

x y
-2 -1 $(-2, -1)$
-1 1 $(-1, 1)$
$0 \rightarrow$ $\boxed{2x + 3}$ $\Rightarrow$ 3 $(0, 3)$
1 5 $(1, 5)$
2 7 $(2, 7)$

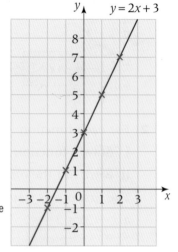

$y = 2x + 3$

You can write the coordinate pairs for a function using a table.

x	-2	-1	0	1	2
y	$2 \times -2 + 3 = -1$	1	3	5	7
	$(-2, -1)$	$(-1, 1)$	$(0, 3)$	$(1, 5)$	$(2, 7)$

You can plot these coordinate pairs on a grid.

- A function is **linear** if its **graph** is a straight line.

Example

a Copy and complete the table of values for $y = 3x - 2$.

x	-2	-1	0	1	2
y					

b Write the coordinate pairs.
c Draw the graph of $y = 3x - 2$.

a

x	-2	-1	0	1	2
y	-8	-5	-2	1	4

b $(-2, -8)$ $(-1, -5)$ $(0, -2)$ $(1, 1)$ $(2, 4)$

c

$y = 3x - 2$

1 **a** Copy and complete the table of values for $y = 3x + 3$.

x	-2	-1	0	1	2
y		0			9

b Write the coordinate pairs.

c Copy the coordinate grid on the right on to square grid paper.

d Plot the coordinate pairs from part **b** on your grid.

e Join these points with a straight line.

f Label the line with its equation.

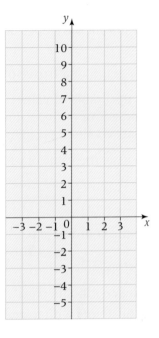

2 **a** Copy and complete the table of values for $y = -x + 3$.

x	-2	-1	0	1	2
y	$-1 \times -2 + 3$ $= 2 + 3 = 5$			2	

b Write the coordinate pairs.

c Copy the coordinate grid from question **1** on to squared grid paper.

d Plot the coordinate pairs from part **b** on your grid.

e Join these points with a straight line.

f Label the line with its equation.

3 **a** Copy and complete the table of values for $x + y = 6$.

x	-2	-1	0	1	2
y	8		6		

b Write the coordinate pairs.

c Copy the coordinate grid from question **1** on to square grid paper.

d Plot the coordinate pairs from part **b** on your grid.

e Join these points with a straight line.

f Label the line with its equation.

4 **a** Copy and complete the table of values for $y = 2x - 5$.

x	-2	-1	0	1	2
y	-9			-3	

b Write the coordinate pairs.

c Draw an appropriate coordinate grid on to square grid paper.

d Plot the coordinate pairs from part **b** on your grid.

e Join these points with a straight line.

f Label the line with its equation.

More linear graphs

This spread will show you how to:

- Plot straight line graphs of functions

Keywords

Explicitly
Implicit form
Implicitly
Subject

To plot a graph of a **function**

For example, $y = x - 2$

- Draw up a table of values.
  1. Choose four or five values of x, including negative values, positive values and zero.

  For example, $x = -2, -1, 0, 1, 2$

  2. Calculate the value of y for each value of x.

  $y = x - 2$

x	-2	-1	0	1	2
y	-4	-3	-2	-1	0

- Write the coordinate pairs.

  $(-2, -4)\ (-1, -3)\ (0, -2)\ (1, -1)\ (2, 0)$

- Draw a suitable grid.

  The x-axis needs to go from -2 to 2
  The y-axis needs to go from -4 to 0

- Plot the coordinate pairs on the grid.
- Join the points with a straight line.
- Label the line with its equation.

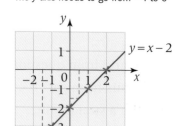

You can read other values from a graph.

When $x = 0.5$, $y = -1.5$
When $y = -3.5$, $x = -1.5$

You can also work these out from the function

When $x = 0.5$, $y = 0.5 - 2 = -1.5$
When $y = -3.5$, $-3.5 = x - 2$
$\qquad\qquad\quad 2 - 3.5 = x - 2 + 2$
$\qquad\qquad\quad -1.5 = x$
$\qquad\qquad\qquad\quad x = -1.5$

- An equation gives y **explicitly** in terms of x when y is the **subject** of the equation.
  $y = x - 2$ gives y explicitly in terms of x.

- An equation gives y **implicitly** in terms of x when y is **not** the subject of the equation.
  $x + y = 4$ gives y **implicitly** in terms of x.

For an equation in **implicit form**

$x + y = 4$ $\qquad$ $x + 0 = 4$ so
$\qquad\qquad\qquad\qquad x = 4$

- Draw up a table of values.
- Calculate **a** the value of y when $x = 0$
  and $\qquad$ **b** the value of x when $y = 0$.

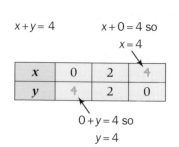

$0 + y = 4$ so
$\qquad y = 4$

1 Draw a graph of each of these functions.

   a $y = 3x + 1$ **b** $y = 2x - 2$ **c** $y = \frac{1}{2}x + 6$ **d** $y = -3x + 2$

2 Draw a graph of each of these functions given in implicit form.

   a $x + y = 5$ **b** $y - x = 3$ **c** $2x + y = 6$ **d** $5x + y = 10$

> In each of these questions choose values of x from −2 to 2. Work out the values of y, then draw appropriate axes.

3 Draw a graph of $y = -2x + 3$.
  Use your graph to find
  - the value of y when $x = 0.5$
  - the value of x when $y = 0$.

4 Draw a graph of $y = 4x + 1$.
  Use your graph to find
  - the value of y when $x = -0.5$
  - the value of x when $y = 7$.

5 Draw a graph of $y = -\frac{1}{2}x + 3$.
  Use your graph to find
  - the value of y when $x = \frac{1}{2}$
  - the value of x when $y = 3\frac{1}{4}$.

6 Draw a graph of $x + y = -2$.
  Rearrange the equation to find
  - the value of y when $x = -2$
  - the value of x when $y = -5$.
  Use your graph to check your answers.

7 Draw graphs of these three functions on the same grid.

   a $y = 2x + 1$ **b** $y = 2x - 2$ **c** $y = 2x + 3$

   What do you notice?

8 Draw graphs of these three functions on the same grid.
  What do you notice?

   a $y = -2x + 1$ **b** $y = -2x - 2$ **c** $y = -2x + 3$

> Compare your graphs from questions 7 and 8. What do you notice?

9 A straight line has the equation $y = 3x + 5$.

   a The point P lies on the line. P has x-coordinate 3.
      Find the y-coordinate of point P.

   b The point Q also lies on the line. Q has y-coordinate −4.
      Find the x-coordinate of point Q.

Horizontal and vertical graphs

This spread will show you how to:

● Understand the equation forms of horizontal and vertical graphs

The points on this **horizontal** graph are
(−3, 2) (−2, 2) (−1, 2) (0, 2) (1, 2) (2, 2) (3, 2)

The y-coordinate is always 2.
The equation of this graph is $y = 2$.

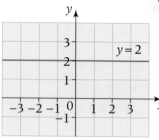

● The equation of a horizontal graph is always y = a number.

To find the number, look at where the graph cuts
the y-axis.

Where a graph
cuts the y-axis
is called the
y-intercept.

The points on this **vertical** graph are
(−1, −3) (−1, −2) (−1, −1) (−1, 0) (−1, 1)
(−1, 2) (−1, 3)

The x-coordinate is always −1.
The equation of this graph is $x = -1$.

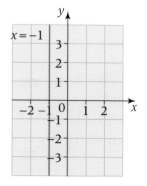

● The equation of a vertical graph is always x = a number.

To find the number, look at where the graph cuts
the x-axis.

Example

a Draw the graphs of $y = 3$ and $x = 2$
on the same pair of axes.

b Find the coordinates of
the point P where the two
graphs cross.

a

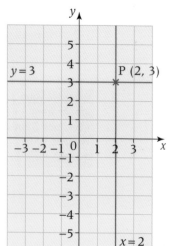

b The coordinates of P are (2, 3).

$y = 3$ is a horizontal graph.
It cuts the y-axis at 3.
$x = 2$ is a vertical graph.
It cuts the x-axis at 2.

1 Write down the equations of these horizontal and vertical graphs.

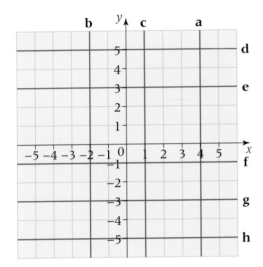

2 Copy the grid from question **1** without the graphs.
Draw these graphs on the same grid.

a $y = 4$ **b** $x = 5$ **c** $y = -2$ **d** $x = -2$ **e** $x = -4$

3 Draw a table like this:

Horizonal lines	Vertical lines

Write these equations into the correct columns of your table:

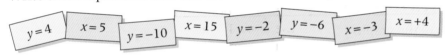

$y = 4$ $x = 5$ $y = -10$ $x = 15$ $y = -2$ $y = -6$ $x = -3$ $x = +4$

4 Use your graphs from question **2** to find the coordinates of the points where these pairs of graphs cross.

a $x = -2$ and $y = 4$ **b** $x = 5$ and $y = -2$ **c** $x = -4$ and $y = 4$

5 Write the coordinates of the points where these pairs of lines cross.

a $x = 2$ and $y = -3$ **b** $x = 1$ and $y = 6$ **c** $x = 3$ and $y = -1$

6 **a** Copy the grid from question **1** without the graphs.
    b Draw a square on your grid using two vertical and two horizontal lines.
    c Write the equations of the four lines.

7 **a** Draw a grid with the x-axis and the y-axis going from -5 to $+5$.
    b Draw the line $y = 0$ on your grid. What is another name for this line?
    c Draw the line $x = 0$ on your grid. What is another name for this line?

8 **a** Draw the graph of $y = 3x + 1$.
    b On the same grid, draw the graph of $y = 7$.
    c Write the coordinates of the point P where the graphs cross.

This spread will show you how to:

- Understand the equation form of a general straight line graph
- Understand that parallel lines have the same gradient

Keywords
Gradient
Intercept
Parallel

- Straight line graphs can be vertical, horizontal or diagonal.

Examples of vertical lines:	Examples of horizontal lines:
$x = 1, x = 5, x = -2, ...$	$y = 2, y = 7, y = -1, ...$

The line $y = 2x + 1$ is a diagonal line.

You can describe a diagonal line by

- how steep it is and
- where it crosses the y-axis (the y-**intercept**).

Gradient measures steepness.

The graph $y = 2x + 1$ has gradient 2.
For every 1 unit across, the graph goes up 2 units.

The graph $y = 2x + 1$ has y-intercept 1.
It crosses the y-axis at $(0, 1)$.

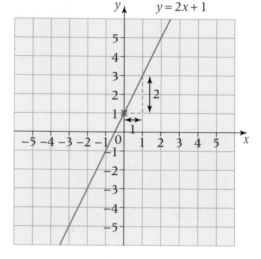

- Diagonal lines have an equation of the form

  $y = mx + c$ where m is the gradient and c is the
                  y-intercept.

Match the equations to the graphs.

a $x = 2$	**b** $y = 3$
c $y = 3x + 2$	**d** $y = 3x - 1$

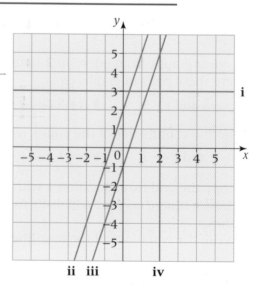

a → **iv**   ($x = 2$ is a vertical graph)

b → **i**   ($y = 3$ is a horizontal graph)

c → **ii**   ($y = 3x + 2$ has y-intercept 2)

d → **iii**   ($y = 3x - 1$ has y-intercept –1)

In the example above, the graphs of $y = 3x + 2$ and $y = 3x - 1$ are **parallel**.

- Parallel lines have the same gradient.

1 Write the gradient and y-intercept for each of these equations.

   a $y = 3x - 1$ **b** $y = 2x + 5$ **c** $y = 4x - 3$ **d** $y = \frac{1}{2}x + 2$

   e $y = 5x + 1$ **f** $y = -3x + 7$

2 Match the equations to the graphs.

   a $y = 3x + 1$

   b $y = 3$

   c $y = 2x + 4$

   d $x = -2$

   e $y = x + 3$

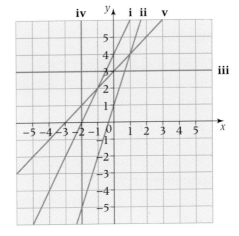

3 Rearrange these equations in the form $y = mx + c$.

   a $x + y = 5$ **b** $y - x = 3$ **c** $x + y = -2$ **d** $x - y = 3$

   e $2x + y = 6$ **f** $5x + y = 9$ **g** $3x + y = -2$ **h** $y - 2x = 5$

   i $2y + x = 4$ **j** $2y - x = 8$ **k** $2x + 4y = 16$ **l** $6x + 2y = 8$

4 List the equations from question **3** whose graphs are parallel to

   a $y = x$ **b** $y = -x$ **c** $y = -3x$ **d** $y = -\frac{1}{2}x$

5 Here are the equations of five straight lines.
   Which three are parallel?

   a $y = 2x + 4$ **b** $2x - y = 3$ **c** $y + 2x = 7$ **d** $4y + 2x = 8$

6 Write these equations for straight lines in order of steepness, starting with the least steep.

   $y = 4x + 3$ $y = 2x - 2$ $y = 3x + 1$ $y = \frac{1}{2}x - 9$ $y = x + 11$

7 Write the equation of a straight line that is parallel to $y = 3x - 1$.

8 Write the equation of a straight line that is parallel to $y + 4x = 2$.

9 Write the equation of the straight line that is parallel to $y = \frac{1}{2}x - 3$ and passes through the point $(0, 4)$.

10 Draw the graph of $y = -x$.
   What can you say about the slope of the graph?
   Is this true for all graphs with negative gradient?
   Draw more graphs to test your idea.

Exam review

Key objectives

- Plot graphs of functions in which y is given explicitly in terms of x or implicitly

- Understand that the form $y = mx + c$ represents a straight line and that m is the gradient of the line and c is the value of the y-intercept

1 Match the equations to the description of their corresponding graphs.

a $y = 3$ **i**   horizontal line

b $y = x + 1$ **ii**   vertical line

c $x = -2$ **iii** diagonal line sloping upwards (from left to right)

d $y = -3x + 2$ **iv** diagonal line sloping downwards (from left to right)   (4)

2 a Copy and complete the table of values for $y = 2x + 3$:   (2)

x	-2	-1	0	1	2	3
y		1	3			

b Copy the grid and use it to draw the graph of $y = 2x + 3$.   (2)

c Use your graph to find

  i   the value of y when $x = -1.3$

  ii the value of x when $y = 5.4$.   (2)

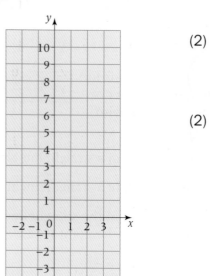

(Edexcel Ltd., 2004)

D3

This unit will show you how to

- Use vocabulary of probability to interpret results
- List all outcomes for single events and identify different mutually exclusive outcomes
- Understand and use the probability scale
- Understand two-way tables and use them to calculate probabilities
- Understand and use estimates or measures of probability and relative frequency
- Compare experimental data and theoretical probabilities

Before you start ...

You should be able to answer these questions.

Review

1 Choose a number from the rectangle that is

4	7	3		9
		10	1	
5		2	8	6

a prime   **b** square
c triangular   **d** a multiple of 3
e a factor of 8

Key stage 3

2 Cancel these fractions to their simplest form.

a $\frac{6}{9}$ **b** $\frac{5}{10}$ **c** $\frac{15}{20}$ **d** $\frac{2}{8}$ **e** $\frac{20}{20}$

Unit N3

3 Copy and complete these calculations.

a $\frac{3}{4} + \frac{1}{4} = ?$ **b** $\frac{7}{10} + \frac{3}{10} = ?$
c $1 - \frac{7}{10} = ?$ **d** $1 - \frac{3}{5} = ?$

Unit N3

4 Copy and complete these calculations.

a $1 - 0.1 = ?$ **b** $1 - 0.6 = ?$
c $1 - 0.15 = ?$

Key stage 3

5 Calculate

a $\frac{1}{3} \times 21$ **b** $\frac{2}{3} \times 21$
c 0.2×80 **d** 0.4×50
e 0.3×60

Unit N1, Unit N3

6 Convert these fractions into decimals.

a $\frac{1}{100}$ **b** $\frac{25}{100}$ **c** $\frac{35}{100}$ **d** $\frac{5}{100}$ **e** $\frac{36}{100}$

Unit N3

This spread will show you how to:

- List all outcomes for single events and identify different mutually exclusive outcomes

Keywords
Equally likely
Event
Outcome
Probability
Systematically

- **An event is an activity.**
  Picking a ball from a bag to see who washes up is an event.

- **An outcome is a possible result of an event.**
  The outcome is either: picking a red ball, Gaz does the washing up; or picking a green ball, Gaz doesn't do the washing up.

Each outcome is **equally likely** as the balls are identical in size and shape.

Probability measures how likely it is that an outcome will happen.

- You can calculate probability using the formula:

  $$\text{Probability of an outcome happening} = \frac{\text{Number of ways the outcome can happen}}{\text{Total number of all possible outcomes}}$$

All probabilities have a value between 0 and 1.
The probability of an outcome can be written as P(outcome).

0 means
impossible.
1 means certain.

Example

An ordinary dice is rolled.

a List the possible outcomes.
b Calculate the probability of choosing
  i a 5
  ii an even number.

a
  or 1, 2, 3, 4, 5, 6.

Draw the 6
outcomes in order
or **systematically**.

b i There is one 5.
  There are 6 possible equally likely outcomes.
  $P(5) = \frac{1}{6}$

ii There are 3 even numbers.
  There are 6 possible outcomes.
  $P(\text{even}) = \frac{3}{6} = \frac{1}{2}$

1 Copy these tables and put each outcome in the appropriate table.

The outcome is impossible
Probability is 0

The outcome is certain
Probability is 1

   a Picking a blue ball from a bag of blue balls.

   b Picking a red ball from a bag of blue balls.

   c Next month will have 7 days.

   d Next year will have 12 months.

   e You will roll an 8 on an ordinary six-sided dice.

2 List all the possible outcomes for these events.

   a spinning a coin

   b rolling a tetrahedron dice (4 faces, numbered 1, 2, 3, 4)

   c picking a letter from C H A N G E

   d spinning the spinner shown on the right

   e picking a day from all the days of the week.

3 Answer each of these questions for each bag A to E.

   A   B   C   D   E

   a List the 4 possible outcomes, when a ball is taken from the bag.

   b Calculate the probability of taking out a blue ball.

   c Calculate the probability of taking out a red ball.

   d Which colour ball is the most likely to be taken out?

   e Which colour ball is the least likely to be taken out?

4 A raffle has only one prize. 250 tickets are sold. Calculate the probability of winning the prize if you buy

   a one ticket   **b** ten tickets.

5 There are 48 boys and 72 girls in a year group at a school. One student is selected at random. Calculate the probability that the student is

   a a boy   **b** a girl.

This spread will show you how to:

● Understand and use the probability scale

Keywords
Chance
Mutually
   exclusive
Outcome
Probability
Probability scale

The **chance** of an outcome happening is measured by the **probability**.

All probabilities have a value between 0 and 1 and can be marked on a **probability scale**.

You can use fractions or decimals on the probability scale.

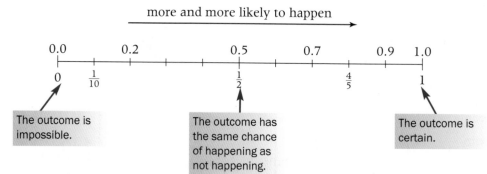

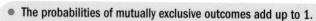

An equilateral triangle is made into a spinner as shown. The possible **outcomes** are Orange, Orange and Green.

These outcomes are **mutually exclusive** because if you get one outcome you cannot get the other one.

Probability of spinning orange = $\frac{2}{3}$

Probability of **not** spinning orange = $\frac{1}{3}$

● The probabilities of mutually exclusive outcomes add up to 1.

● Probability of an outcome not happening = 1 − probability of the outcome happening

$\frac{2}{3} + \frac{1}{3} = 1$

$\frac{1}{3} = 1 - \frac{2}{3}$

The probability of picking a coloured counter from the tin is shown.

Colour	Red	Orange	Yellow
Probability	0.4	0.25	

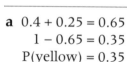

a Calculate the probability of picking a yellow counter.
b Which colour counter is the least likely to be picked?

a 0.4 + 0.25 = 0.65
    1 − 0.65 = 0.35
    P(yellow) = 0.35
b Orange, as orange has the smallest probability.

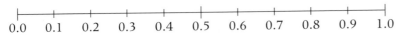
1 Draw a 10 cm line. Put a mark at every centimetre.
Label the marks 0.0, 0.1, 0.2, ..., 0.9, 1.0 as shown.

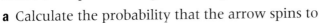

0.0   0.1   0.2   0.3   0.4   0.5   0.6   0.7   0.8   0.9   1.0

On your probability scale, mark the position of

a an impossible outcome

b an even chance outcome

c a certain outcome.

2 A bag contains 1 yellow, 3 green and 6 red balls.
One ball is taken out at random.

a Calculate the probability that the ball is

i yellow   **ii** green   **iii** red.

b Draw a probability scale as in question 1.
On your scale, mark the positions of P(yellow), P(green) and
P(red).

c Which colour is the least likely to be picked?

d Which colour is the most likely to be picked?

e Add the answers P(yellow), P(green) and P(red).

3 A spinner is made from a regular octagon.
There are 6 pink and 2 green triangles.

a Calculate the probability that the arrow spins to

i a pink triangle

ii a green triangle.

b Draw a probability scale as in question 1.
On your scale, mark the positions of P(pink) and P(green).

c Which colour is the least likely?

d Which colour is the most likely?

e Add the answers P(pink) and P(green).

4 The probability of winning a raffle is 0.01.
What is the probability of not winning the raffle?

5 A bag contains red, yellow and green counters.
One counter is taken out at random.
The probability that the counter is a particular colour is
shown in the table.

Colour	Red	Yellow	Green
Probability	0.3	0.1	

Calculate the probability of taking a green counter out of the bag.

D3.3 Two-way tables

This spread will show you how to:

● Understand two-way tables and use them to calculate probabilities

Keywords

Equally likely
Random
Two-way table

● A **two-way table** links two types of information.

23 children and adults attend a birthday party.
The two-way table shows this information.

	Male	Female
Adult	0	4
Child	7	12

7 + 12 = 19 children at the party.

There were no adult males.

4 + 12 = 16 females at the party.

You can use two-way tables to calculate probabilities.

Example

The shoe sizes of fifty Y10 students are shown in the two-way table.

	Size 6	Size 7	Size 8	Size 9
Boy	5	8	9	8
Girl	8	9	2	1

One of the students is selected at random.
Calculate the probability that the student is

a a boy

b a girl

c a girl who wears size 7 shoes

d a student who wears size 8 shoes.

a 5 + 8 + 9 + 8 = 30 boys

$P(boy) = \frac{30}{50} = \frac{3}{5}$

b $P(girl) = 1 - \frac{3}{5} = \frac{2}{5}$

c $P(girl\ with\ size\ 7\ shoes) = \frac{9}{50}$

d 9 + 2 = 11

$P(size\ 8) = \frac{11}{50}$.

1 The numbers of passengers in 50 cars are recorded.
The results are shown in the two-way table.
Calculate the probability that a car has

a 0 passengers   **b** 1 passenger

c 2 passengers   **d** 3 or more passengers.

Number of passengers	Number of cars
0	20
1	15
2	10
3 or more	5

2 A tray contains brown and white eggs. Some of the eggs are cracked.
The two-way table shows the number of eggs in each category.

	Cracked	Not cracked
Brown	2	6
White	4	12

a Calculate the number of eggs that are

  i on the tray   **ii** brown   **iii** white

  iv cracked   **v** not cracked.

One egg is selected at random.

b Calculate the probability that the egg is

  i brown and cracked   **ii** white and not cracked

  iii a brown egg   **iv** a white egg

  v a cracked egg   **vi** an uncracked egg.

3 An athletic club enters 10 athletes in
various races at a meeting. Each athlete
enters only one race. The two-way table
shows the number of athletes that won
or didn't win for each race.

One athlete is selected at random for a
drugs test.

Calculate the probability that the
selected athlete

a is the 200 m winner

b entered the 100 m race

c entered the 400 m race

d won a race

e didn't win a race.

	Won	Didn't win
100 m	0	5
200 m	1	0
400 m	0	0
800 m	0	1
1500 m	1	2

Expected frequency

This spread will show you how to:

- Understand and use estimates or measures of probability

Keywords

Expect
Expected
  frequency
Trial

If you know the probability of an outcome, you can calculate how many times you **expect** the outcome to happen.

Example

A dice is rolled 60 times.
Calculate the number of

a fours

b even numbers you would expect.

a $P(4) = \frac{1}{6}$ or 1 four for every 6 rolls
                  or 10 fours for every 60 rolls.

b $P(\text{even}) = \frac{1}{2}$ $\frac{1}{2}$ of 60 = 30 times should be even.

- The **expected frequency** is the number of times you expect an outcome to happen.
- Expected frequency = probability × number of trials.

Each roll of the dice is called a **trial**.

Example

Red, yellow and green balls are put in a bag.
The probability of taking out each colour of ball is given in the table.

Red	Yellow	Green
0.1	0.3	

a Calculate the probability of taking out a green ball.

b Which colour is the most likely to be taken out?

c There are 60 balls in the bag.
How many of them are red, yellow and green?

a   0.1 + 0.3 = 0.4
      1 − 0.4 = 0.6
  P(green) = 0.6

b Green is the most likely as 0.6 is the biggest probability.

c Red: 0.1 × 60 = 6 red balls
   Yellow: 0.3 × 60 = 18 yellow balls
   Green: 0.6 × 60 = 36 green balls

The outcomes of taking out a red or a yellow or green are mutually exclusive.

1 A crisp manufacturer claims that '3 out of every 4 people prefer Potayto Crisps'.
If 100 people are asked, how many would you expect to prefer Potayto Crisps?

2 The probability of a drawing pin landing point up when dropped, is 0.8.
If 100 drawing pins are dropped, how many of them would you expect to land point up?

3 Research has shown that when you take a dog for a daily walk, the probability that you will have a conversation with someone is $\frac{3}{10}$.
If you walked a dog daily throughout September, how many times would you expect to have a conversation with someone?

'30 days has September, April June and November.'

4 A spinner is made from a circle divided into 12 equal sectors, coloured green, yellow and pink.
If the spinner is spun 60 times, how many times would you expect the colour to be

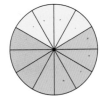

a green

b yellow

c pink?

5 The probability of rolling each number for this biased dice is shown in the table.

Number	1	2	3	4	5	6
Probability	0.1	0.15	0.3	0.2	0.1	

a Calculate the probability of rolling a 6.

b Calculate the expected frequencies for each number, if the dice is rolled

   i 100 times

   ii 500 times

   iii 1000 times.

6 In a 'roll a penny' game, a penny is rolled into the box.
To win you need to land the penny off any black lines.
It costs 1p to have a go and winners are given 10p back.
The probability of landing the penny off the black lines is $\frac{1}{20}$.

1p a go
Roll the penny off the black lines and get 10p back

If 200 pennies are rolled into the box, how much profit would you expect the game to make?

This spread will show you how to:

- Understand and use estimates or measures of probability and relative frequency
- Compare experimental data and theoretical probabilities

Keywords
Biased
Equally likely
Estimate
Experiment
Fair
Relative
  frequency
Trial

- A dice is **fair** if the numbers are all **equally likely** to be rolled.
  You would normally expect a dice to be fair, as each face is identical.

- A spinner is **biased** if the colours are **NOT** all equally likely to happen.
  This spinner is not fair as the size and shape of each colour are not identical.

It is not always possible to calculate the theoretical probability.

- You can **estimate** the probability from experiments.

Example

Sam knows the probability of a Head when spinning a coin should be $\frac{1}{2}$ (or 0.5).
She thinks the coin is biased and so she spins the coin 50 times. The results are shown in the frequency table.

	Frequency
Head	35
Tail	15

a Estimate the probability of getting a Head when spinning the coin.
b Do you think the coin is biased? Explain your answer.

a Sam got a Head on 35 out of 50 occasions.
Estimated probability of getting a Head = $\frac{35}{50} = \frac{7}{10} = 0.7$
b The spinner could be biased as 0.7 is significantly larger than 0.5.
However, Sam needs to spin the coin a lot more times before she can make the decision.

- **Estimated probability is called the relative frequency.**

Each spin of the coin is called a **trial**.

In the example, if Sam calculated the relative frequency of getting a Head after each spin, she could graph the results.

Highest relative frequency is 1.

Lowest relative frequency is 0.

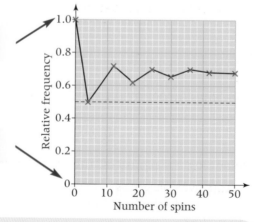

$P(\text{Head}) = \frac{1}{2} = 0.5$
This is the theoretical probability of spinning a Head.

- The estimated probability becomes more reliable as you increase the number of trials.

1 The colours of 50 cars are recorded. The colours are shown

Blue	Red	Other	Silver	Blue	Red	Silver	Silver	Blue
Other	Red	Silver	Silver	Blue	Red	Red	Other	Silver
Silver	Red	Red	Silver	Silver	Blue	Blue	Silver	Silver
Red	Red	Other	Blue	Red	Red	Other	Red	Red
Red	Silver	Blue	Blue	Blue	Other	Silver	Other	Other
Other	Silver	Red	Red	Blue				

a Copy and complete the frequency chart to show the 50 colours.

b State the modal colour.

c Give an estimate of the probability that the next car will be

    i blue   **ii** red   **iii** silver.

Colour	Tally	Frequency
Blue		
Red		
Silver		
Other		

2 A spinner is made from a regular pentagon. The scores are recorded

```
1  2  3  4  3  5  1  2
5  4  2  1  3  1  5  4
2  2  3  1  4  5  4  2
3  1  2  2  4  4  5  5
1  2  3  4  2  4  1  1
```

a Draw a frequency chart to show the scores.

b State the modal score.

c How many times is the spinner spun?

d Estimate the probability of scoring

    i a 1   **ii** a 2   **iii** a 3   **iv** a 4   **v** a 5.

e If the spinner is fair, how many times would you expect to spin a 3 from 100 spins?

3 There are 10 coloured balls in a bag.
One ball is taken out and then replaced in the bag.
The colours of the balls are shown in the frequency table.

Colour	Red	Green	Blue
Frequency	9	14	27

a How many times was a ball taken out of the bag?

b Estimate the probability of taking out

    i a red ball   **ii** a green ball   **iii** a blue ball.

c How many balls of each colour do you think are in the bag?

d How could you improve this guess?

Exam review

Key objectives

- Understand and use the probability scale
- Understand and use estimates or measures of probability from theoretical models, or from relative frequency
- Identify different mutually exclusive outcomes and know that the sum of the probabilities of all these outcomes is 1

1 A bag contains coloured balls. The probability of choosing a ball of a certain colour at random from the bag is shown in this table:

Colour	Red	Blue	Yellow	Green
Probability	0.4	0.25	0.2	

a Work out the probability of choosing a green ball.

Explain your answer. (2)

b What is the probability of choosing a white ball from the bag?

Explain your answer. (1)

2 The probability that a biased dice will land on a four is 0.2.

Pam is going to roll the dice 200 times.

Work out an estimate for the number of times the dice will land on a four. (2)

(Edexcel Ltd., 2004)

This unit will show you how to

- Use decimals, fractions and percentages to describe proportions
- Use proportions to make simple comparisons
- Understand and use ratio, proportion and direct proportion in problem solving
- Calculate missing amounts when two quantities are in direct proportion
- Calculate exchange rates and solve problems involving exchange rates
- Solve problems involving compound measures

Before you start ...

You should be able to answer these questions.

Review

1 What proportion of this shape is shaded?

Unit N3

2 Neil buys 2 pizzas at a cost £7.00. What is the cost of 8 pizzas?

Unit N3

3 John weighs 50 kg. Kevin weighs 75 kg. How many times heavier than John is Kevin?

Unit N3

4 What is $56 \div 14$?

Unit N2

5 Krishna earns £8.50 per hour. How much does he get paid for 8 hours work?

Unit N3

6 Beatrice is driving her car. She travels 200 miles in 4 hours. What is her average speed?

Unit N2

This spread will show you how to:

- Use decimals, fractions and percentages to describe proportions
- Use proportions to make simple comparisons

Keywords

Decimal
Equivalent
Fraction
Percentage
Proportion

> A **proportion** is a part of the whole.
> You can use **percentages**, **fractions** and **decimals** to describe proportions.

Example

a What proportion of this shape is shaded?

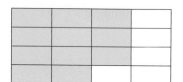

b What proportion of cars are blue?

Colours of cars

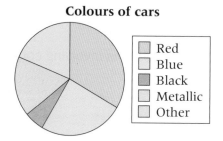

- Red
- Blue
- Black
- Metallic
- Other

a The proportion shaded is $\frac{11}{16}$

$= 11 \div 16$
$= 0.6875$
$= 68.75\%$

b The sector representing blue cars is 90 degrees.

Fraction of blue cars $= \frac{90}{360} = \frac{1}{4}$
$= 1 \div 4$
$= 0.25$
$= 25\%$

Change the fraction to a decimal by division.
Change the decimal to a percentage by multiplying by 100.

> You can use proportions to make simple comparisons.

Example

John scores $\frac{26}{40}$ in his Maths exam and 63% in his English exam.
In which exam did he score the highest mark?

Change the Maths mark into a percentage:

$\frac{26}{40} = 26 \div 40$
$= 0.65$
$= 0.65 \times 100\%$
$= 65\%$

Maths mark $= 65\%$ English mark $= 63\%$

John scored a higher mark in his Maths exam.

It is easier to compare proportions by converting them to percentages.

1   Write the proportion of each of these shapes that is shaded. Write each of your answers as

   i a fraction in its simplest form

   ii a percentage (to 1 decimal place as appropriate).

a 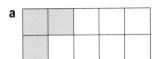   **b** 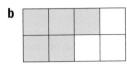   **c**

d 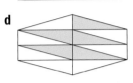   **e**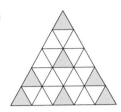

2   Put these fractions, decimals and percentages in order from lowest to highest.
Do these without a calculator.

   a $\frac{3}{5}$, 61%, 0.63   **b** $\frac{7}{10}$, $\frac{17}{25}$, 69%, 0.71   **c** $\frac{7}{20}$, $\frac{2}{5}$, $\frac{3}{8}$, 0.36, 34%

   Do these with a calculator.

   d $\frac{3}{7}$, 42%, $\frac{2}{5}$ **e** 15%, $\frac{3}{19}$, 0.14, $\frac{1}{5}$ **f** 81%, $\frac{8}{9}$, 0.93, 0.9, $\frac{19}{20}$

3   Solve each of these without using a calculator.
Express each of your answers

   i as a fraction in its lowest form

   ii as a percentage.

   a Brian's mark in a Geography test was 42 out of 70.
What proportion of the test did he answer correctly?

   b Hannah collects dolls. She has 25 dolls altogether.
13 of the 25 dolls are from Russia.
What proportion of Hannah's dolls are from Russia?

   c A restaurant makes a service charge of 3p in every 20p.
Work out 3p as a proportion of 20p.

   d Class 11X2 has 30 students.
21 of these students are boys.
What proportion of the class are boys?

   e Sakarako makes cakes. On Friday she makes 60 cakes.
Sakarako puts icing on 48 of the cakes.
What proportion of the cakes have icing on them?

This spread will show you how to:

- Calculate missing amounts when two quantities are in direct proportion

Keywords
Direct proportion
Ratio
Unitary method

- A **ratio** tells you how many times bigger one number is compared to another number. You can calculate a ratio using division.

- Numbers or quantities are in **direct proportion** when the ratio of each pair of corresponding values is the same.

Here is a price list for the cost of different-sized tins of paint.

Number of litres	Total cost (£)
2	9.00
3	13.50
5	22.50
10	45.00

a Are the number of litres of paint in proportion to the total cost?
b What is the ratio between the number of litres and the total cost?

For 2 tins of paint   Ratio of 'number of litres' to 'total cost' = $\frac{9}{2}$ = 4.5
For 3 tins of paint   Ratio of 'number of litres' to 'total cost' = $\frac{13.5}{5}$ = 4.5
For 5 tins of paint   Ratio of 'number of litres' to 'total cost' = $\frac{22.5}{5}$ = 4.5
For 10 tins of paint   Ratio of 'number of litres' to 'total cost' = $\frac{45}{10}$ = 4.5

Remember: to find the ratio of two numbers you divide them.

a The ratio is the same, so the numbers are in direct proportion.
b The total cost is always 4.5 times bigger than the number of litres.

- You can use the **unitary method** to solve problems involving direct proportion. In this method you always find the value of one unit of a quantity.

Here is a recipe for mushroom soup.
Work out the number of grams of mushrooms needed to make mushroom soup for eight people.

Mushroom Soup
(for 3 people)

270 g of button mushrooms
45 ml of white wine
450 ml of vegetable stock
3 tbsp of olive oil
3 garlic cloves

Number of people   Grams of mushrooms

÷3 (3   270) ÷3
      1   90
×8 (   ) ×8
      8   720

The number of grams of mushrooms is in direct proportion to the number of people.

You need 720 g of mushrooms for eight people.

1 How many times bigger than

    a 12 is 60   **b** 3 is 24   **c** 12 is 84

    d 20 is 90   **e** 18 is 27   **f** 9 m is 30 m

    g 16 km is 50 km   **h** £10 is £72   **i** 36 kg is 240 kg

    j $25 is $215   **k** 10 mm is 18 mm   **l** 220p is 300p?

    (Give your answers to 1 dp as appropriate.)

2 What proportion of

    a 15 is 5   **b** 20 is 10   **c** 10 cm is 3 cm

    d 12 kg is 3 kg   **e** 4 cm is 15 mm   **f** £30 is £12

    g 3 m is 50 cm   **h** 40 km is 60 km   **i** £8 is £16?

3 Which of these sets of numbers are in direct proportion?
Explain your reasoning.

a

A	B
3	12
30	120
6	24
1.5	6

b

C	D
4	13
35	115
7	21
15	47

c

E	F
2	3.6
7	12.6
15	27
13	23.4

d

G	H
12	37.2
8	24.8
19	58.9
45	139.5

4 Sven works as a manager. He is paid by the hour. Copy and complete
this table to help him work out his pay.

Hours worked	6	1	3	30	38	48
Pay (£)	£300					

5 In each of these questions the items are all the same price.

    a 2 pizzas cost £7.50. What is the cost of 5 pizzas?

    b 4 sweets cost £1.40. What is the cost of 17 sweets?

    c 11 packets of seeds cost £17.49. What is the cost of 7 packets of seeds?

    d 5 tennis balls cost £2.60. What is the cost of 12 tennis balls?

    e 5 kg of apples cost £3.95. What is the cost of 12 kg of apples?

    f There are 2640 megabytes of memory on 11 identical memory
sticks. How much memory is there on 3 memory sticks?

    g 30 protractors cost £3.30. What is the cost of 17 protractors?

    h Del needs 10 litres of lemon drink to fill 25 cups. Work out how
many litres of lemon drink are needed to fill 30 cups.

    i Three 1 litre tins of paint cost a total of £23.85. Find the cost of
seven of the 1 litre tins of paint.

Direct proportion

This spread will show you how to:

• Calculate missing amounts when two quantities are in direct proportion

• You can calculate a **ratio** using division.

Example

Morgan is 150 cm tall. Peter is 180 cm tall.

a How many times taller than Morgan is Peter?
b What fraction of Peter's height is Morgan?

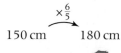

---

a Ratio of Peter's height to Morgan's height $= \dfrac{180}{150} = \dfrac{18}{15} = \dfrac{6}{5}$

Peter is $\frac{6}{5}$ or 1.2 times taller than Morgan.

b Ratio of Morgan's height to Peter's height $= \dfrac{150}{180} = \dfrac{15}{18} = \dfrac{5}{6}$

Morgan is $\frac{5}{6}$ of the height of Peter.

• When a problem involves two sets of numbers which are in **direct proportion** you can use ratios to solve it.

Example

Rio buys 144 cakes for a party with £80. Gabby buys £150 of cakes at the same price. How many cakes does Gabby buy?

Ratio of Gabby's money: Rio's money $= \dfrac{150}{80} = \dfrac{15}{8}$

Multiply Rio's number of cakes by this ratio:

$\times\frac{15}{8}\left(\begin{array}{l}\text{£80\ \ buys\ \ 144 cakes}\\[4pt]\text{£150\ \ buys\ \ 270 cakes}\end{array}\right)\times\frac{15}{8}$

This is sometimes called the scaling method.

Example

These two sets of numbers are in direct proportion. Find the value of y.

Set A	Set B
£4	£7
£9	£y

Ratio of numbers in set B: numbers in set A $= \frac{7}{4}$

Set A $\quad \times\frac{7}{4} \quad$ **Set B**

$\quad 4 \xrightarrow{\hspace{1cm}} 7$

$\quad 9 \xrightarrow[\times\frac{7}{4}]{\hspace{1cm}} y$

This is sometimes called the ratio method.

Multiply the number in set A by this ratio.

$y = 9 \times \frac{7}{4} = \frac{63}{4} = £15.75$

1 How many times bigger than

   a 15 is 30   **b** 10 m is 35 m   **c** £6 is £21

   d 12 km is 40 km?

> In questions 1 and 2, give your answers to 2 dp as appropriate.

2 What proportion of

   a 30 is 15   **b** 35 m is 10 m   **c** £21 is £6

   d 40 km is 12 km?

3 Stefan is looking at the vegetables he has planted in his garden. The broad beans are 50 cm tall. The sweetcorn is 100 cm tall.

   a How many times taller than the broad beans is the sweetcorn?

   b What proportion of the height of the sweetcorn are the broad beans?

4 Bobby and Wendy are comparing their weights. Bobby is 60 kg. Wendy is 48 kg.

   a How many times heavier than Wendy is Bobby?

   b What proportion of the weight of Bobby is Wendy?

5 Rudi and Colin are comparing their wages.
Rudi earns £250 per week. Colin earns £400 per week.

   a How many times bigger is Colin's wage compared to Rudi's wage?

   b What proportion of Colin's wage does Rudi earn?

6 Copy and complete each of these direct proportion problems using the scaling method.

   a Trevor buys 4 kg of apples for £3.20. Gerry buys 7 kg of the same apples. How much does Gerry have to pay for his apples?

$$\times\tfrac{7}{4}\left(\begin{array}{l}4\,\text{kg} \quad\text{costs}\quad £3.20 \\[4pt] 7\,\text{kg} \quad\text{costs}\quad \underline{\hspace{2em}}\end{array}\right)\times\tfrac{7}{4}$$

   b Jermaine owns a sports equipment shop. He sells five tennis balls for £1.90. What is the cost of seven tennis balls?

$$\times\underline{\hspace{1.5em}}\left(\begin{array}{l}5\ \text{tennis balls} \quad\text{cost}\quad £1.90 \\[4pt] 7\ \text{tennis balls} \quad\text{cost}\quad \underline{\hspace{2em}}\end{array}\right)\times\underline{\hspace{1.5em}}$$

   c Horace works for 9 hours a day. He is paid £76.05. He is paid the same amount for each hour he works. How much will he earn if he works for 20 hours?

   d 12 cans of tomato soup weigh 5040 g. What is the weight of 15 cans?

This spread will show you how to:

- Calculate exchange rates and solve problems involving exchange rates

Keywords

Rate
Ratio
Scale

- A **rate** is a way of comparing two quantities. It tells you how many units of one quantity there are compared to one unit of another quantity. You can calculate a rate using division.

Example

Tariq is paid £374 a week. Each week he works for 44 hours.
What is his hourly rate of pay?

The rate of pay = £374 for every 44 hours

$$= \frac{£374}{44} \text{ for every 1 hour}$$

$$= £8.50 \text{ for every hour}$$

$$= £8.50 \text{ per hour}$$

- An exchange rate is a way of comparing two currencies. It tells you how many units of one currency there are compared to one unit of another currency.

Example

Katherine went to France. She changed £300 into €480.

a What was the exchange rate of euros to the pound?
b What was the exchange rate of pounds to the euro?

a Rate of euros to pounds = $\frac{€480}{£300}$

$$= 480 \div 300 \text{ euros for every pound}$$

$$= 1.6 \text{ euros for every pound}$$

Exchange rate is £1 = €1.6 (£1 will buy you €1.6).

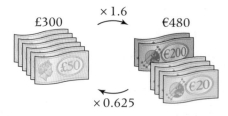

b Rate of pounds to euros = $\frac{£300}{€480}$

$$= 300 \div 480 \text{ pounds for every euro}$$

$$= 0.625 \text{ pounds for every euro}$$

Exchange rate is €1 = £0.625 (€1 will buy you £0.625 or 62.5p).

1 Work out the hourly rate of pay for each person.

Person	Money earned (£)	Hours worked (hours)	Hourly rate of pay (£ per hour)
Leonard	£210	30	
Pavel	£216	32	
Andy	£554.40	48	

2 Work out the rate for each of these.

a Wendy works for 3 hours. She gets paid £22.26.
What is her hourly rate of pay?

b Brian is a bricklayer. On average, he lays 680 bricks in 4 hours.
What is his hourly rate of laying bricks?

c Gustav travels in his car for 6 hours. He travels 330 km.
What is his average speed?

How far does he travel each hour?

3 Work out the exchange rate into pounds for each of these currencies.

Country	Number of pounds (£)	Number of other currency	Exchange rate (= £1)
Lithuania	£13	65 litas	£1 = ? litas
Namibia	£260	3003 dollars	£1 = ? dollars
Qatar	£82.40	519.12 riyals	£1 = ? riyals

4 Each of these people change amounts of money from pounds into euros. The exchange rate is £1 = €1.44.
Work out the number of euros each person receives.

Person	Amount (£)	Exchange rate (£1 = €1.44)	Amount (€)
Bernice	£240	£1 = €1.44	
Ingeborg	£720	£1 = €1.44	
Andrew	£6300	£1 = €1.44	

5 Each of these people change amounts of money from euros into pounds. The exchange rate is £1 = €1.44.
Work out the number of pounds each person receives.

Person	Amount (€)	Exchange rate (£1 = €1.44)	Amount (£)
Ann	€360	£1 = €1.44	
Raul	€768	£1 = €1.44	
Nicolas	€2448	£1 = €1.44	

You need to work out the exchange rate of pounds to the euros first.

This spread will show you how to:

- Solve problems involving compound measures

Keywords

Compound
measure
Rate

Rates are always expressed using two units, for example petrol consumption is expressed in miles and litres. These are called **compound measures** because they involve two separate units of measurement.

Example

Priti's car uses 35 litres of petrol to travel 310 miles.
What is the rate of petrol consumption?

The rate of petrol consumption = 310 miles for every 35 litres
$$= \frac{310}{35} \text{ for every 1 litre}$$
$$= 8.857\ 14\dots \text{ miles for every litre}$$
$$= 8.9 \text{ miles per litre (1 decimal place)}$$

This means that for every 1 litre of petrol used the car travels 8.9 miles.

$$\div 8.9$$
310 miles ⟶ 35 litres
$$\times 8.9$$

Example

Mark runs in a race. He travels 100 m in 10.23 seconds.
What is his average speed?

The speed (rate of travel) of Mark = 100 m in every 10.23 seconds
$$= \frac{100\text{ m}}{10.23} \text{ in every 1 second}$$
$$= 9.775\ 17\dots \text{ m in every 1 second}$$
$$= 9.8 \text{ m/s (1 decimal place)}$$

This means that in every second Mark covers a distance of 9.8 m.

$$\times 9.8$$
10.23 secs ⟶ 100 m
$$\div 9.8$$

- You can solve problems involving rates by multiplying or dividing by the rate.

Example

Harry travels 360 km at an average speed of 80 km/h.
How long does it take him to complete his journey?

Express the speed as a rate.

Speed 80 km/h

$$\div 80$$
80 km ⟶ 1 hour
$$\times 80$$

Divide the distance by the speed (rate of travel).

360 km = 360 ÷ 80 hours
$$= 4.5 \text{ hours} = 4\tfrac{1}{2} \text{ hrs}$$

1 Work out the rate of petrol consumption for each person's car
   (give your answer to 2 dp as appropriate).

Person	Miles travelled (miles)	Petrol used (litres)	Rate of petrol consumption (miles per litre)
Mr Sibbit	300 miles	25 litres	
Mr Griffin	676 miles	52 litres	
Miss Ahmed	500 miles	48 litres	

DID YOU KNOW?

Hybrid vehicles combine an internal combustion engine with an electric motor and battery to reduce fuel consumption. Some use half as much fuel as a normal car over the same distance.

2 **a** Tina's car uses 45 litres of petrol to travel 414 miles.
      What is the rate of petrol consumption?

   b Mandy is paid £480.70. She works a 38 hour week.
      What is her hourly rate of pay?

   c A 250 g serving of breakfast cereal contains 460 kCal.
      What is the number of kCal in every 100 g?

3 **a** There are 48 inches in 4 feet. What is the conversion rate to
      change feet into inches?

   b There are 33 pounds in 15 kg. What is the conversion rate to
      change kg into pounds?

   c There are 40 km in 25 miles. What is the conversion rate to change
      miles into kilometres?

4 **a** For each of these sprinters, work out their average speed.

Person	Distance travelled (metres)	Time taken (seconds)	Speed or rate of travel (metres per second)
Bobby	100 m	9.97	
Mark	60 m	5.88	
Eugene	110 m	10.28	
Victor	200 m	19.43	
Alan	400 m	38.93	
Janet	200 m	19.81	

   b Put the sprinters in order from fastest to slowest.

5 **a** Eve's car uses petrol at the rate of 12.5 km per litre.

   i How far can she travel with 14 litres of petrol?

   ii How much petrol does she need to travel 200 km?

   b Louise is paid £8.56 per hour.

   i How much does she earn if she works for 37.5 hours?

   ii How many hours does she have to work to earn £1000?

Exam review

Key objectives

- Use knowledge of operations and inverse operations, and of methods of simplification, in order to select and use suitable strategies and techniques to solve problems and word problems, including those involving ratio and proportion, fractions, percentages and measures and conversion between measures, and compound measures defined within a particular situation

1 John is painting a fence. There are 80 fence posts in total.

  a It takes John 2 hours to paint 20 fence posts.
    How long will it take him to paint the whole fence? (2)

  b John uses 5 tins of paint to paint the whole fence.
    How many tins of paint would he need to paint a fence
    made of 50 fence posts? (2)

2 A group of students visited the USA. The table shows information about the numbers of hamburgers the students bought on the visit:

Number of hamburgers	Number of students
0	1
1	1
2	4
3	8
4	8
5	7

  a Work out the total number of hamburgers that these students bought. (3)

One of these students bought a pair of sunglasses in the USA.
He paid $35.50.
In England, an identical pair of sunglasses costs £26.99.
The exchange rate is £1 = $1.42.

  b In which country were the sunglasses cheaper, and by how much?
    Show all your working. (3)

(Edexcel Ltd., 2004)

This unit will show you how to

- Understand, recognise and describe reflections, rotations and translations
- Transform triangles and other 2-D shapes by reflection, rotation, translation and a combination of these transformations
- Understand congruence
- Recognise that translations, rotations and reflections preserve length and angle
- Recognise reflection symmetry of 2-D and 3-D shapes and rotational symmetry of 2-D shapes

Before you start ...

You should be able to answer these questions.

Review

1 Give the coordinates of

a A   **b** B

c C   **d** D

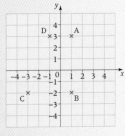

Key stage 3

2 State the direction of the turn.

a   **b**

Key stage 3

3 Give the equation of each straight line.

Key stage 3

a 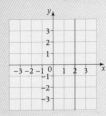   **b**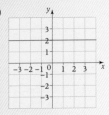

c 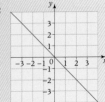   **d**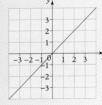

4 State the sum of the three angles *a*, *b*, *c*.

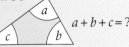

$a + b + c = ?$

Unit S2

This spread will show you how to:

● Understand, recognise and describe reflections, rotations and translations

Keywords
Congruent
Equation
Equidistant
Flip
Mirror line
Reflection
Transformation

A reflection **flips** a shape over.

● You describe a **reflection** using the **mirror line** or reflection line.

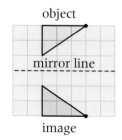

object

mirror line

image

Choose a point on the object to find the corresponding point on the image.

Corresponding points are **equidistant** from the mirror line.

Example

a Draw a mirror line so that shape B is a reflection of shape A.
b Give the **equation** of the mirror line.

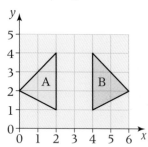

a

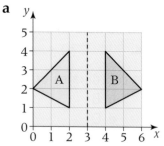

b Choose some coordinates on the line: (3, 0) (3, 1) (3, 2). The x-coordinates are all 3. The line is $x = 3$.

Example

a Draw the reflection of the shaded shape in the mirror line.
b Give the equation of the mirror line.

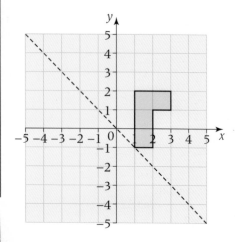

a

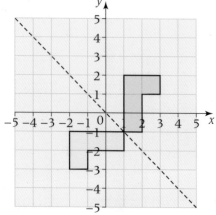

b Choose some coordinates on the line:
(−2, 2), (3, −3), (5, −5)
The line is $y = −x$

1 Copy and complete the diagrams to show the reflections of the triangles in the mirror line $x = 2$.

a 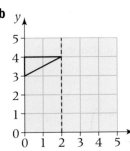 **b** 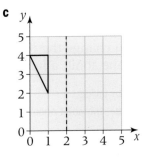 **c**

2 Give the equation of the mirror line for each reflection.

a 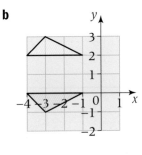 **b** 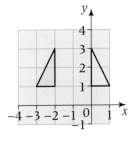 **c**

3 **a** Copy the diagram.

b Reflect the triangle in the mirror line.

c Give the equation of the mirror line.

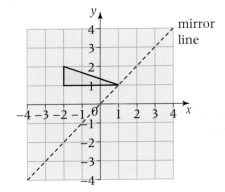

4 **a** Copy the diagram.

b Plot the points (0, 1) (3, 1) (3, 2) to form a triangle.

c Reflect the triangle in the mirror line.

d Give the coordinates of the reflected points.

e Give the equation of the mirror line.

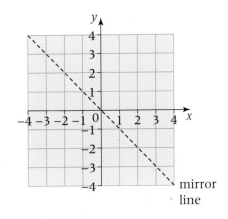

This spread will show you how to:

● Transform triangles and other 2-D shapes by reflection, rotation, translation and a combination of these transformations

Keywords

Anticlockwise
Centre of
   rotation
Clockwise
Congruent
Rotation
Transformation

A **transformation** can change the position of a shape.
A **rotation** turns a shape about a fixed point.

● You describe a rotation by giving:
   ● the **centre of rotation** – the point about which it turns
   ● the angle of turn
   ● the direction of turn – either **clockwise** or **anticlockwise**.

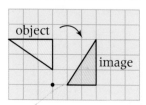

The dot is the centre of rotation.
The turn is 90°.
The direction is clockwise.

The two shapes
are **congruent**.
They are exactly
the same size and
the same shape.

Example

a Draw the position of the red triangle after a rotation of 90° clockwise about the origin.
b Give the coordinates of the point A **after** the rotation.

a

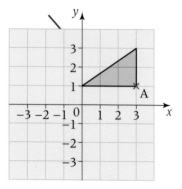

b (1, −3)

The origin is the point (0, 0).

Use tracing paper to find the position of the blue triangle.

Example

A regular pentagon is divided into five isosceles triangles. The centre of the pentagon is marked with a dot (●). The green triangle is rotated about the dot onto the yellow triangle.

a State whether the green and yellow triangles are congruent or similar.
b Calculate the angle and direction of the rotation.

a Congruent – same size and same shape.
b The five angles at the dot total 360°.
   One angle at the dot is 360° ÷ 5 = 72°.
   Rotation is 72° clockwise about the dot.

1 State the angle and direction of turn for each of these rotations about the dot (●), green shape to blue shape:

a **b** **c** **d** **e**

f **g** **h** **i** **j**

k **l** **m** **n** **o**

2 The diagram shows the pattern made by repeated 90° rotations of a right-angled triangle about the dot (●).
Draw a similar pattern using repeated 45° rotations about the dot (●).

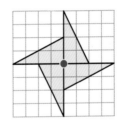

3 Copy this grid.

   a Plot and join the points
      O (0, 0), A (2, 1), B (3, 0) and C (2, −1).

   b Give the mathematical name of this shape.

   c Rotate the shape through 90° anticlockwise about the origin.

   d Give the coordinates of the point A after the rotation.

   e Are the two shapes congruent?

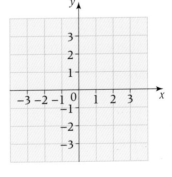

4 **a** Copy the shape and axes on square grid paper.

   b Rotate the triangle by 90° anticlockwise about the point (1, 2).

   c Give the coordinates of the vertices of the triangle after the rotation.

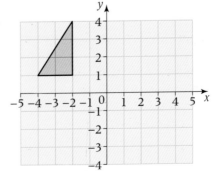

Translations

This spread will show you how to:

- Understand, recognise and describe reflections, rotations and translations

Keywords
Congruent
Slide
Transformation
Translation
Vector

A **transformation** can change the size and position of a shape.

A **translation** is a **sliding** movement.

To get from the green shape to the blue shape, you translate the object 1 unit right and 3 units down.

You can write this translation as a **vector**, $\begin{pmatrix} 1 \\ -3 \end{pmatrix}$.

- To describe a translation you give
  - the distance moved left or right, then
  - the distance moved up or down.
- You can use a **vector** to describe the translation.

You can **transform** an object into a **congruent** image using a translation.

The two shapes are **congruent**.

Choose a point on the object to locate the corresponding point on the image.

This is a translation of $\begin{pmatrix} 3 \\ 1 \end{pmatrix}$.

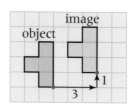

Congruent shapes are the same size and shape.

Example

a Give the mathematical name of the shaded shape.
b Describe fully the transformation that moves the shaded shape to shape A.
c Draw the shaded shape after a translation of $\begin{pmatrix} 3 \\ -1 \end{pmatrix}$.

   Label the new shape B.

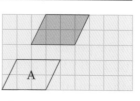

a Parallelogram
b Translation of $\begin{pmatrix} -2 \\ -3 \end{pmatrix}$.

c

1 Which shapes are translations of the green shape?

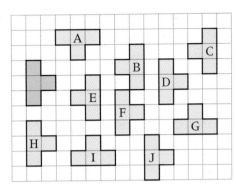

2 Describe the translation that moves the green triangle to the other triangles.

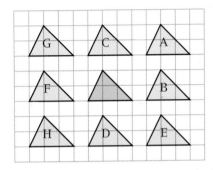

3 Describe these translations.

  a A to B   **b** D to B

  c B to D   **d** A to C

  e C to D   **f** D to A

  g C to A   **h** B to A

  i B to C   **j** A to D

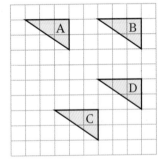

4 **a** State the coordinates of point A.

  b What is the mathematical name of the shape?

  c Draw the shape after a translation of $\begin{pmatrix} 5 \\ -2 \end{pmatrix}$.

  d State whether the two shapes are congruent.

  e Give the coordinates of the point A after the translation.

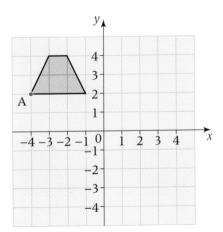

This spread will show you how to:

- Understand congruence
- Recognise that translations, rotations and reflections preserve length and angle

Keywords
Congruent
Reflection
Rotation
Transformation
Translation

- **Congruent** shapes are exactly the same size and the same shape.

Congruent shapes fit exactly on top of each other.

Corresponding angles are equal and corresponding sides are equal.

A rotation moves one triangle to the other triangle.

These **transformations** produce congruent shapes.

reflection   **rotation**   **translation**

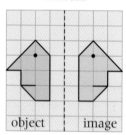 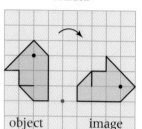 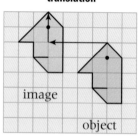

Example

This is triangle A.

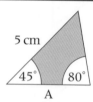

5 cm
45° 80°
A

Which of these triangles are congruent to triangle A?

 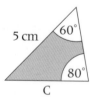 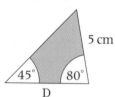 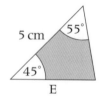

55° 5 cm
80°
B

5 cm 60°
80°
C

5 cm
45° 80°
D

5 cm 55°
45°
E

Fill in the missing information (angles in a triangle add to 180°).

  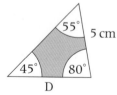 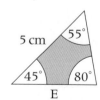

55° 5 cm
80° 45°
B

5 cm 60°
40° 80°
C

55° 5 cm
45° 80°
D

5 cm 55°
45° 80°
E

Yes, congruent to A   No, 40° is wrong   No, 5 cm is wrong   Yes, congruent to A

1 How many pairs of congruent triangles are there in this kite?

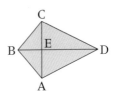

2 Which of these triangles are congruent to triangle A?

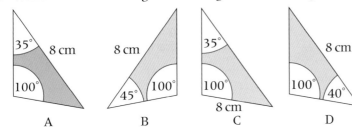

3 a Copy this shape and grid. Translate triangle A by $\begin{pmatrix} 3 \\ 0 \end{pmatrix}$.

Label the image B.

b Translate triangle A by $\begin{pmatrix} 2 \\ -4 \end{pmatrix}$. Label the image C.

c Describe the transformation of triangle C to triangle B.

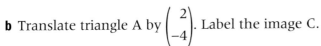
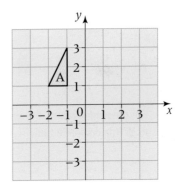

4 a Copy this shape and grid. Rotate triangle A through 90° anticlockwise about the origin. Label the image B.

b Rotate triangle A through 180° about the origin. Label the image C.

c Describe the transformation of triangle C to triangle B.

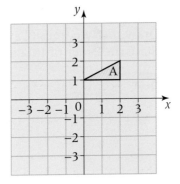

5 a Copy this shape and grid. Reflect triangle A in the *x*-axis. Label the image B.

b Reflect triangle A in the *y*-axis. Label the image C.

a Describe the transformation of triangle C to triangle B.

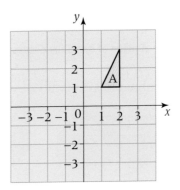

Symmetry

This spread will show you how to:

● Recognise reflection symmetry of 2-D and 3-D shapes and rotational symmetry of 2-D shapes

Keywords
Cross-section
Line of symmetry
Plane of
    symmetry
Polygon
Reflection
    symmetry
Regular
Rotational
    symmetry

You can describe shapes by their **symmetry**.

A shape has **reflection symmetry** if the shape divides into two identical halves.

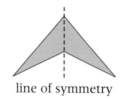

line of symmetry

The **line of symmetry** divides the shape into identical halves.

A shape has **rotational symmetry** if the shape looks like itself more than once in a full turn.

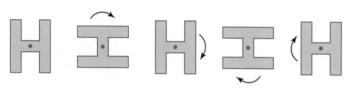

The order of rotational symmetry is 2.

● The **order of rotational symmetry** is the number of times a shape looks exactly like itself in a complete turn.

Example

a Add one extra square so that the shaded shape has 2 lines of symmetry.
b Draw the two lines of symmetry.
c State the order of rotational symmetry of the final shape.

a, b

c Rotational symmetry of order 2

● A **plane of symmetry** divides a 3-D shape into two identical halves.

A cuboid has 3 planes of symmetry.

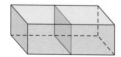  

A **cross-section** is a plane through a 3-D shape (in red).

1 a Write the 26 letters of the alphabet, in upper case.
  b Draw any lines of symmetry on each letter.

2 State the order of rotational symmetry of these 2-D shapes.

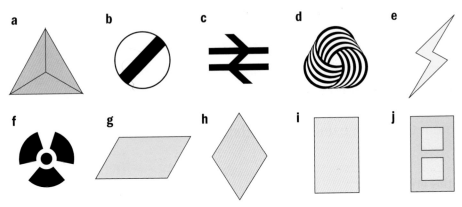

3 Copy these regular polygons.

  a Draw the lines of symmetry for each shape.

  b State the order of rotational symmetry for each shape.

> A regular polygon has equal sides and equal angles.

4 Make two copies of this grid.

  a On one copy, shade in squares so that there are two lines of symmetry.

  b On the other copy, shade in squares so that there is rotational symmetry of order 4.

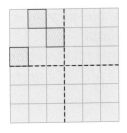

5 Draw copies of these 3-D shapes.
On each diagram draw one plane of symmetry.
Write the number of planes of symmetry for each shape.

a

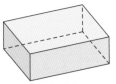

cuboid

b

square-based
pyramid

c

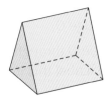

isosceles
triangular prism

Exam review

Key objectives

- Use congruence to show that translations, rotations and reflections preserve length and angle, so that any figure is congruent to its image under any of these transformations

- Transform triangles and other 2-D shapes by rotation, translation and reflection, recognising that these transformations preserve length and angle, so that any figure is congruent to its image under any of these transformations

1 Copy the grid.

  a Describe the transformation from shape ABCD to shape A′B′C′D′. (2)

  b Reflect shape ABCD in the line $y = 0$. Label this shape A″B″C″D″. (1)

  c Describe the single transformation that takes shape A′B′C′D′ to shape A″B″C″D″. (2)

  d Draw a shape, A‴B‴C‴D‴, so that the whole diagram is symmetrical in the y-axis.
Describe the transformation from shape A″B″C″D″ to shape A‴B‴C‴D‴. (3)

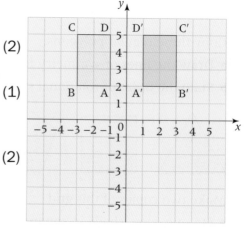

2 The triangle P has been drawn in the grid.
Copy the grid and

  a reflect the triangle P in the line $x = 2$. Label the image Q. (2)

  b rotate triangle Q through 180° about (2, 1). Label this image R. (2)

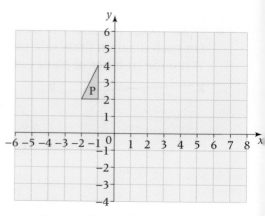

(Edexcel Ltd., 2000)

This unit will show you how to

- Use powers and index notation for small positive integer powers
- Use the square, square root, cube and cube root functions of a scientific calculator
- Understand and use reciprocals
- Make and justify estimates and approximations of calculations
- Multiply and divide by powers of 10
- Use simple index laws including negative indices
- Recognise prime factors and express a number as a product of its prime factors
- Express standard index form both in conventional notation and on a calculator display
- Find the highest common factor and least common multiple of two numbers

Before you start ...

You should be able to answer these questions.

	Review
1 Calculate **a** 12^2 **b** $\sqrt{81}$	Key stage 3
2 Calculate **a** 5^3 **b** $\sqrt[3]{8}$	Key stage 3
3 Calculate **a** 2^4 **b** 10^6	Key stage 3
4 Write all the factors of 24.	Unit N1
5 Write the first 6 prime numbers.	Key stage 3
6 Work out the value of each of these expressions. **a** $3^2 \times 5$ **b** $2^2 \times 5^2$	Unit N2

This spread will show you how to:

- Use powers and index notation for small positive integer powers
- Use the square and square root functions of a scientific calculator

Keywords
Index
Power
Square number
Square root

- A **square number** is the result of multiplying a whole number by itself.

Square numbers can be written using **index** notation.

$1^2 = 1 \times 1 = 1$ $2^2 = 2 \times 2 = 4$ $3^2 = 3 \times 3 = 9$

Your calculator should have an $\boxed{x^2}$ function key.

- A **square root** is a number that when multiplied by itself it is equal to a given number. Square roots are written using $\sqrt{}$ notation.

$\sqrt{225} = 15$ and -15 because $15 \times 15 = 225$ and $-15 \times -15 = 225$

You can write $\sqrt{225} = \pm 15$

Example

a Calculate the value of $\sqrt{300}$ using a calculator.
b Find $\sqrt{900}$ using a calculator.

Use a calculator to find a square root

using the $\boxed{\sqrt{x}}$ function key.

a Using the calculator you would type

$\boxed{\sqrt{x}}\ \boxed{3}\ \boxed{0}\ \boxed{0}\ \boxed{=}$ $\boxed{\begin{array}{l}\text{√300}\\ \textit{17.32050808}\end{array}}$

So $\sqrt{300} = 17.32$ (2 dp)

Check: $17.32^2 \approx 17^2$
$17^2 < 20^2 = 400$
$17^2 > 15^2 = 225$
17.32^2 is greater than 225 but less than 400.

b $\begin{aligned} \sqrt{900} &= \sqrt{9 \times 100}\\ &= \sqrt{9} \times \sqrt{100}\\ &= 3 \times 10\\ &= 30 \end{aligned}$

You can use trial and improvement to **estimate** the square root of a number to a given number of decimal places.

Example

Use trial and improvement to find $\sqrt{30}$ to 1 decimal place.

Examiner's tip:
In these GCSE questions you get most of the marks for your working out.

Estimate	Check (square of estimate)	Answer	Result
5	5^2	25	Too small
6	6^2	36	Too big
5.5	5.5^2	30.25	Too big
5.4	5.4^2	29.16	Too small
5.45	5.45^2	29.7025	Too small

So $\sqrt{30} = 5.5$ (1 decimal place)

1 Write

   a the 5th square number   **b** the 11th square number

   c the 15th square number   **d** the 17th square number.

2 In each of these lists of numbers, identify the square numbers.

   a 8, 16, 24, 30, 36   **b** 49, 59, 69, 79, 99

   c 140, 121, 135, 144, 136   **d** 214, 218, 223, 225, 222

3 Use your calculator to work out each of these. Give your answer to 2 decimal places as appropriate.

   a 16^2 **b** 3.7^2 **c** 50^2 **d** 6.7^2

   e 17.8^2 **f** $(-4.2)^2$ **g** 1.9^2 **h** 0.1^2

   i $(-3.9)^2$ **j** 2.1^2 **k** $(-0.7)^2$ **l** 13.25^2

4 Calculate each of these using a calculator, giving your answer to 2 dp as appropriate. Remember to give your answer as both a positive and a negative square root.

   a $\sqrt{529}$ **b** $\sqrt{157}$ **c** $\sqrt{41}$ **d** $\sqrt{0.16}$

   e $\sqrt{6.76}$ **f** $\sqrt{800}$ **g** $\sqrt{1345}$ **h** $\sqrt{38.6}$

   i $\sqrt{7093}$ **j** $\sqrt{234.652}$

5 Without a calculator, write the whole number that is closest in value to

   a $\sqrt{50}$ **b** $\sqrt{80}$ **c** $\sqrt{30}$ **d** $\sqrt{40}$

   e $\sqrt{120}$ **f** $\sqrt{150}$ **g** $\sqrt{8}$ **h** $\sqrt{5}$

6 Use your calculator to work out these problems.

   a $\sqrt{7} = 2.645751$

       Calculate $(2.645751)^2$.

       Explain why the answer is not 7.

   b Two consecutive numbers are multiplied together. The answer is 3192. What are the two numbers?

7 **a** Use a trial and improvement method to find the square root of 20 to 1 decimal place.

Estimate	Check	Answer	Result
4	4^2	16	Too small
5	5^2	25	
4.5			

   b Use a similar method to find

       i $\sqrt{40}$ **ii** $\sqrt{60}$ **iii** $\sqrt{95}$

This spread will show you how to:

- Use powers and index notation for small positive integer powers
- Use the square, square root, cube and cube root functions of a scientific calculator

Keywords

Cube number
Cube root
Index
Power

- A **cube number** is the result of multiplying a whole number by itself and then multiplying by that number again.

Your calculator should have a x^3 function key.

Cubes of numbers are written using **index** notation.

$1^3 = 1 \times 1 \times 1 = 1$ $2^3 = 2 \times 2 \times 2 = 8$ $3^3 = 3 \times 3 \times 3 = 27$

- A **cube root** is a number that when multiplied by itself and then multiplied by itself again is equal to a given number. Cube roots are written using $\sqrt[3]{}$ notation.

$\sqrt[3]{4913} = 17$ because $17^3 = 17 \times 17 \times 17 = 4913$

- A positive number has a positive cube root and a negative number has a negative cube root.

$\sqrt[3]{-125} = -5$ because $(-5)^3 = -5 \times -5 \times -5 = -125$

Example

Calculate the value of $\sqrt[3]{200}$.

Using a calculator you might type

```
3√200
5.848035476
```

So $\sqrt[3]{200} = 5.85$ (2 dp)

Check: $5.85^3 \approx 6^3$
        $5.85^3 < 6^3 = 216$
        $5.85^3 > 5^3 = 125$
        5.85^3 is greater than 125 but less than 216.

Use a calculator to find a cube root using the

$\sqrt[3]{x}$ function key.

You can use trial and improvement to estimate cube roots.

Example

Use trial and improvement to find $\sqrt[3]{18}$ to 1 decimal place.

Estimate	Check (cube of estimate)	Answer	Result
2	2^3	8	Too small
3	3^3	27	Too big
2.5	2.5^3	15.625	Too small
2.6	2.6^3	17.576	Too small
2.7	2.7^3	19.683	Too big
2.65	2.65^3	18.609 625	Too big

So $\sqrt[3]{18} = 2.6$ (1 decimal place)

Examiner's tip
In these GCSE questions you get most of the marks for your working out.

Note you can also use this technique for **square** roots.

1 Write

  a the 7th cube number   **b** the 10th cube number

  c the 13th cube number   **d** the 19th cube number.

2 In each of these lists of numbers, identify the square and cube numbers.

  a 4, 11, 16, 27, 35   **b** 24, 44, 64, 84, 124, 144

  c 156, 196, 216, 256, 286   **d** 700, 800, 900, 1000, 1200

3 Use your calculator to work out each of these. Give your answer to 2 decimal places as appropriate.

  a 8^3 **b** 2.4^3 **c** 20^3 **d** 3.9^3

  e 11.7^3 **f** $(-2.8)^3$ **g** 8.9^3 **h** 0.5^3

  i $(-5.4)^3$ **j** 9.9^3 **k** $(-0.1)^3$ **l** 16.85^3

4 Calculate these using a calculator, giving your answers to 2 dp as appropriate.

  a $\sqrt[3]{729}$ **b** $\sqrt[3]{100}$ **c** $\sqrt[3]{64}$ **d** $\sqrt[3]{86}$

  e $\sqrt[3]{7.6}$ **f** $\sqrt[3]{2.7}$ **g** $\sqrt[3]{1.331}$ **h** $\sqrt[3]{56.3}$

  i $\sqrt[3]{12\ 167}$ **j** $\sqrt[3]{-216}$ **k** $\sqrt[3]{-70}$ **l** $\sqrt[3]{0.015\ 625}$

5 **a** Use a trial and improvement method to find the cube root of each of these numbers to 1 decimal place.

    i $\sqrt[3]{20}$

Estimate	Check (cube of estimate)	Answer	Result
2	2^3	8	Too small
3	3^3	27	
2.5			

    ii $\sqrt[3]{50}$

Estimate	Check (cube of estimate)	Answer	Result
3	3^3	27	Too small
4	4^3		

    iii $\sqrt[3]{80}$ **iv** $\sqrt[3]{150}$ **v** $\sqrt[3]{300}$ **vi** $\sqrt[3]{500}$ **vii** $\sqrt[3]{900}$ **viii** $\sqrt[3]{1500}$

  b Use the cube root key on your calculator to check your answers.

This spread will show you how to:

- Use powers and index notation for small positive integer powers
- Understand and use reciprocals
- Multiply and divide by powers of 10

Keywords

Index
Power
Powers of 10
Reciprocal

● You can use **index** notation to describe **powers** of any number.

$$4.6^5 = 4.6 \times 4.6 \times 4.6 \times 4.6 \times 4.6$$

To work out 4.6^5 you might type: 5

The calculator display should read 2059.629 76.
So $4.6^5 = 2059.63$ (2 dp).

Some calculators may have a different key, for example $\boxed{x^y}$ or $\boxed{\wedge}$ or $\boxed{\text{EXP}}$.

● Powers of the same number can be multiplied and divided.

When multiplying, you add the indices.

$$5^3 \times 5^4 = (5 \times 5 \times 5) \times (5 \times 5 \times 5 \times 5) = 5^7$$
$$5^{3+4} \qquad\qquad\qquad\qquad\qquad = 5^7$$

When dividing, you subtract the indices.

$$3^5 \div 3^2 = \frac{3 \times 3 \times 3 \times 3 \times 3}{3 \times 3} = 3 \times 3 \times 3 = 3^3$$
$$3^{5-2} \qquad\qquad\qquad\qquad\qquad = 3^3$$

● **Any number raised to the power of zero is equal to 1.**

$$7^0 = 1 \qquad\qquad\qquad 10^0 = 1$$

● The **reciprocal** of a number is 1 divided by that number.

Reciprocal of $10 = \frac{1}{10} = 0.1$ Reciprocal of $4^2 = \frac{1}{4^2} = \frac{1}{16} = 0.0625$

To calculate reciprocals use the $\boxed{\frac{1}{x}}$ or function key on your calculator.

● A **negative power** represents the reciprocal of a number.

$$8^{-1} = \frac{1}{8} = 0.125 \qquad\qquad 10^{-2} = \frac{1}{10^2} = \frac{1}{100} = 0.01$$

The decimal system is based upon **power of ten**.

Example

Calculate   **a** 6.3×10^3 **b** $120 \div 10^4$

a

Thousands	Hundreds	Tens	Units	•	tenths	hundredths	
			6	•	3		$\times 10^3$
6	3	0	0	•			

$6.3 \times 10^3 = 6300$

When you multiply by 10^3, all the digits move **three** places to the left.

b

Hundreds	Tens	Units	•	tenths	hundredths	thousandths	
1	2	0	•				$\div 10^4$
			•	0	1	2	

$120 \div 10^4 = 0.012$

When you divide by 10^4, all the digits move **four** places to the right.

1 Calculate these without using a calculator.

a 4^2 b 2^5 c 5^3 d 7^4 e 9^3

2 Use the $\boxed{x^y}$ function key on your calculator to work out these, giving your answers to 2 decimal places where appropriate.

a 15^3 b 3^6 c 2^{10} d 21.6^4 e 13^3

3 Use your calculator to work out each of these.

a $2^4 + 3^2$ b $10^3 \div 5^2$ c $8^6 - 13^3$ d $10^6 \div 5^3$ e $\left(\frac{1}{4}\right)^4 + \left(\frac{1}{8}\right)^2$

4 Use the $\boxed{x^y}$ function key on your calculator to find the value of x.

a $3^x = 27$ b $5^x = 625$ c $10^x = 10\ 000$ d $4^x = 16\ 384$ e $x^2 = 529$

5 Calculate these.

a 3.4×10^2

Thousands	Hundreds	Tens	Units	•	tenths	hundredths	
			3	•	4		$\times 10^2$
				•			

b 76.6×10^3 c $85 \div 10^3$ d 2.3×10^4 e 0.312×10^6

f 5.62×10^4 g $2960 \div 1000$

6 Simplify each of these, leaving your answer as a single power of the number.

a $3^2 \times 3^2$ b $7^3 \times 7^2$ c $2^7 \times 2^5$ d $10^7 \div 10^4$

e $3^{10} \div 3^6$ f $4^2 \times 4^3 \times 4^2$ g $10^5 \times 10^2 \times 10^3$

h $7^4 \times 7^1 \times 7$ i $\dfrac{2^3 \times 2^5}{2^2}$ j $\dfrac{10^3 \times 10^4}{10^2}$ k $\dfrac{4^2 \times 4^2 \times 4^2}{4^6}$

7 Use your calculator to work out the reciprocal of each of these numbers.

a 10   b 8   c 1000   d 3   e 7   f 13

8 Calculate each of these without using a calculator.

a 4^0 b 5^{-1} c 13^0

9 Copy these and fill in the missing numbers.

a $540 \div 10^2 = \underline{\quad}$ b $6850 \div 10^? = 6.85$

c $3.12 \times \underline{\quad} = 31\ 200$ d $1.73 \times 10^6 = \underline{\quad}$

10 Simplify each of these, leaving your answer as a single power of the number or letter where appropriate.

a $y^2 \times y^3$ b $4^8 \times 4^2$ c $w^{12} \div w^7$ d $4^y \div 4^2$ e $\dfrac{g^6 \times g^3}{g^5}$ f $3^2 \times 4^3$

This spread will show you how to:

- Understand and use standard form in calculations with large and small numbers
- Use calculators to calculate in standard form

You can use **standard form** to represent large numbers.

- In **standard form**, a number is written as $A \times 10^n$.
    - A is a number between 1 and 10 (but not including 10). Using algebra, $1 \leqslant A < 10$.
    - The value of n is an integer.
    For example, $856 = 8.56 \times 10^2$ and $43\,994 = 4.3994 \times 10^4$.

13×10^5 is *not* in standard form, because 13 is larger than 10.

0.75×10^4 is *not* in standard form, because 0.75 is less than 1.

You can calculate with numbers in standard form.

- Multiplication works like this:
$(3 \times 10^5) \times (4 \times 10^3) = (3 \times 4) \times 10^{(5+3)} = 12 \times 10^8 = 1.2 \times 10^9$
- Division works like this:
$(1.4 \times 10^8) \div (7 \times 10^5) = (1.4 \div 7) \times 10^{(8-5)} = 0.2 \times 10^3 = 2 \times 10^2$

The correct version is 1.3×10^6

The correct version is 7.5×10^3

Multiplication – add the indices

Division – subtract the indices

Example

Write these numbers in standard form.

a 235 **b** 12 492 **c** 15×10^4 **d** 0.23×10^6

a $235 = 2.35 \times 10^2$ **b** $12\,492 = 1.2492 \times 10^4$
c $15 \times 10^4 = 1.5 \times 10^5$ **d** $0.23 \times 10^6 = 2.3 \times 10^5$

You can use a calculator to input standard form. On a standard Casio you use the [EXP] key.

Example

Calculate

a $(4.2 \times 10^3) \times (2 \times 10^2)$ **b** $(3.6 \times 10^5) \div (1.2 \times 10^3)$ **c** $(5.4 \times 10^4) \times (2 \times 10^3)$

a $(4.2 \times 10^3) \times (2 \times 10^2) = (4.2 \times 2) \times (10^3 \times 10^2)$
$= 8.4 \times 10^{(3+2)} = 8.4 \times 10^5$
b $(3.6 \times 10^5) \div (1.2 \times 10^3) = (3.6 \div 1.2) \times (10^5 \div 10^3)$
$= 3 \times 10^{(5-3)} = 3 \times 10^2$
c $(5.4 \times 10^4) \times (2 \times 10^3) = (5.4 \times 2) \times (10^4 \times 10^3)$
$= 10.8 \times 10^7 = 1.08 \times 10^8$

To do part **a** on a calculator:

4.2 [EXP] 3 [×] 2 [EXP] 2

However, your calculator may give the answer 840 000. Why?

Example

The Andromeda Galaxy has a radius of about 1 040 700 000 000 000 000 km. Write this in standard form.

$1\,040\,700\,000\,000\,000\,000 = 1.0407 \times 10^{18}$

1 Write these numbers as powers of 10.

    a 100   **b** 10   **c** 100 000   **d** 1

2 Write these numbers in standard form.

    a 200   **b** 800   **c** 9000   **d** 650

    e 6500   **f** 952   **g** 23.58   **h** 255.85

3 These numbers are in standard form. Write each of them as an 'ordinary' number.

    a 5×10^2 **b** 3×10^3 **c** 1×10^5 **d** 2.5×10^2

    e 4.9×10^3 **f** 3.8×10^6 **g** 7.5×10^{11} **h** 8.1×10^{18}

4 Although they are written as multiples of powers of 10, these numbers are not in standard form. Rewrite each of them correctly in standard form.

    a 60×10^1 **b** 45×10^3 **c** 0.65×10^1 **d** 0.05×10^8

5 Work out these calculations, giving your answers in standard form. Do not use a calculator.

    a $(2 \times 10^2) \times (2 \times 10^3)$ **b** $(3 \times 10^4) \times (3 \times 10^3)$

    c $(5 \times 10^3) \times (5 \times 10^4)$ **d** $(8 \times 10^7) \times (3 \times 10^5)$

6 Evaluate these, showing your working. Do not use a calculator; give your answers in standard form.

    a $(4 \times 10^4) \div (2 \times 10^2)$ **b** $(8.4 \times 10^9) \div (4.2 \times 10^5)$

    c $(2 \times 10^6) \div (4 \times 10^4)$ **d** $(3 \times 10^5) \div (4 \times 10^2)$

7 Use a calculator to find these. Give your answers in standard form, to 3 significant figures.

    a $(2.5 \times 10^5) \times (3.9 \times 10^4)$ **b** $(4.1 \times 10^6) \div (3 \times 10^2)$

    c $(4.95 \times 10^3) \times (8.11 \times 10^7)$ **d** $(3.7 \times 10^{11}) \div (1.8 \times 10^3)$

8 The speed of light is approximately 3×10^8 metres per second. Copy and complete the table to show the time taken for light from the Sun to reach the various planets.

Planet	Mean distance from Sun (m)	Light travel time
Mercury	5.79×10^{10}	
Earth	1.50×10^{11}	
Mars	2.28×10^{11}	
Jupiter	7.78×10^{11}	
Pluto	5.90×10^{12}	

Prime factor decomposition

This spread will show you how to:

Keywords
Factor
HCF
LCM
Prime factor
Prime number

- Recognise prime factors and express a number as a product of its prime factors
- Find the HCF and LCM of two numbers

> - A **prime factor** is a factor of a number which is also prime.

Look back to page 10 to remind yourself about factors.

Factors of 28 are {1, 2, 4, 7, 14, 28}.
Prime factors of 28 are {2, 7}

> - Every whole number can be written as the product of its **prime factors**.

There are two common methods to find the prime factors.

Factor trees

Split the number into a **factor** pair. Continue splitting until you reach a prime factor.

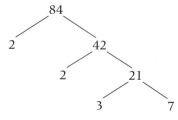

$84 = 2 \times 2 \times 3 \times 7$

Division by prime numbers

Divide the number by the smallest **prime number**. Repeat dividing by larger prime numbers until you reach a prime number.

2	84
2	42
3	21
	7

$84 = 2 \times 2 \times 3 \times 7$

- You can find the **highest common factor (HCF)** by using prime factors.

For example, the HCF of 30 and 135:

$30 = 2 \times 3 \times 5 \qquad = 2 \times 3 \times 5$

2	30
3	15
	5

$135 = 3 \times 3 \times 3 \times 5 = 3 \times 3 \times 3 \times 5$

3	135
3	45
3	15
	5

$\text{HCF} = 3 \times 5 = 15$

- Write each number as the product of its prime factors.
- Pick out the common factors 3 and 5.
- Multiply these together to get the HCF.

- You can find the **least common multiple (LCM)** by using prime factors.

For example, the LCM of 28 and 126:

$28 = 2^2 \times 7 = 2 \times 2 \times 7$

2	28
2	14
	7

$126 = 2 \times 3^2 \times 7 = 2 \times 3 \times 3 \times 7$

2	126
3	63
3	21
	7

$\text{HCF} = 2 \times 7 = 14$
$\text{LCM} = 2 \times 3 \times 3 \times 14 = 252$

- Write each number as the product of its prime factors.
- Pick out the common factors 2 and 7.
- Multiply these together to get the HCF – 14.
- Multiply the HCF by the remaining factors – the remaining factors are 2, 3 and 3.

1 Work out the value of each of these expressions.

   a 3×5^2 **b** $2^3 \times 5$ **c** $3^2 \times 7$ **d** $2^2 \times 3^2 \times 5$ **e** $3^2 \times 7^2$

2 Express these numbers as products of their prime factors.

   a 18   **b** 24   **c** 40   **d** 39

   e 48   **f** 82   **g** 100   **h** 144

   i 180   **j** 315   **k** 444   **l** 1350

3 In each of these questions, Jack has been asked to write each of the numbers as the product of its prime factors.

   i Mark his work and identify any errors he has made.

   ii Correct any of Jack's mistakes.

   a 126   **b** 210   **c** 221

Answer: $126 = 2 \times 3^2$

Answer: $2 \times 3^2 \times 7$

Answer: 221

4 **Investigation**

   The number 18 can be written as $2 \times 3 \times 3$.
   You can say that 18 has three prime factors.

   a Find three numbers with exactly three prime factors.

   b Find five numbers with exactly four prime factors.

   c Find four numbers between 100 and 300 with exactly five prime factors.

   d Find a two-digit number with exactly six prime factors.

5 Find the HCF of

   a 9 and 24   **b** 15 and 40   **c** 18 and 24

   d 96 and 144   **e** 12, 15 and 18   **f** 425 and 816.

6 Find the LCM of

   a 9 and 24   **b** 15 and 40   **c** 18 and 24

   d 20 and 30   **e** 12, 15 and 18   **f** 48, 54 and 72.

7 Cancel these fractions to their simplest forms using the HCF of the numerator and denominator to help.

   a $\frac{6}{8}$ **b** $\frac{12}{18}$ **c** $\frac{60}{96}$

   d $\frac{36}{54}$ **e** $\frac{117}{169}$ **f** $\frac{26}{65}$

Key objectives

- Use standard index form expressed in conventional notation and on a calculator display
- Use index laws for multiplication and division of integer powers
- Understand highest common factor, least common multiple, prime number and prime factor decomposition

1 Calculate:

   a $3^2 \times 3^2$ (1)

   b $3^3 \div 3$ (1)

   c 3^{-2} (1)

2 a Express 108 as the product of powers of its prime factors.   (3)

   b Find the highest common factor (HCF) of 108 and 24.   (1)

(Edexcel Ltd., 2004)

This unit will show you how to

- Understand and use the words equation, formula, identity, and expression
- Substitute values into expressions, functions and formulae
- Solve equations by rearranging formulae and using the balance method
- Use formulae from mathematics and other subjects
- Write formulae to represent everyday situations
- Change the subject of simple formulae
- Understand the difference between a practical demonstration and a proof
- Use a counter-example to show that a statement is false

Before you start ...

You should be able to answer these questions.	**Review**
1 Work out the value of each expression when $y = 3$.	Unit A2
a $2y$ **b** $4y - 1$	
c y^2 **d** $4y \div 2$	
2 Multiply out	Unit A1
a $3(x + 1)$ **b** $2(x - 1)$	
c $4(2x + 3)$ **d** $3(4x - 2)$	
3 Solve, using the balance method	Unit A2
a $2x + 3 = 11$ **b** $3y - 4 = 14$	
4 Factorise	Unit A1
a $4x + 8$ **b** $6x + 2$	
c $3y - 9$	
5 Write the prime numbers from this list.	Unit N1
2 3 5 7 8	
11 13 15 17 19	

Formulae, equations and identities

This spread will show you how to:

- Understand and use the words equation, formula, identity, and expression

Keywords
Equation
Expression
Formula
Function
Identity
Substitute

In algebra you use letters to represent numbers.

- An **expression** is made up of algebraic terms. It has no equals sign.

  $2x + 3b$ and $2(l + w)$ are expressions.

- A **function** links two variables. When you know one, you can work out the other.

  $x \rightarrow 3x + 2$ or $y = 3x + 2$ is a function.

- A **formula** is a rule linking two or more variables.

  $P = 2l + 2w$ is a formula for the perimeter of a rectangle.

- An **equation** is only true for one unique value of a variable. You can solve the equation to find this value, the solution.

  $x + 4 = 10$ is an equation. Its solution is $x = 6$.

- An **identity** is true for any values of the variables.

  $a + a + a + a \equiv 4a$ is an identity.

  The sign $\equiv$ means identically equal to.

You can **substitute** values into expressions, functions and formulae.

Formulae is the plural of formula.

Example

Work out the value of each expression when $x = 2$, $y = 4$, $z = 3$.

a $xy - z$ **b** $3x + 5y$ **c** $\dfrac{x + y}{z}$

$xy = x \times y$

a $xy - z = 2 \times 4 - 3$

$= 8 - 3 = 5$

b $3x + 5y = 3 \times 2 + 5 \times 4$

$= 6 + 20 = 26$

c $\dfrac{x + y}{z} = \dfrac{2 + 4}{3} = \dfrac{6}{3} = 2$

Write in the multiplication sign.

You can solve equations using the balance method.

Example

Solve $3x + 5 = 17$.

$3x + 5 = 17$

$3x + 5 - 5 = 17 - 5$ Subtract 5 from both sides.

$3x = 12$

$3x \div 3 = 12 \div 3$ Divide both sides by 3.

$x = 4$

Do the same to both sides.

1 Work out the value of each expression when
$a = 6$, $b = 3$, $c = \frac{1}{2}$, $d = 4$.

a ad **b** $2b$ **c** ab **d** $a + cd$

e $ad + b$ **f** $3b - d$ **g** $2dc - a$ **h** $ab - dc$

2 Work out the value of each expression when $e = -2$, $f = 3$, $g = -6$.

a $ef + g$ **b** $eg + f$ **c** $2e^2 - g$ **d** $\dfrac{fg}{e}$

3 For each function, work out the value of y

   i when $x = 4$
   ii when $x = -2$.

a $y = 4x + 3$ **b** $y = 2x - 6$ **c** $y = \frac{1}{2}x + 10$

d $y = 6x - 1$ **e** $y = x^2$ **f** $y = 2x^2 + 4$

4 Solve these.

a $2x + 3 = 15$ **b** $2y - 5 = 17$ **c** $4x + 15 = 7$

d $3y - 13 = -10$ **e** $23 = 6b + 5$ **f** $7 = 19 + 3c$

g $15 - 7f = 1$ **h** $60 - 3g = 72$

5 Multiply out the brackets and write each of these as an identity.
The first one has been done for you.

a $7(x + 4) \equiv 7 \times x + 7 \times 4 \equiv 7x + 28$

b $3(x - 2)$ **c** $2(3 + x)$ **d** $5(2 - x)$

6 Copy and complete these identities by factorising.

a $8m + 4 \equiv 4 ($ $)$ **b** $12n - 9 \equiv \square ($ $)$ **c** $15p + 55 \equiv \square ($ $)$

d $q^2 + 2q \equiv q ($ $)$ **e** $16r - 28 \equiv \square ($ $)$ **f** $4pq - 10q \equiv \square ($ $)$

7 Copy the table.

Expressions	Equations	Functions	Formulae	Identities

Write these under the correct heading in your table.

a $a + bc = bc + a$ **b** $y = 3x + 2$ **c** $a + bc = d$

d $3a + 5 = -4$ **e** $4xy + 3x - z$ **f** $E = mc^2$

g $s = ut$ **h** $x - 1 = y$

Substituting into formulae

This spread will show you how to:

● Substitute values into expressions, functions and formulae

Keywords

Formula
Substitute

● You can **substitute** numbers into a **formula** written in words.

The formula for the perimeter of a regular hexagon is

    Perimeter = 6 × length of one side

This regular hexagon has sides of length 3 cm.
Its perimeter = 6 × 3 cm = 18 cm.

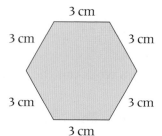

3 cm
3 cm
3 cm
3 cm
3 cm
3 cm

● You can substitute numbers into a formula written using letters.

Example

Apples cost 20p each and bananas cost 25p each.

The formula for the cost (in pence) of a apples and b bananas is

    cost = 20a + 25b

Find the cost of 8 apples and 3 bananas.

25p each   20p each

a apples cost
a × 20p.
b bananas cost
b × 25p.

Cost = 20 × 8 + 25 × 3
    = 160 + 75
    = 235 pence or £2.35

Substitute $a = 8$
and $b = 3$

● You can solve an equation to find a value from a formula.

Example

In the formula $v = u + at$

a find v when $u = 2$, $a = 5$, $t = 20$ **b** find u when $v = 50$, $a = 2$, $t = 15$

---

a $v = u + at$
  $v = 2 + 5 × 20$
    $= 2 + 100 = 102$

b $v = u + at$
  $50 = u + 2 × 15$
  $50 = u + 30$
  $50 - 30 = u + 30 - 30$
    $20 = u$

Subtract 30 from
both sides.

1 The area of card needed to make an open cube-shaped box is calculated by

    Area of card = 5 × area of one side of box
Use this formula to work out the area of card needed for a box with

a area of one side 12 cm^2 **b** area of one side 20 cm^2

c area of one side 1 m^2 **d** area of one side 2.3 m^2

2 The bill for a mobile phone is calculated using the formula
    Cost in pounds = 0.05 × number of texts + 0.10 × minutes of calls

a Use the formula to work out the bills for

   i   Nadia: 40 texts and 20 minutes of calls

   ii Saleem: 5 texts and 70 minutes of calls

   iii Marcus: 32 texts and 15 minutes of calls.

b What is the cost for a call lasting 1 minute?
Give your answer in pence.

3 The cost of hiring a van is given by the formula $C = 25d + 40$
where C is the cost in pounds and d is the number of days.
Work out the cost of

a hiring the van for 3 days   **b** hiring the van for 10 days.

4 In the formula $v = u + at$ find v when

a $u = 3$, $a = 5$, $t = 2$ **b** $u = 12$, $a = 4$, $t = 9$

5 In the formula $V = lwh$ find V when $l = 3$, $w = 6$, $h = 8$.

6 Use the formula $s = ut + \frac{1}{2}at^2$ to find the value of s when

a $u = 2$, $a = 3$, $t = 5$ **b** $u = -3$, $t = 4$, $a = 12$

7 Use the formula $t = \dfrac{v - u}{a}$ to find t when

a $v = 35$, $u = 27$, $a = 4$ **b** $v = 12$, $u = 16$, $a = -2$

8 In the formula $A = 2b + c$, find c if $A = 14$ and $b = 5$.

9 $P = 2l + 2w$
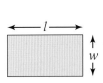

a Find w when $P = 18$, $l = 6$.   **b** Find l when $P = 20$, $w = 8$.

10 Using the simple interest formula, $I = \dfrac{PRT}{100}$

a find P when $I = 12$, $R = 20$, $T = 30$.

b find R when $I = 3.6$, $T = 18$, $P = 10$.

11 Gemma and Paul evaluated $5x^2$ when $x = 6$.

Who was right? Explain why.

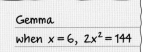

Gemma
when $x = 6$, $2x^2 = 144$

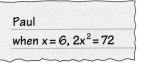

Paul
when $x = 6$, $2x^2 = 72$

This spread will show you how to:

- Write formulae to represent everyday situations
- Use formulae from mathematics and other subjects

Keywords
Formula

A **formula** can save time when you have to work out similar calculations over and over again.

- You can write a formula to represent an everyday situation.
  - Write the formula in words and then using letters.
  - Explain what the letters represent.

Example

A plumber charges £25 for a callout and £30 per hour of work. Write a formula for the plumber's charge.

Charge in pounds = 25 + 30 × number of hours of work

$$C = 25 + 30h$$

where C = charge in pounds, h = number of hours of work.

Example

A bus ticket to town costs £3 for an adult and 90p for a child.

a Write a formula to work out the cost in pounds of bus tickets for different numbers of adults and children.
b Use your formula to work out the cost of tickets for 3 adults and 5 children.
c Mr and Mrs Karim and their children paid £8.70 for bus tickets.
  How many children bought tickets?

a Cost in pounds = 3 × number of adults + 0.90 × number of children

$$C = 3n + 0.90m$$

where C = cost in pounds, n = number of adults, m = number of children.

90p = £0.90

b $C = 3n + 0.90m$
  $= 3 \times 3 + 0.90 \times 5$
  $= 9 + 4.50 = £13.50$

$n = 3, m = 5$

Write the answer in pounds.

c $C = 3n + 0.90m$
  $8.70 = 3 \times 2 + 0.90m = 6 + 0.90m$
  $8.70 - 6 = 6 - 6 + 0.90m$
  $2.70 = 0.90m$
  $2.70 \div 0.90 = 0.90m \div 0.90$
  $3 = m$
  3 children bought tickets.

Substitute $C = 8.70$ and $n = 2$.

1 An electrician charges £35 for each job + £20 per hour.

  a Write a formula for the electrician's charge in pounds.

  b Use your formula to find the charge of a job that takes 3 hours.

2 The cost of a taxi is £2 for a callout + 60p for each mile.

  a Write a formula for the cost of a taxi in pounds.

  b Work out the cost for a journey of

   i 5 miles   **ii** 15 miles.

3 In Spain a hire car costs €75 plus €35 a day.

  a Write a formula for the cost of hiring a car in euros.

  b How much does it cost to hire a car for 7 days?

  c Louise paid €495 to hire a car.
  How many days did she hire it for?

4 Pencils are arranged in rectangles.
The number of pencils needed to make a rectangle is
    2 × number of pencils along the bottom + 2

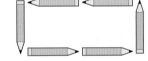

  a Write this formula using letters.

  b Check that your formula gives the correct answer for a rectangle of
  length 5.

  c Work out how many pencils are needed for a rectangle of length 8.

  d A rectangle uses 48 pencils. What is its length?

5 Cinema tickets cost £6.80 for adults and £4.50 for children.
5 adults took a group of children to the cinema.
The tickets cost £97 in total.
How many children went to the cinema?

> Write a formula first.

6 The cost of hiring a steam cleaner is
  ● £32.50 for the first day
  ● £24.75 for each extra day.
Tariq paid £131.50 to hire the steam cleaner.
How many days did he hire it for?

7 Tickets for a fun day cost £3 for adults and £1.50 for children.
The total cost of tickets for a group of adults and children was £54.

  a Write a formula for the cost for n adults and m children.

  In the group there were 4 children for every adult.

  b Write this information using algebra: $m = 4 \times \ldots$

  c Substitute your expression from part **b** into your formula from
  part **a**.

  d Use your formula from part **c** to work out the number of adults in
  the group.

Changing the subject of a formula

This spread will show you how to:

● Change the subject of simple formulae

Keywords

Subject

● The **subject** of a formula is the letter on its own on one side of the equals sign.

The formula for the number of slabs in a rectangular patio is

$$N = lw$$

where l is the number of slabs along the length and w is the number along the width.

N is the subject of the formula. You can substitute values for l and w to find N.

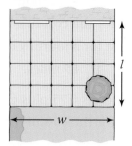

Rick has 24 slabs. He is trying to decide on the dimensions for a patio. For a patio 6 slabs long, he substitutes $N = 24$ and $l = 6$ into the formula:

$$24 = 6w$$

He solves to find w

$24 \div 6 = 6w \div 6$, so $w = 4$.

To work out w for different values of l, each time he has to:

● substitute for N and l

● solve the equation.

To save time, he can rearrange the formula to make w the subject.

● You can change the subject of a formula using the balance method.

$N = lw$

$\dfrac{N}{l} = \dfrac{lw}{l}$

$\dfrac{N}{l} = w$

w is multiplied by l.

To get w on its own, use the inverse operation 'divide by l'.

Do the same to both sides.

Example

Rearrange these formulae to make x the subject.

a $y = x - a$ **b** $y = mx + c$ **c** $y = \dfrac{x}{2} - b$

a $\quad y = x - a$

$\quad y + a = x - a + a$

$\quad\quad x = y + a$

b $\quad y = mx + c$

$\quad y - c = mx + c - c$

$\quad y - c = mx$

$\quad \dfrac{y - c}{m} = \dfrac{mx}{m}$

$\quad \dfrac{y - c}{m} = x$

c $\quad y = \dfrac{x}{2} - b$

$\quad y + b = \dfrac{x}{2}$

$\quad 2(y + b) = x$

Exercise A5.4

1 $v = u + at$
Find u when

   a $v = 20$, $a = 2$, $t = 6$ **b** $v = 8$, $a = 5$, $t = 2$

2 $y = mx + c$
Find c when

   a $y = 10$, $m = 2$, $x = 3$ **b** $y = 8$, $m = 3$, $x = -2$

3 $3y = 2x - 4$
Find x when

   a $y = 6$ **b** $y = 3$

4 $R = \dfrac{V}{I}$. Find V when

   a $R = 6$, $I = 10$ **b** $R = 7.2$, $I = 20$

5 $s = \dfrac{D}{T}$. Find t when

   a $s = 70$, $d = 35$ **b** $s = 13$, $d = 52$

6 Rearrange each formula

   a $y = mx + c$, make x the subject   **b** $v = u + at$, make t the subject
   c $y = \frac{x}{2} + d$, make x the subject   **d** $x + 3y = 4$, make y the subject

7 For each of these formulae make t the subject.

   a $s = 3t - 6$ **b** $2x = 5t + 9$ **c** $12 + 2t = 3x$

8 Rearrange each formula to make y the subject.

   a $4x + 6y = 2$ **b** $3y - 2x = 6$ **c** $3x - 5y = z$

9 These patterns are made with pencils.
The formula to work out the number
of pencils (P) in a row of n huts is

     $P = 4n + 1$

 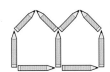 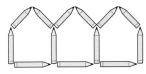

      5 pencils   9 pencils   13 pencils

   a Rearrange this formula to make
     n the subject.

   b Use your formula to work out the number of huts you can make
     with

     i 37 pencils   **ii** 53 pencils   **iii** 229 pencils.

10 The formula for calculating the cost in pounds of an electricity bill is
     $C = 17.5 + 0.1u$ where u is the number of units used.
By rearranging the formula, work out the numbers of units used
when the cost is

   a £37.50   **b** £32.50   **c** £74.50

This spread will show you how to:

- Understand the difference between a practical demonstration and a proof

Keywords
Counter-example
Prove
Show

- You can **show** that a formula is true by writing expressions and simplifying.

Example

This triangle has height $2x$ and base $x + 1$.
The area of the triangle is A.
Show that $A = x^2 + x$.

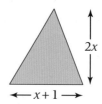

$2x$

$\longleftarrow x + 1 \longrightarrow$

Area of a triangle $= \frac{1}{2} \times$ base $\times$ height

So $A = \frac{1}{2} \times (x + 1) \times 2x$

$\quad = \frac{1}{2} \times 2x(x + 1)$

$\quad = x(x + 1)$

$\quad = x^2 + x$

$(x + 1) \times 2x \equiv$
$2x \times (x + 1)$

- You can **prove** a statement by showing that it is true for all possible values of the variables.

Example

The expressions $(n - 1)$, n and $(n + 1)$ represent three consecutive numbers.
When $n = 4$, the three consecutive numbers are 3, 4 and 5.
$3 + 4 + 5 = 12$, which is divisible by 3.
When $n = 20$, $19 + 20 + 21 = 60$, which is divisible by 3.

Use the expressions $(n - 1)$, n and $(n + 1)$ to prove that the sum of any three consecutive numbers is divisible by 3.

The sum of any three consecutive numbers is

$\quad n - 1 + n + n + 1 = n + n + n - 1 + 1 = 3n$

$3n$ is always divisible by 3.
So the sum of any three consecutive numbers is always divisible by 3.

- You can show that a statement is not true by finding a **counter-example**.

A counter-example is an example or value that doesn't fit the statement.

Example

Find a counter-example to show that this statement is not true:
'the sum of two prime numbers is always a prime number'.

Try some pairs of prime numbers.
$\quad$ 2 and 3 are prime, and $2 + 3 = 5$, which is prime.
$\quad$ 3 and 5 are prime, and $3 + 5 = 8$, which is not prime.
So the statement is false.

2 and 3 fit the statement.
3 and 5 do not fit – this is a counter-example.

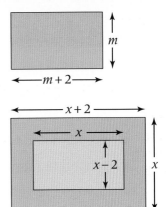

1 This rectangle has length m and width $m + 2$.
The area of the rectangle is A.
Show that $A = m^2 + 2m$.

2 A rectangular photo frame is made by cutting a
smaller rectangle out of a rectangular piece of card.

  a Write an expression for the area of the larger
rectangle.

  b Write an expression for the area of the smaller
rectangle.

  c Show that A, the area of card in the frame, is $4x$.

3 The integers 1, 2, 3, 4, ... follow this pattern:
odd, even, odd, even, ...

  a Copy and complete these statements.

    For any two consecutive numbers, one is ___ and one is ___

    Even + even = ___

    Odd + odd = ___

    Odd + even = ___

  b Use statements from part **a** to prove that:
The sum of any two consecutive numbers is odd.

  c Prove that the sum of any four consecutive numbers is even.

4 Any even number is a multiple of 2.
So any even number can be represented by $2n$, for some value of n.

  a What type of number does $2n + 1$ represent?

  b Use these results to write the calculation
    even number × odd number
in terms of n.

  c Multiply out the brackets in your expression.

  d Copy and complete:

    $4n^2 \div 2 =$ ___ For any n, $4n^2$ is a multiple of ___

  e Use your answers to show that

    even number × odd number = even number

5 Find a counter-example for each of these statements.

  a If x is a prime number, $3x$ is an odd number.

  b If x is a prime number, x^2 is an odd number.

  c If x and y are prime numbers, $x^2 + y^2$ is an even number.

A5 Exam review

Key objectives

- Know the meaning of and use the words equation, formula, identity and expression
- Use formulae from mathematics and other subjects
- Substitute numbers into a formula
- Change the subject of a simple formula
- Understand the difference between a practical demonstration and a proof

1 a Make x the subject of the equation   (2)

$$y = \frac{2x}{3} + 5$$

b Hence find the value of x when $y = 7$.   (2)

2 Tayub said, 'When $x = 3$, then the value of $4x^2$ is 144'.

Bryani said, 'When $x = 3$, then the value of $4x^2$ is 36'.

a Who was right?

Explain why.   (2)

b Work out the value of $4(x + 1)^2$ when $x = 3$.   (1)

(Edexcel Ltd., 2003)

This unit will show you how to

- Use angle properties of equilateral, isosceles and right-angled triangles
- Recall the geometric properties of quadrilaterals
- Investigate 3-D shapes made from cuboids, using 2-D representations of 3-D shapes
- Analyse 3-D shapes through plans and elevations
- Understand and use coordinates in one, two and three dimensions

Before you start ...

You should be able to answer these questions.

Review

1 Name the types of angles *a* and *b* in the diagram.

Unit S2

2 Give the coordinates of
  a A
  b B
  c C
  d D

Key stage 3

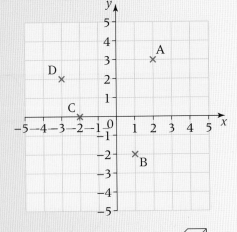

3 How many cubes are needed to make this shape?

Key stage 3

4 Calculate the volume of this cuboid, stating the units of your answer.

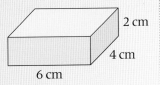

2 cm
4 cm
6 cm

Key stage 3

This spread will show you how to:

- Use angle properties of equilateral, isosceles and right-angled triangles

Keywords

Equilateral
Isosceles
Regular
Right-angled
  triangle
Scalene
Triangle

A **triangle** is a 2-D shape with 3 sides and 3 angles.

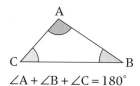

$\angle A + \angle B + \angle C = 180°$

- **The angles in a triangle add to 180°.**

You need to know the properties of these triangles.

Triangle		Properties	Reflection symmetry	Rotational symmetry
Right-angled		One 90° angle marked ⌐	No lines of symmetry	Order 1
Equilateral		3 equal angles 3 equal sides	3 lines of symmetry	Order 3
Isosceles		2 equal angles 2 equal sides	1 line of symmetry	Order 1
Scalene		No equal angles No equal sides	No lines of symmetry	Order 1

The equilateral triangle is a **regular** shape as it has equal sides and equal angles. All its interior angles are 60°.

Example

The side lengths of this spinner are equal.

The spinner is rotated about the dot.
What does this rotation show about the angles in the triangle?

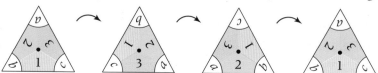

Each position looks identical to the previous one.
The angles are exactly the same.

1 Calculate the third angle of each of these triangles and state the type of triangle.

  a 60°, 60°   **b** 37°, 53°   **c** 114°, 33°

  d 53°, 48°   **e** 45°, 90°

2 The points A(−1, −2) and B(3, −2) are shown. Give the coordinates of a point C, so that triangle ABC

  a is isosceles

  b is right-angled but scalene

  c is right-angled and isosceles

  d is scalene

  e is equilateral (only an approximate value of y is possible)

  f has an area of 4 cm².

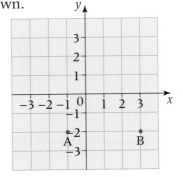

3 Here is a regular hexagon.
The yellow triangles are equilateral.
The green triangles are isosceles.
Calculate the three angles in the

  a yellow triangle

  b green triangle.

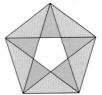

4 A regular pentagon is shown.
Find the number of isosceles triangles with each of these designs.

  a   **b**   **c**

  d   **e**   **f**

5 Calculate the area of triangle

  a ABC

  b ABD

  c ABE

  d ABF

  e ABG.

6 Can a triangle have a reflex angle? Justify your answer.

Properties of quadrilaterals

This spread will show you how to:

- Recall the geometric properties of quadrilaterals

Keywords

Diagonal
Parallel
Quadrilateral
Line symmetry
Rotational
    symmetry

A **quadrilateral** is a 2-D shape with 4 sides and 4 angles.

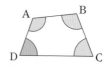

- **The angles in a quadrilateral add to 360°.**

$$\angle A + \angle B + \angle C + \angle D = 360°$$

You need to know the properties of these quadrilaterals.

Square	Rectangle	Rhombus	Parallelogram
4 right angles 4 equal sides 2 sets parallel sides 4 lines of symmetry Rotational symmetry of order 4	4 right angles 2 sets equal sides 2 sets parallel sides 2 lines of symmetry Rotational symmetry of order 2	2 pairs equal angles 4 equal sides 2 sets parallel sides 2 lines of symmetry Rotational symmetry of order 2	2 pairs equal angles 2 sets equal sides 2 sets parallel sides No lines of symmetry Rotational symmetry of order 2

Trapezium	Isosceles trapezium	Kite	Arrowhead (Delta)
1 set of parallel sides No lines of symmetry Rotational symmetry of order 1	2 sets equal angles 1 set equal sides 1 set parallel sides 1 line of symmetry Rotational symmetry of order 1	1 pair equal angles 2 sets equal sides No parallel sides 1 line of symmetry Rotational symmetry of order 1	1 pair equal angles 2 sets equal sides No parallel sides 1 reflex angle 1 line of symmetry Rotational symmetry of order 1

Example

a Plot the points A(−2, 1), B(1, 3) and C(3, 1) on the grid.
b Give the coordinates of the point D, so that ABCD is a kite.
c Draw any lines of symmetry for the kite.

a,c

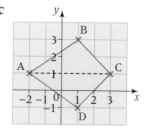

b D(1, −1)

1 State the value of each unknown angle.

a

square

b
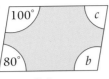
parallelogram

c

arrowhead

d
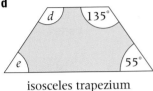
isosceles trapezium

e
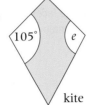
kite

f
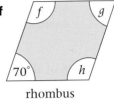
rhombus

2 The **diagonals** of a rectangle

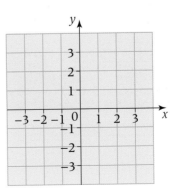

- are equal in length
- bisect each other
- are not perpendicular.

Copy and complete the table of results for the diagonals of these shapes.

Shape	Equal in length	Bisect each other	Perpendicular
Rectangle	✓	✓	✗
Kite			
Isosceles trapezium			
Square			
Parallelogram			
Rhombus			
Ordinary trapezium			

3 Plot the points $(-2, -1)$, $(0, -1)$ and $(1, 2)$ on a copy of this grid.
These points are three vertices (corners) of a parallelogram.

a Write the coordinates of the fourth point.

b Draw the parallelogram.

c Calculate the area of the parallelogram.

2-D and 3-D shapes

This spread will show you how to:

- Investigate 3-D shapes made from cuboids, using 2-D representations of 3-D shapes

Keywords
Cube
Cuboid
Edge
Face
Net
Prism
Pyramid
Solid
Three-dimensional
(3-D)
Vertex

- A **solid** is a **three-dimensional (3-D)** shape.

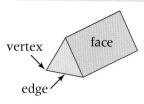

A **face** is a flat surface of a solid.
An **edge** is the line where two faces meet.
A **vertex** is a point at which three or more edges meet.

You need to know the names of these 3-D shapes.

The plural of vertex is vertices.

A **cube** has 6 square faces
    12 equal edges
    8 vertices

A **cuboid** has 6 rectangular faces
    12 edges
    8 vertices

A **prism** has a constant cross-section.

A **pyramid** has faces that taper to a common point.

You name a prism by the shape of its cross-section.

hexagonal prism

square-based pyramid

You name a pyramid by the shape of its base.

- A **net** is a 2-D shape that can be folded to form a 3-D shape.

Example

The nets of four solids are shown. Name the solid that can be made from each net.

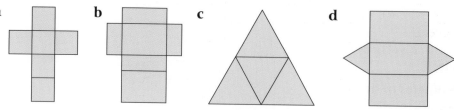

a   **b**   **c**   **d**

a cube
b cuboid
c tetrahedron
d triangular prism

A tetrahedron has 4 faces – all equilateral triangles.

198

1 Give the mathematical name of each of these solids.

a b c d e

f g h i j

2 Draw

  a a prism with a square cross-section

  b a pyramid with a hexagonal base

  c a tetrahedron.

3 This solid consist of eight triangles.
It is called an octahedron.
Write

  a the number of faces

  b the number of edges

  c the number of vertices of this solid.

DID YOU KNOW?

In Science, a prism is a triangular glass solid that bends, or refracts, white light to separate the rainbow of colours within.

4 a Copy and complete this table.

Name of solid	Number of faces (f)	Number of edges (e)	Number of vertices (v)
Cuboid	6	12	8
Triangular prism			
Square-based pyramid			
Tetrahedron			
Pentagonal prism			
Square-based prism			
Cube			
Hexagonal pyramid			
Octagonal prism			
Pentagonal pyramid			

  b Write a relationship between f, e and v.

5 Sketch six different nets of a cube.

This spread will show you how to:

● Analyse 3-D shapes through plans and elevations

Keywords

3-D
Front elevation
Plan
Side elevation

The plan is the 'birds-eye view'.

You can look at this car from different directions.

from above, …   from the front, …   and from the side.

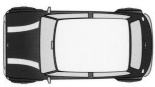

Plan   **Front elevation**   **Side elevation**

Example

This solid is made from 8 cubes.
Draw

a the plan
b the side elevation
c the front elevation

on square grid paper.

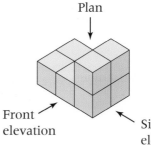

Plan

Front elevation

Side elevation

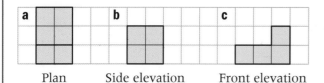

Plan   Side elevation   Front elevation

Notice the extra bold line in the plan, when the level of the cubes alters.

Example

The plan and front elevation of a prism are shown.

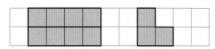

Plan   Front elevation

a Draw a 3-D sketch of the prism.
b Draw the side elevation on square grid paper.

a

b

Side elevation

1 On square grid paper, draw the plan (P), the front elevation (F) and the side elevation (S) for each solid.

a
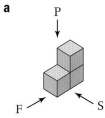

b
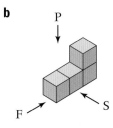

c
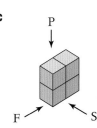

d
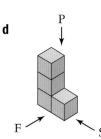

e
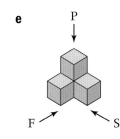

f
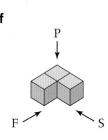

2 The plan, front elevation and side elevation are given for these solids made from cubes. Draw a 3-D sketch of each solid and state the number of cubes needed to make it.

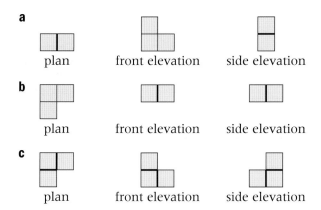

3 Sketch the plan (P), the front elevation (F) and the side elevation (S) for each solid.

a
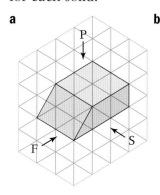

b
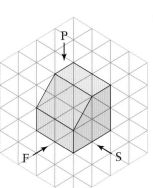

c
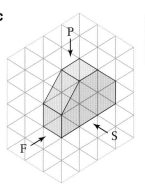

These solids are drawn on an **isometric grid**.

This spread will show you how to:

● Understand and use coordinates in one, two and three dimensions

Keywords
Coordinates
1 dimension (1-D)
2 dimensions (2-D)
3 dimensions (3-D)

In **1 dimension (1-D)**, you only need **one** number to show a point.

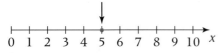

The point is $x = 5$.

This is an ordinary number line.

In **2 dimensions (2-D)**, you need **two** numbers to show a point.

$x = 5, y = 4$
The point is (5, 4).

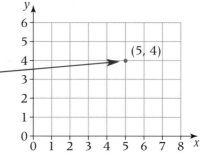

(5, 4)

The x-axis and the y-axis are at right angles.

In **3 dimensions (3-D)**, you need **three** numbers to show a point.

$x = 4, y = 2, z = 5$
The point is (4, 2, 5).

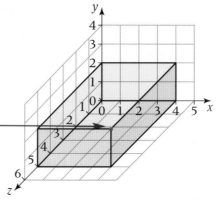

The x-axis, the y-axis and the z-axis are at right angles to each other.

Example

A 2 by 3 by 4 cuboid is placed on the axes as shown.

a Give the values of p, q and r.
b Complete the **coordinates** of A, B, C and D.
  A(_, _, _)
  B(3, 0, 4)
  C(_, _, _)
  D(_, _, _)
c Calculate the volume of the cuboid.

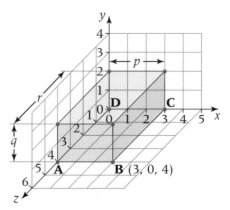

B (3, 0, 4)

a $p = 3$, $q = 2$, $r = 4$
b A(0, 0, 4), B(3, 0, 4), C(3, 0, 0), D(0, 0, 0)
c Volume $= 4 \times 3 \times 2 = 24$ cubic units

1 For each diagram, write the coordinates of the point P.

a

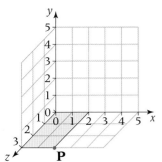

b

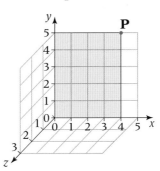

c

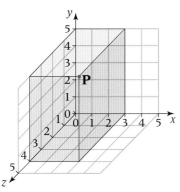

d

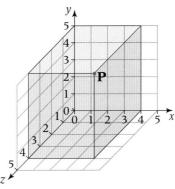

2 Draw diagrams to illustrate these points.

   a (0, 2, 0)   **b** (0, 3, 1)   **c** (2, 0, 3)

   d (5, 3, 4)   **e** (4, 4, 4)

3 A 3 cm by 3 cm by 3 cm cube is placed on the axes as shown.
Give the coordinates of these points.

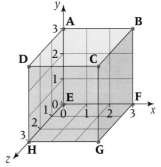

   a A   **b** B

   c C   **d** D

   e E   **f** F

   g G   **h** H

4 A 2 by 4 by 5 cuboid is placed on the axes as shown.

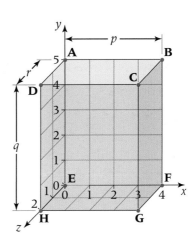

   a Give the values of p, q and r.

   b Give the coordinates of A to H.

   c Calculate the volume of the cuboid.

203

Exam review

Key objectives

- Use angle properties of equilateral, isosceles and right-angled triangles
- Classify quadrilaterals by their geometric properties
- Use 2-D representations of 3-D shapes and analyse 3-D shapes through 2-D projections and cross-sections, including plan and elevation
- Understand that one coordinate identifies a point on a number line, two coordinates identify a point in a plane and that three coordinates identify a point in space, using the terms '1-D, 2-D and 3-D'

1 a What type of triangle is shown in the diagram? (1)

  b What is the size of angle *x*? (2)
Show your working.

2 a Write down the mathematical name of these 3-D shapes:

  b Here are nets of two different 3-D shapes: (2)

Write down the mathematical name of each of these 3-D shapes. (2)

(Edexcel Ltd., 2004)

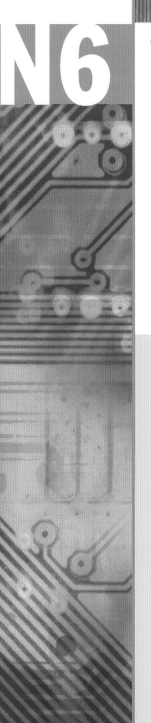

This unit will show you how to

- Know and use the order of operations, including brackets
- Multiply and divide by powers of 10 and by decimals between 0 and 1
- Use checking procedures, including approximation to estimate the answer to multiplication and division problems
- Use a range of mental and written methods for calculations with whole numbers and decimals
- Solve multi-step problems
- Use calculators to carry out more complex calculations
- Give answers to an appropriate degree of accuracy

Before you start ...

You should be able to answer these questions.

1 Calculate.

$5 \times 3 + 4 \times 8$

2 Calculate.

a $13 \div 10$　　　　**b** 0.03×10

3 Given that $12 \times 35 = 420$, what is the value of

a 12×3.5?　　　**b** $420 \div 12$?

4 Use an appropriate method of calculation to work out

a 15×3.2　　　　**b** $26.6 \div 7$

5 Hugo estimates the value of

$$\frac{6.89 \times 12.07}{3.88} \text{ to be 21.}$$

Write three numbers Hugo could use to get his estimate.

Review

Unit N2

Unit N2

Unit N2

Unit N2

Unit N2

This spread will show you how to:

● Know and use the order of operations, including brackets

Keywords
Brackets
Index
Order of
    operations
Power

When you do long calculations you must work them out according to the **order of operations**.

Order of operations
Brackets Work out the contents of any **brackets** first.
Powers or Indices Work out any **powers** or roots.
Division and Multiplication Work out any multiplications and divisions.
Addition and Subtraction Finally, work out any additions and subtractions.

To calculate $\dfrac{(6+4)^2}{5} + 8 \times 2$

Start by working out the contents of any brackets.

$\dfrac{(6+4)^2}{5} + 8 \times 2 = \dfrac{(6+4)^2}{5} + 8 \times 2$ (work out the contents of the bracket)

$= \dfrac{10^2}{5} + 8 \times 2$ (work out any powers)

$= \dfrac{100}{5} + 8 \times 2$ (work out any divisions and multiplications)

$= 20 + 16$ (work out any additions and subtractions)
$= 36$

● Brackets are used when you need to do an operation in a different order to normal.

● Calculations with brackets need to be thought about carefully.

Calculate **a** $\dfrac{34 \times 8}{5 + 11}$ **b** $11 + 13(8^2 - 47)$ **c** $30 \div (15 - (12 - 7))$

a $\dfrac{34 \times 8}{5 + 11} = \dfrac{(34 \times 8)}{(5 + 11)}$

$\quad = (34 \times 8) \div (5 + 11)$ (work out the brackets)
$\quad = 272 \div 16$ (work out the division)
$\quad = 17$

Always write the calculation a line at a time, so you can see each operation clearly.

b $11 + 13(8^2 - 47) = 11 + 13(8^2 - 47)$ (work out the brackets)
$\quad = 11 + 13(64 - 47)$ (work out the index)
$\quad = 11 + 13 \times 17$ (work out the multiplication)
$\quad = 11 + 221$ (work out the addition)
$\quad = 232$

c $30 \div (15 - (12 - 7)) = 30 \div (15 - (12 - 7))$ (work out the innermost brackets)
$\quad = 30 \div (15 - 5)$ (work out the next set of brackets)
$\quad = 30 \div 10$ (work out the division)
$\quad = 3$

Example

1 Calculate these using the order of operations.

   a $2 + 8 \times 3$ **b** $4 \times 11 - 7$ **c** $4 \times 3 + 5 \times 8$

   d $5 + 12 \div 6 + 3$ **e** $(2 + 9) \times 3$ **f** $(1.5 + 18.5) \div 4$

   g $(12 + 3) \times (14 - 2)$ **h** $5 + (3 \times 8) \div 6$

2 Calculate these using the order of operations.

   a $(4 + 3) \times 2^2$ **b** $3^2 \times (15 - 7)$ **c** $(6^2 - 16) \div 4$

   d $2^4 \times (3^2 - 2 \times 4)$ **e** $128 \div (2 + 2 \times 3)^2$ **f** $(8^2 - 7^2) \times 5$

3 Copy each of these calculations.
   Insert brackets where necessary to make each of the calculations correct.

   a $5 \times 2 + 1 = 15$ **b** $5 \times 3 - 1 \times 4 = 40$ **c** $20 + 8 \div 2 - 7 = 17$

   d $2 + 3^2 \times 4 + 3 = 65$ **e** $2 \times 6^2 \div 3 + 9 = 33$ **f** $4 \times 5 + 5 \times 6 = 150$

4 **a** Karen and Pete answered the same question. Who is correct?

 $5 + (2 \times 9 - 4)$ is 15.

 $5 + (2 \times 9 - 4)$ is 19.

   b Duncan said $(5 \times 4)^2$ means the same as 5×4^2.
   Is this correct? Explain your answer.

   c Use your calculator to work out $(2.4 + 1.65)^2 \times 3.4$.

      i Write all the figures on your calculator display.

      ii Round your answer to 1 decimal place.

5 Calculate each of these.

   a $\dfrac{7^2 - 9}{5 \times 8}$ **b** $\dfrac{4 \times 8}{4^2}$ **c** $\dfrac{15 \times 4}{6 \times 5}$

   d $\dfrac{2 \times (3 + 4)^2}{7}$ **e** $\dfrac{(6 + 4)^2}{20} + 7 \times 5$ **f** $\dfrac{6 + (2 \times 4)^2 + 7}{11}$

6 Calculate each of these.

   a $12 + 6 - 4$ **b** $5 \times 4 \div 2$ **c** $40 \div 10 \div 2$ **d** $28 - 12 - 4$

   e $13(2 + 5)$ **f** $14(2 + 6)$ **g** $5^2 + 9(8 - 3)$ **h** $4^2 + 3(16 - 9)$

   i $4 + (12 - (3 + 2))$ **j** $120 \div (8 \times (7 - 2))$

7 Solve each of these calculations.

   a $(15.7 + 1.3) \times (8.7 + 1.3)$ **b** $\dfrac{7^2}{(2.3 \times 4)^2}$ **c** $\dfrac{(7 + 5)^2}{(25 + 7 \times 8)}$

> Decide whether to use a mental, written or calculator method. Where appropriate give your answer to 2 decimal places.

Estimation

This spread will show you how to:

- Multiply and divide by powers of 10 and by decimals between 0 and 1
- Use checking procedures, including approximation to estimate the answer to multiplication and division problems

---

- You can multiply or divide a number by a power of 10. Move the digits of the number to the left or to the right.

$$\times 10$$
or $\div 0.1$

$$1.8 \qquad 18$$

$$\div 10$$
or $\times 0.1$

$$\times 100$$
or $\div 0.01$

$$12.4 \qquad 1240$$

$$\div 100$$
or $\times 0.01$

$\times 0.1$ is the same as $\div 10$.
$\times 0.01$ is the same as $\div 100$.

$\div 0.1$ is the same as $\times 10$.
$\div 0.01$ is the same as $\times 100$.

- You can multiply and divide by any decimal between 0 and 1 using mental methods.

Example

Calculate   **a** 12×0.3 **b** $3.6 \div 0.04$ **c** $2 \div 0.05$

a $12 \times 0.3 = 12 \times 3 \times 0.1$
$\qquad\qquad = 36 \times 0.1$
$\qquad\qquad = 36 \div 10$
$\qquad\qquad = 3.6$

b $36 \div 0.04 = 36 \div (4 \times 0.01)$
$\qquad\qquad = 36 \div 4 \div 0.01$
$\qquad\qquad = 9 \div 0.01$
$\qquad\qquad = 9 \times 100$
$\qquad\qquad = 900$

c $2 \div 0.05 = \dfrac{2}{0.05}$
$\qquad\qquad = \dfrac{200}{5} = 40$
$\qquad\qquad = 40$

- You can **estimate** the answer to a calculation by first rounding the numbers in the calculation.

Example

Estimate the answers to these calculations.

a $\dfrac{8.93 \times 28.69}{0.48 \times 6.12}$

b $\dfrac{17.4 \times 4.89^2}{0.385}$

A good strategy is to round each number in the calculation to 1 significant figure.

a $\dfrac{8.93 \times 28.69}{0.48 \times 6.12} \approx \dfrac{9 \times 30}{0.5 \times 6}$
$\qquad\qquad\qquad = \dfrac{270}{3} = 90$

b $\dfrac{17.4 \times 4.89^2}{0.385} \approx \dfrac{20 \times 5^2}{0.4}$
$\qquad\qquad\qquad = \dfrac{20 \times 25}{0.4} = \dfrac{500}{0.4}$
$\qquad\qquad\qquad = \dfrac{5000}{4} = 1250$

1 Round each of these numbers to the nearest   **i** 1000   **ii** 100   **iii** 10.

    a 1548.9   **b** 5789.47   **c** 17 793.8 kg

    d €35 127.35   **e** 236 872

2 Round each of these numbers to
   i 3 dp   **ii** 2 dp   **iii** 1 dp   **iv** the nearest whole number.

    a 4.3563   **b** 9.8573   **c** 0.9373   **d** 19.4963

    e 26.8083   **f** 19.9999   **g** 0.004896   **h** 3896.6567

3 Calculate these.

    a 3×0.1 **b** $15 \div 0.1$ **c** 8×0.01 **d** 2.8×100

    e $3.8 \div 0.1$ **f** 0.4×0.1 **g** $9.23 \div 0.1$ **h** $44.6 \div 0.01$

4 Here are five number cards.

    | 0.1 | | 10 | | 0.01 | | 1000 | | 10^2 |

    Fill in the missing numbers in each of these statements using one of these cards.

    a $3.24 \times ? = 324$ **b** $14.7 \times ? = 0.147$ **c** $6.3 \div ? = 630$

    d $2870 \div ? = 2.87$ **e** $0.43 \div ? = 4.3$ **f** $2.04 \div ? = 204$

5 Round each of these numbers to   **i** 3 sf   **ii** 2 sf   **iii** 1 sf.

    a 9.4837   **b** 27.73   **c** 46.73   **d** 387.63

    e 2.4058   **f** 4905.81   **g** 0.009 483   **h** 3489.7

    i 9.8765   **j** 25.1407   **k** 2314.17   **l** 237 415

6 Work out these calculations using a mental method.

    a 12×0.2 **b** 8×0.07 **c** $15 \div 0.3$

    d $3 \div 0.15$ **e** 1.2×0.4 **f** $28 \div 0.07$

7 Write a suitable estimate for each of these calculations.
   In each case clearly show how you estimated your answer.

    a 3.76×4.22 **b** 17.39×22.98 **c** $\dfrac{4.59 \times 7.9}{19.86}$ **d** $54.31 \div 8.8$

8 Write a suitable estimate for each of these calculations.
   In each case clearly show how you estimated your answer.

    a $\dfrac{29.91 \times 38.3}{3.1 \times 3.9}$ **b** $\dfrac{16.2 \times 0.48}{0.23 \times 31.88}$ **c** $\{4.8^2 + (4.2 - 0.238)\}^2$

    d $\dfrac{63.8 \times 1.7^2}{1.78^2}$ **e** $\sqrt{(2.03 \div 0.041)}$ **f** $\sqrt{(27.6 \div 0.57)}$

This spread will show you how to:

● Use a range of mental and written methods for calculations with whole numbers and decimals

Keywords

Compensation
Mental method
Multiple
Partitioning
Place value

There are lots of **mental methods** you can use to help you work out calculations in your head.

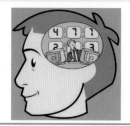

You can use **place value**.

Example

Use the fact that 35 × 147 = 5145 to write the value of

a 3.5 × 1.47   **b** 0.35 × 147 000   **c** 51.45 ÷ 3.5

a 3.5 × 1.47 = (35 ÷ 10) × (147 ÷ 100)   **b** 0.35 × 147 000 = (35 ÷ 100) × (147 × 1000)
$\qquad\qquad$ = 35 × 147 ÷ 1000 $\qquad\qquad\qquad\qquad$ = 35 × 147 × 10
$\qquad\qquad$ = 5145 ÷ 1000 $\qquad\qquad\qquad\qquad\quad$ = 5145 × 10
$\qquad\qquad$ = 5.145 $\qquad\qquad\qquad\qquad\qquad\quad$ = 51 450

c $51.45 \div 3.5 = \dfrac{51.45}{3.5} = \dfrac{514.5}{35}$

$\qquad\qquad = \dfrac{(5145 \div 10)}{35}$

$\qquad\qquad = 147 \div 10$

$\qquad\qquad = 14.7$

You can use **partitioning**.

Example

a Calculate 18.5 − 7.7.   **b** Calculate 6.3 × 12.

a 18.5 − 7.7 = 18.5 − 7 − 0.7
$\qquad\qquad$ = 11.5 − 0.7
$\qquad\qquad$ = 10.8

b $\qquad$ 12 = 10 + 2

6.3 × 12 = (6.3 × 10) + (6.3 × 2)
$\qquad\quad$ = 63 + 12.6
$\qquad\quad$ = 75.6

Split **12** into **10 + 2**.
Then work out **10** × 6.3 and **2** × 6.3.
Add your two answers together.

You can use **compensation**.

Example

Calculate   **a** 12.4 − 4.9   **b** 23.2 × 1.9

a 12.4 − 4.9 = 12.4 − 5 + 0.1
$\qquad\qquad$ = 7.4 + 0.1
$\qquad\qquad$ = 7.5

b $\qquad$ 1.9 = 2 − 0.1

23.2 × 1.9 = (23.2 × 2) − (23.2 × 0.1)
$\qquad\quad$ = 46.4 − 2.32
$\qquad\quad$ = 44.08

Rewrite **1.9** as **2 − 0.1**.
Work out **2** × 23.2 and **0.1** × 23.2.
Subtract your two answers.

---

1 Calculate these.

a 9×7 **b** $121 \div 10$ **c** 2×2.7 **d** $48.4 \div 2$

e 3.6×100 **f** $430 \div 100$ **g** 23.6×10 **h** $0.78 \div 100$

2 Use an appropriate mental method to calculate these. Show the method you have used.

a 1.4×11 **b** 21×9 **c** 5.3×11 **d** 41×2.8

e 19×7 **f** 12×5.3 **g** $147 \div 3$ **h** $276 \div 4$

i 3.2×11 **j** 31×5.6 **k** 14.9×9 **l** 25.3×31

m 14×8 **n** $51 \div 1.5$ **o** $81 \div 4.5$ **p** 4.4×4.5

3 Use the mental method of partitioning to work out each of these.

a $19.5 - 7.6$ **b** $45.3 + 12.6 + 7.2$ **c** $132.6 - 21.4$

d 7.2×13 **e** 8.4×12 **f** 11×19.2

g $129 \div 3$ **h** $292 \div 4$

4 Use the mental method of compensation to work out each of these.

a $19.5 - 7.9$ **b** $48.4 - 12.8$ **c** $164.5 - 15.9$

d 8.1×19 **e** 36×3.9 **f** 17×5.9

5 Use an appropriate mental method to calculate each of these.

a $27.6 + 21.7$ **b** $1623 - 897$ **c** 32×2.1 **d** 2.9×23

e 19×1.4 **f** 9×7.5 **g** $2.4 \div 0.2$ **h** $\dfrac{30 \times 0.2}{0.15}$

6 **a** Using the information that $69 \times 147 = 10\,143$, write the value of each of these.

     i 69×1470 **ii** 690×1470 **iii** 6.9×147 **iv** 0.69×14.7

     v 6.9×0.147 **vi** 690×1.47 **vii** 0.069×14.7 **viii** 0.69×0.147

   b Using the information that $37 \times 177 = 6549$, write the value of each of these.

     i 3.7×17.7 **ii** 0.37×1770 **iii** $654.9 \div 177$ **iv** $65.49 \div 3.7$

7 **a** Using the information that $43 \times 217 = 9331$, write the value of each of these.

     i 4.3×2170 **ii** 0.43×2.17 **iii** $933.1 \div 4.3$ **iv** $93.31 \div 0.217$

   b Using the information that $48 \times 164 = 7872$, write the value of each of these.

     i 4.8×16.4 **ii** $0.48 \times 16\,400$ **iii** $787.2 \div 1640$ **iv** $78.72 \div 4.8$

This spread will show you how to:

- Use a range of mental and written methods for calculations with whole numbers and decimals
- Use checking procedures, including approximation to estimate the answer to multiplication and division problems

Keywords
Dividend
Divisor
Estimate
Grid method
Standard
  method
Whole number

You can multiply decimals by replacing them with an equivalent **whole-number** calculation that is easier to work out.

Example

Carol is working out the area of carpet she needs for her floor. The floor is in a rectangle with a length of 4.8 m and a width of 3.12 m. What is the area of Carol's floor?

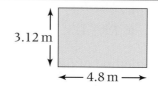

3.12 m

← 4.8 m →

$4.8 \times 3.12 = (48 \div 10) \times (312 \div 100)$
$= 48 \times 312 \div 1000$

×	300	10	2
40	40 × 300 = 12 000	40 × 10 = 400	40 × 2 = 80
8	8 × 300 = 2400	8 × 10 = 80	8 × 2 = 16

$48 \times 312 = 12\,000 + 400 + 80 + 2400 + 80 + 16 = 14\,976$

The area of Carol's floor is $4.8 \times 3.12 = 48 \times 312 \div 1000$
$= 14\,976 \div 1000$
$= 14.98 \text{ m}^2 \text{ (2 decimal places)}$

Estimate the answer first.
$4.8 \times 3.12 \approx 5 \times 3$
$= 15 \text{ m}^2$

You can divide a number by a decimal by rewriting the calculation as an equivalent whole-number division.

Example

Mandy has a floor with an area of 91 m². She fills the floor with carpet tiles which have an area of 2.8 m².
How many tiles does she need to cover the floor?

$91 \div 2.8 = 910 \div 28$

```
   28)910
     −840    28 × 30
       70
      −56    28 × 2
      14.0
     −14.0   28 × 0.5      30 + 2 + 0.5 = 32.5
        0
```

$910 \div 28 = 91 \div 2.8 = 32.5$

Mandy needs $91 \div 2.8 = 32.5$ tiles.

Estimate the answer first.
$9.1 + 2.8 \approx 90 \div 3$
$= 30$

1 Use a written method for each of these calculations.

    a $16.4 + 9.68$ **b** $27.3 + 5.41$ **c** $9.51 - 6.7$

    d $24.3 + 7.69$ **e** $34.76 - 8.29$ **f** $38.29 - 24.8$

    g $16.5 - 12.67 + 5.34$ **h** $78.7 - 14.92 + 16.66 - 12.9$

2 Use an appropriate method of calculation to work out each of these.

    a 15×3.4 **b** 5.6×18 **c** 8.4×13

    d 23×7.6 **e** 28×4.2 **f** 9.7×49

3 Use an appropriate method of calculation to work out each of these.

    a $27.3 \div 7$ **b** $36.6 \div 6$ **c** $70.4 \div 8$

    d $73.8 \div 6$ **e** $119.7 \div 9$ **f** $119.2 \div 8$

4 Use a mental or written method to solve each of these problems.

    a Oliver sells tomatoes at the market. On Thursday he sells 78.6 kg; on Saturday he sells 83.38 kg. What mass of tomatoes has he sold during the two days?

    b A mobile phone without a battery weighs 188.16 g. When the battery is inserted the combined mass of the mobile phone and battery is 207.38 g. What is the mass of the battery?

    c A recycling box is full of things to be recycled.
    The empty box weighs 1.073 kg.

        Bottles   12.45 kg
        Cans   1.675 kg
        Paper   8.7 kg
        Plastic objects   ? kg

    The total weight of the box and all the objects to be recycled is exactly 25 kg. What is the weight of the plastic objects?

DID YOU KNOW?

At least half the household waste produced in the UK each year could be recycled. Unfortunately in 2005 only 12% was recycled!

5 Use an appropriate method of calculation to work out each of these.

    a 2.3×1.74 **b** 1.6×2.75 **c** 1.7×44.3

    d 2.5×5.88 **e** 8.7×4.79 **f** 38×4.78

    g 3.4×4.45 **h** 0.54×8.28 **i** 0.93×3.87

6 **a** Scooby buys 1.8 m of carpet. Each metre costs £1.85. How much does this cost in total?

    b Shaggy buys 7.8 kg of apples. Each kilogram of apples costs £1.45. How much money does Shaggy pay for the apples?

    c Brian is a gardener. He plants trees at a rate of 11.8 trees per hour. How many trees does he plant in 6.4 hours?

    d Clarke works as a car mechanic. He charges £31.70 per hour for his work. How much does he charge for working 2.5 hours?

This spread will show you how to:

- Use calculators to carry out more complex calculations
- Use checking procedures, including approximation to estimate the answer to multiplication and division problems
- Give answers to an appropriate degree of accuracy

Keywords

Appropriate degree of accuracy
Brackets
Order of operations

You can use the bracket keys on a scientific calculator to do calculations where the **order of operations** is not obvious.

Example

a Use a calculator to work out the value of

$$\frac{21.42 \times (12.4 - 6.35)}{(63.4 + 18.9) \times 2.83}$$

Write all the figures on the calculator display.

b Put brackets in this expression so that its value is 45.908.

$$8.2 + 3.4 \times 2.7 - 4.3$$

a Rewrite the calculation as $(21.42 \times (12.4 - 6.35)) \div ((63.4 + 18.9) \times 2.83)$

Type this into the calculator:

| (21.42×(12.4−6.35))÷((63.4+18.9)×2.83) | ➡ | (21.42×(12.4−
0.55640 1856 |

Estimate:
$$\frac{20 \times (12 - 6)}{(60 + 20) \times 3}$$
$$= \frac{120}{240} = 0.5$$

So the answer is 0.556 401 856.

b By inserting a pair of brackets: $(1.4 + 3.9 \times 2.2) \times 4.6$
The calculator should display 45.908.   ✓ This is the correct answer.

You can solve multi-step problems using a calculator. You will need to give your answer to an **appropriate degree of accuracy**.

Example

The diagram shows a box in the shape of a cuboid.

a Work out the volume, in m^3, of the box.
b Saleem builds boxes of different sizes.
He charges £7.89 for each m^3 of a box's volume.
Work out Saleem's charge for building this box.

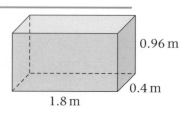

0.96 m
0.4 m
1.8 m

a Volume of a cuboid
= length × width × height

Volume ≈ $2 \times 1 \times 0.4 = 0.8 \ m^3$
Volume = $1.8 \times 0.4 \times 0.96$
= $0.6912 \ m^3$
= $0.7 \ m^3$

b Saleem's charge
= cost for each m^3 × number of m^3

Estimate: Saleem's charge ≈ £8 × 0.8
= £6.40
Type: Saleem's charge = £7.89 × 0.6912
= £5.453 568
= £5.45

1 Put brackets into each of these expressions to make them correct.

a $2.4 \times 4.3 + 3.7 = 19.2$

b $6.8 \times 3.75 - 2.64 = 7.548$

c $3.7 + 2.9 \div 1.2 = 5.5$

d $2.3 + 3.4^2 \times 2.7 = 37.422$

e $5.3 + 3.9 \times 3.2 + 1.6 = 24.02$

f $3.2 + 6.4 \times 4.3 + 2.5 = 46.72$

2 Use your calculator to work out each of these. Write all the figures on your calculator.

a $\dfrac{165.4 \times 27.4}{(0.72 + 4.32)^2}$

b $\dfrac{(32.6 + 43.1) \times 2.3^2}{173.7 \times (13.5 - 1.78)}$

c $\dfrac{24.67 \times (35.3 - 8.29)}{(28.2 + 34.7) \times 3.3}$

d $\dfrac{1.45^2 \times 3.64 + 2.9}{3.47 - 0.32}$

e $\dfrac{12.93 \times (33.2 - 8.34)}{(61.3 + 34.5) \times 2.9}$

f $\dfrac{24.7 - (3.2 + 1.09)^2}{2.78^2 + 12.9 \times 3}$

3 Work out each of these using your calculator. In each case give your answer to an appropriate degree of accuracy.

a Véronique puts carpet in her bedroom. The bedroom is in the shape of a rectangle with a length of 4.23 m and a width of 3.6 m. The carpet costs £6.79 per m^2.

   i Calculate the floor area of the bedroom.

   ii Calculate the cost of the carpet which is required to cover the floor.

b Calculate $\frac{1}{3}$ of £200.

4 Barry sees a mobile phone offer.

Vericheep Fone OFFER
Monthly fee £12.99
FREE – 200 texts every month
FREE – 200 voice minutes every month
Extra text messages 3.2p each
Extra voice minutes 5.5p each

Barry decides to see if the offer is a good idea for him.
His current mobile phone offers him unlimited texts and voice minutes for £22.99 per month.

a In February, Barry used 189 texts and 348 voice minutes. Calculate his bill using the new offer.

b In March, Barry used 273 texts and 219 voice minutes. Calculate his bill using the new offer.

c Explain if the new offer is a good idea for Barry.

Exam review

Key objectives

- Use the hierarchy of operations
- Use an extended range of function keys, relevant across this programme of study
- Make mental estimates of the answers to calculations
- Develop a range of strategies for mental calculation
- Use standard column procedures for multiplication of integers and decimals
- Select and justify appropriate degrees of accuracy for answers to problems

1 a Calculate the following, giving your answers to 1 decimal place:

   i $1.5 + 2.2$

   ii 2.2×3.1

   iii $2.2 - 1.5$

   iv 3.7×3.1 (4)

b Hence put brackets in the following calculation so that the answer is correct:

$$1.5 \;+\; 2.2 \;\times\; 3.1 \;=\; 11.47 \hspace{2cm} (2)$$

2 Use your calculator to work out the value of $\dfrac{6.27 \times 4.52}{4.81 + 9.63}$.

a Write down all the figures on your calculator display.   (2)

b Write your answer to part **a** to an appropriate degree of accuracy.   (1)

(Edexcel Ltd., 2004)

This unit will show you how to

- Expand brackets within an algebraic expression
- Solve linear equations using the balance method, including equations with fractional or negative solutions
- Solve equations with the unknown on both sides
- Solve equations involving fractions and negative signs
- Use systematic trial and improvement to estimate the solutions of an equation

Before you start ...

You should be able to answer these questions.

Review

1 Expand the brackets.

   a $2(x + 4)$ **b** $3(y - 2)$

   c $5(2x + 3)$ **d** $-2(3x - 1)$

Unit A1

2 Work out the perimeter of these shapes.

   a   **b**

Unit S1

3 Solve using the balance method.

   a $2x + 3 = 13$ **b** $4y - 7 = 9$

Unit A2

4 Work out

   a $\frac{3}{2} \times 2$ **b** $\frac{4}{5} \times 5$

   c $3 \times \frac{2}{3}$ **d** $\frac{5}{6} \times 6$

Unit N3

5 One box holds n tins.

   a Write an expression for the number of tins in 6 boxes.

   b Write an expression for the number of tins if a box is half full.

Unit A5

Solving equations with brackets

This spread will show you how to:

- Expand brackets within an algebraic expression

Keywords

Brackets
Expand
Solve

- You can **expand brackets** in an algebraic expression.
  - You multiply each term inside the bracket by the term outside.

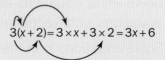
$$3(x+2) = 3 \times x + 3 \times 2 = 3x + 6$$

- To **solve** an equation with brackets:
  - Expand the brackets
  - Solve using the balance method.

Solve

a $4(x + 1) = 12$ **b** $3(y - 3) = 6$

a
$$4(x + 1) = 12$$ Expand the brackets.
$$4 \times x + 4 \times 1 = 12$$
$$4x + 4 = 12$$
$$4x + 4 - 4 = 12 - 4$$
$$4x = 8$$ Divide both sides by 4.
$$x = 2$$

b
$$3(y - 3) = 6$$
$$3 \times y + 3 \times -3 = 6$$ Keep each term with its sign.
$$3y - 9 = 6$$ $3 \times -3 = -9$
$$3y - 9 + 9 = 6 + 9$$
$$3y = 15$$ Divide both sides by 3.
$$y = 5$$

Solutions may be negative numbers or fractions.

Solve the equations.

a $5(a + 3) = 10$ **b** $2(z - 2) = 1$

a
$$5(a + 3) = 10$$
$$5a + 15 = 10$$
$$5a + 15 - 15 = 10 - 15$$
$$5a = -5$$ Divide both sides by 5.
$$a = -1$$

b
$$2(z - 2) = 1$$
$$2z - 4 = 1$$ Add 4 to both sides.
$$2z = 5$$ Divide both sides by 2.
$$z = \frac{5}{2} \text{ or } 2\frac{1}{2}$$

1 Expand the brackets in these expressions.

   a $4(x+3)$ **b** $2(y-4)$ **c** $5(3-a)$ **d** $3(-b+2)$

2 Expand the brackets and solve these equations.

   a $3(x+1)=15$ **b** $4(s-2)=16$ **c** $2(t-3)=0$ **d** $4(-v+1)=-8$

3 Expand the brackets in these expressions.

   a $-2(c+4)$ **b** $-3(d-3)$ **c** $2(4m-1)$ **d** $-4(2n-3)$

4 Expand and solve these.

   a $3(a+4)=-6$ **b** $2(b-5)=-12$

   c $-4(6-c)=-16$ **d** $3(2d-3)=26$

5 Solve these.

   a $4(e+1)=10$ **b** $3(f-2)=-4$ **c** $8(2-g)=10$ **d** $-4(h-6)=26$

6 Solve these equations.

   a $-2(x+3)=11$ **b** $-10(y-4)=15$ **c** $12(z-5)=-30$

   Which is the odd one out?

7 The diagram shows an equilateral triangle.
   Each side has length $x-2$.

   a Copy and complete this expression for the
   perimeter of the triangle:

   Perimeter = 3(   )

   b The perimeter of the triangle is 12 cm.
   Use your expression from part **a** to find the value of x.

$x-2$

8 The diagram shows a square with sides $2y+5$ cm.

   a Write an expression for the perimeter of the
   square.

   b The perimeter of the square is 28 cm.
   Find the value of y.

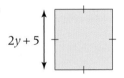

$2y+5$

Perimeter = 4(   )

9 Write an expression for the area of this
   rectangle.
   The area of the rectangle is 8 cm^2.
   Find the value of z.

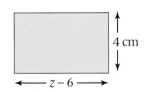

4 cm

$z-6$

Equations with the unknown on both sides

This spread will show you how to:

- Solve linear equations using the balance method, including equations with fractional or negative solutions

Keywords
Solve
Unknown

When you **solve** an equation, you find the value of the letter term or **unknown**.

In some equations the unknown is on both sides of the equals sign.

- You can solve equations with the unknown on both sides using the balance method.

Here is an example

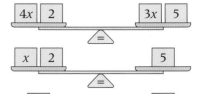

$4x + 2 = 3x + 5$ The 3x term has the smallest number of x.

$4x - 3x + 2 = 3x - 3x + 5$ Subtract 3x from both sides.

$x + 2 = 5$

$x - 2 = 5 - 2$ Subtract 2 from both sides.

$x = 3$

Example

Solve the equation

$3y - 7 = 2y + 3$

$3y - 2y - 7 = 2y - 2y + 3$ The smallest term in y is 2y. Subtract 2y from both sides.

$y - 7 = 3$ Add 7 to both sides.

$y = 3 + 7 = 10$

Example

Here is an equation

$4t + 10 = 2t + 4$

Find the value of t.

$4t - 2t + 10 = 2t - 2t + 4$ The smallest term in t is 2t. Subtract 2t from both sides.

$2t + 10 = 4$

$2t + 10 - 10 = 4 - 10$

$2t = -6$ Divide both sides by 2.

$t = -3$

1 Solve these equations.

    a $4m + 2 = 3m + 7$ **b** $6p - 5 = 5p - 2$

    c $3t + 2 = 2t + 5$ **d** $3n - 11 = 2n - 4$

    e $4q + 2 = 5q - 6$ **f** $5s - 2 = 4s + 6$

2 Solve these.

    a $2s + 5 = 3s + 8$ **b** $4t - 2 = 5t + 2$

    c $6u + 10 = 5u + 8$ **d** $4v - 6 = -15 - 5v$

3 Find the value of the unknown in each of these.

    a $2a + 14 = 6a - 6$ **b** $4b - 2 = 6b + 6$

    c $3c - 4 = c + 1$ **d** $5d + 15 = -6 - 2d$

4 Solve these.

    a $4x + 3 = 18 + 2x$ **b** $4x + 10 = 2x + 4$

    c $8x + 15 = 12x + 14$ **d** $6x - 4 = 10x + 2$

5 Mae doubles a number and adds 5 to get 21.

    a Write an expression for Mae's calculation.
        Use n to represent the number.

                                               $21 = \Box n + \Box$

    b Tim multiplies the same number by 4 and subtracts 11 to get 21.
        Write an expression for Tim's calculation, using n to represent
        the number.

                                               $\Box n - \Box = 21$

    d Write your expressions from parts **a** and **b** as an
        equation.

                     expression **a** = 21, expression **b** = 21

    e Solve your equation to find the value of n.

                          expression **a** = expression **b**

6 Write equations for these 'think of a number' problems as you did in
    question **5**.

    Solve them to find the value of the number.

    a I think of a number, multiply by 2 and add 7. I get the same
        answer when I multiply the number by 4 and subtract 13. $2n + 7 = 4n - 13$

    b I think of a number, multiply by 5 and subtract 8. I get the same
        answer when I double the number and add 10. $\Box n - \Box = \Box n + \Box$

    c I think of a number, multiply by 3 and add 4. I get the same
        answer when I multiply by 5 and add 12.

This spread will show you how to:

● Solve equations with the unknown on both sides

Keywords

Brackets
Expand

This square pattern is made from rectangular tiles.
Each tile has length $x + 3$ and width x.

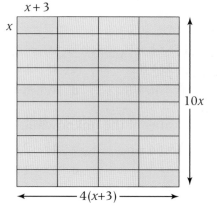

The pattern is 10 tiles wide: $10x$
The pattern is 4 tiles long: $4(x + 3)$

The pattern is a square,
so length = width: $\qquad 4(x + 3) = 10x$

Expand the **brackets**: $\qquad 4x + 12 = 10x$

Subtract $4x$ from both sides: $\quad 12 = 10x - 4x$
$\qquad\qquad\qquad\qquad\qquad 12 = 6x$

Divide both sides by 6: $\qquad 2 = x$
$\qquad\qquad\qquad\qquad\qquad$ So $x = 2$.

The dimensions of the square are 20 units long by 20 units wide.

● To solve equations with the unknown on both sides and brackets:
  • Expand the brackets
  • Use the balance method.

Example

Solve

a $2(y + 4) = 4y$

b $6r - 2 = 4(r + 3)$

a $2(y + 4) = 4y$ $\qquad\qquad$ Expand the brackets.
$\quad\ 2y + 8 = 4y$ $\qquad\qquad$ Subtract $2y$ from both sides.
$\qquad\ 8 = 4y - 2y$
$\qquad\ 8 = 2y$ $\qquad\qquad\qquad$ Divide both sides by 2.
$\qquad\ 4 = y$

b $\qquad 6r - 2 = 4(r + 3)$
$\qquad\quad 6r - 2 = 4r + 12$ $\qquad$ Subtract $4r$ from both sides.
$\quad 6r - 4r - 2 = 4r - 4r + 12$
$\qquad\quad 2r - 2 = 12$ $\qquad\qquad$ Add 2 to both sides.
$\qquad\qquad 2r = 12 + 2$
$\qquad\qquad 2r = 14$ $\qquad\qquad\quad$ Divide both sides by 2.
$\qquad\qquad\ r = 7$

Exercise A6.3

1 Solve these equations.

   a $2(r + 6) = 5r$ **b** $6(s - 3) = 12s$

   c $4(2t + 8) = 24t$ **d** $5(v - 1) = 6v$

2 Solve these equations.

   a $2(a + 5) = 7a - 5$ **b** $3(b - 2) = 5b - 2$

   c $2(c + 6) = 5c - 3$ **d** $3d + 8 = 2(d + 2)$

3 Solve these equations.

   a $3(2x - 4) = 7x - 18$ **b** $2(3y + 2) = 5y - 2$

   c $4(2z + 1) = 6z + 15$ **d** $-4(6m + 1) = -17m - 18$

4 Solve these equations.

   a $2(e + 3) = 4e - 1$ **b** $4f + 3 = 2(f + 2)$

   c $4(2g + 1) = 6g + 1$ **d** $3(2h + 3) = 5h + 8$

5 **a** Choose one expression from each set of cards.

   b Write them as an equation:
      Expression from set 1 = expression from set 2

   c Solve your equation to find the value of x.

   d Repeat for different pairs of expressions.

Set 1

Set 2

6 The triangle and the square have equal perimeter.

   a Write an expression for the perimeter of the triangle.

   b Write an expression for the perimeter of the square.

   c Use your two expressions to write an equation.

   d Solve your equation to find the value of x.

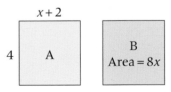

Perimeter of triangle = perimeter of square

7 **a** Write an expression for the area of square A.

   b Square B and square A have equal area.
      Write an equation in x to show this.

   c Solve your equation to find the value of x.

$x + 2$

4 A

B
Area $= 8x$

8 A blouse has m buttons. A shirt has $m + 2$ buttons.

   a Write an expression for the number of buttons on four blouses.

   b Write an expression for the number of buttons on three shirts.

   c Three shirts have the same number of buttons in total as four
      blouses.
      Write an equation and solve it to find the value of m.

   d How many buttons are there on a shirt?

Equations with fractions

This spread will show you how to:

- Solve equations involving fractions and negative signs

Problems in algebra often contain fractions.

Tom and Jas share a packet of sweets.
Tom has half the sweets.
He counts them.
There are 15.

How many sweets were there in the packet?

To solve this problem, you multiply 15×2 to get 30.

You can write the problem in algebra like this:

$$\frac{x}{2} = 15$$

$$x \div 2 = \frac{x}{2}$$

Using the balance method, you do the same to both sides:

$$\frac{x}{2} \times 2 = 15 \times 2$$

$$x = 30$$

The inverse of ÷ is ×

- You can solve equations involving **fractions** using the balance method.

Example

Solve.

a $\dfrac{x}{4} = -3$ **b** $\dfrac{x}{3} + 2 = 7$ **c** $\dfrac{x+3}{2} = 5$ **d** $\dfrac{5-2x}{3} = 7$

a $\dfrac{x}{4} = -3$

$$4 \times \frac{x}{4} = -3 \times 4$$

$$x = -12$$

b $\dfrac{x}{3} + 2 = 7$

$$\frac{x}{3} + 2 - 2 = 7 - 2$$

$$\frac{x}{3} = 5$$

$$3 \times \frac{x}{3} = 5 \times 3$$

$$x = 15$$

c $\dfrac{x+3}{2} = 5$

$$2 \times \frac{x+3}{2} = 5 \times 2$$

$$x + 3 = 10$$

$$x = 10 - 3$$

$$x = 7$$

d $\dfrac{5-2x}{3} = 7$

$$3 \times \frac{5-2x}{3} = 7 \times 3$$

$$5 - 2x = 21$$

$$5 - 2x - 5 = 21 - 5$$

$$-2x = 16$$

$$\frac{-2x}{-2} = \frac{16}{-2}$$

$$x = -8$$

1 Solve these.

a $\dfrac{x}{3} = 3$ **b** $\dfrac{m}{4} = -2$ **c** $\dfrac{-n}{3} = 6$ **d** $\dfrac{m}{5} = 4$

2 Find the value of the unknown in each of these.

a $\dfrac{s}{3} + 5 = 8$ **b** $4 - \dfrac{t}{2} = 1$ **c** $\dfrac{u}{5} + 7 = 5$ **d** $16 = \dfrac{v}{4} + 13$

3 Solve these.

a $\dfrac{2x}{3} + 5 = 9$ **b** $\dfrac{3y}{2} - 5 = 4$ **c** $3 - \dfrac{2z}{5} = -3$ **d** $\dfrac{3q}{2} + 5 = -7$

4 Solve these equations.

a $\dfrac{x+5}{3} = 2$ **b** $\dfrac{x-3}{4} = 2$ **c** $\dfrac{x+9}{2} = -4$ **d** $\dfrac{10-x}{4} = 1$

5 Solve these equations.

a $\dfrac{2x+1}{5} = 5$ **b** $\dfrac{3x-2}{4} = 4$ **c** $\dfrac{11-2x}{3} = -1$ **d** $\dfrac{31-3x}{4} = 4$

6 I think of a number.
I divide my number by 4 and add 6.

  a Write an expression for 'I divide my number by 4 and add 6'.
     Use n to represent the number.

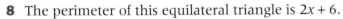

  b My answer is 10.
     Using your expression from part **a**, write an equation to show this.

Expression **a** = 10

  c Solve your equation to find the number, n.

7 Use the method in question **6** to write an equation and find the missing number in these problems.

  a I think of a number.
     I divide it by 3 and subtract 4.
     The answer is 7.

  b I think of a number.
     I half it and add 8.
     The answer is 3.

8 The perimeter of this equilateral triangle is $2x + 6$.

  a Write an expression for the length of one side of
     the triangle.

  b The length of one side of the triangle is 8 cm.
     Find the value of x.

Length of side = $\dfrac{\text{perimeter}}{3}$

9 The perimeter of this square is $4 + x$.
The length of one side is 10 cm.
Write an equation and solve it to find the value of x.

This spread will show you how to:

- Use systematic trial and improvement to estimate the solutions of an equation

Keywords
Estimate
Improvement
Trial

- To solve equations with powers, you can use **trial** and **improvement**.
  - You **estimate** a solution and **try** it in the equation.
  - If your estimate doesn't fit, you **improve** it and try again.

Example

Use trial and improvement to find the value of x in this equation.
$$x^2 = 87$$
Give your answer to 1 dp.

$$x^2 = 87$$

An estimate for x is 9.2
Try 9.2 in the equation: $\quad$ $9.2^2 = 84.64$ $\quad$ too small
Try 9.3 in the equation: $\quad$ $9.3^2 = 86.49$ $\quad$ too small
Try 9.4 in the equation: $\quad$ $9.4^2 = 88.36$ $\quad$ too big

So the solution is between 9.3 and 9.4.
Try the halfway value, 9.35: $\quad$ $9.35^2 = 87.42$ $\quad$ too big
So the solution is between 9.3 and 9.35.

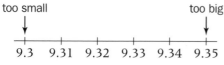

The solution is 9.3 to 1 dp.

$9^2 = 81$, so estimate that x is a bit bigger than 9.

When the answer is too small, improve your estimate by choosing a slightly bigger value.

All these values between 9.3 and 9.35 round to 9.3

- When using trial and improvement you need to work systematically.
  You can show your trials in a table.

Example

The equation
$$x^3 + x = 33$$
has a solution between 3 and 4.
Use trial and improvement to find the solution.
Give your answer correct to 1 decimal place.

x	x^3	$x^3 + x$	Too big or too small?
3.5	42.875	46.375	too big
3.2	32.768	35.968	too big
3.1	29.791	32.891	too small
3.15	31.255...	34.405...	too big

The solution is between 3.1 and 3.15.
The solution is 3.1 to 1 dp.

Draw a table.

The solution is between 3.1 and 3.2. Try the halfway value.

All the values between 3.1 and 3.15 round to 3.1.

1 Bina is using trial and improvement to find a solution to $x^2 = 29$.
  She draws this table

x	x^2	Too big or too small?
5.5	30.25	
5.4		

  a Copy the table and fill in the rest of the rows for the values
     5.5 and 5.4.

  b What value could you try next?
     Write this value in your table and complete the row.

  c Improve your estimate and write the value in the table.
     Complete the row for this estimate.

  d Continue in this way until you have found a solution to
     1 decimal place.

  You may need to add extra rows to your table.

2 The equation $x^2 - x = 13$ has a solution between 4 and 5.
  Copy and complete the table to find this solution to 1 decimal place.
  Draw as many rows as you need.

x	x^2	$x^2 - x$	Too big or too small?
4.5			

3 The equation $x^3 + x = 146$ has a solution between 5 and 6.
  Copy and complete the table to find this solution to 1 decimal place.
  Draw as many rows as you need.

x	x^3	$x^3 + x$	Too big or too small?

4 **a** Substitute $x = 1$, $x = 2$ and $x = 3$ into the equation
     $$x^3 - x = 9$$

  b Use your answers from part **a** to help you estimate a solution to
     the equation $x^3 - x = 9$.

  c Draw up a table for this equation.

  d Use your answer from part **b** as your first estimate in your table.

  e Find the solution to 1 decimal place.

  Your table will be similar to the one in question **3**.

5 Use trial and improvement to find a solution to
     $$x^3 + x = 73$$

Exam review

Key objectives

- Solve linear equations that require prior simplification of brackets, including those that have negative signs occurring anywhere in the equation, and those with a negative solution
- Solve linear equations in one unknown, with integer or fractional coefficients, in which the unknown appears on either side or on both sides of the equation
- Use systematic trial and improvement to find approximate solutions of equations where there is no simple analytical method of solving them

1 The equation

$$x^2 - x = 23$$

has a solution between 5 and 6.

Use trial and improvement to find the solution.

Give your answer correct to 1 decimal place. (4)

2 a Solve $7x + 18 = 74$. (2)

   b Solve $4(2y - 5) = 32$. (2)

   c Solve $5p + 7 = 3(4 - p)$. (3)

(Edexcel Ltd., 2003)

D4

This unit will show you how to

- Recognise the difference between discrete and continuous data
- Calculate the mean, median, mode and range for sets of data
- Use frequency tables for discrete and grouped data
- Compare distributions and make inferences
- Estimate the mean, median and mode for grouped data

Before you start ...

You should be able to answer these questions.

1 Calculate

  a 43 – 17   **b** 136 – 118

  c 8.3 – 2.7

2 Order these numbers in size, smallest first.

  a 6.5, 8, 4, 5.5, 7.

  b 3.2, 2.3, 3.4, 4.3, 4.2, 2.4.

  c 8.6, 7.5, 9.1, 7.9, 8.3.

3 List the ten numbers recorded in each frequency table.

a

Number	Frequency
5	0
6	2
7	1
8	2
9	5

b

Number	Frequency
100	2
101	1
102	2
103	0
104	5

4 Find the mid-value between

  a 1 and 5   **b** 6 and 10

  c 40 and 44   **d** 45 and 49

  e 50 and 54

Review

Unit N2

Unit N1

Unit D3

Key stage 3

Types of data and the range

This spread will show you how to:

- Recognise the difference between discrete and continuous data

Keywords
Continuous data
Discrete data
Range
Spread

- Numerical data can be **discrete** or **continuous**.

- **Discrete data** can only take exact values.

Shoe sizes could be 7, $7\frac{1}{2}$, 8, $8\frac{1}{2}$, 9.
There are no values between them.

The shoe size $7\frac{1}{4}$ does not exist.

- **Continuous data** can take any value within a given range.

Temperature can take
any value between 21°C and 22°C.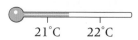

The values of continuous data depend on the accuracy of the measurement.

Continuous data cannot be measured exactly.

A height of 171 cm has been given to the nearest centimetre.

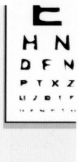

- You can measure the **spread** of a set of data by calculating the **range**.
- The **range** is the highest value minus the lowest value.

Example

There are eight classes in Year 10 of a school. The numbers of students that were absent from each class were 3, 1, 4, 8, 4, 2, 5, 1.
a Calculate the range of absences.
b State whether the data is discrete or continuous.

a Range = highest value − lowest value
        = 8 − 1
        = 7
b Discrete − you cannot have $7\frac{1}{2}$ students.

1 Decide whether each of these are discrete or continuous data.

  a number of people in a room

  b number of cars in a car park

  c length of a piece of wood

  d thickness of a piece of wood

  e amount of water in a pan

  f cost of buying a DVD

  g time taken to walk to the shops

  h weight of a piece of cheese

  i number of tomatoes on a plant

  j temperature in a fridge

  k score on a dice

  l your age

2 Calculate the range for each set of numbers.

  a 0, 0, 1, 2, 2, 2, 3, 4, 4, 5, 5

  b 6, 7, 8, 8, 8, 9, 9, 9, 10

  c 32, 32, 33, 35, 41

  d 48, 48, 48, 49, 49

  e 85, 86, 87, 88, 89, 90, 91, 92

  f 5, 6, 8, 4, 7, 9, 5, 6, 7

  g 31, 34, 18, 25, 31, 26, 35, 27

  h 17, 17, 15, 16, 21, 22, 20, 20

  i $3\frac{1}{2}$, $3\frac{1}{2}$, $4\frac{1}{2}$, 4, $3\frac{1}{2}$, 5, 3, $3\frac{1}{2}$

  j £3.00, £1.25, £4.70, £2.52, 85p

3 Calculate the range of these sets of numbers.

  a 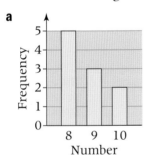 **b** 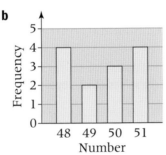 **c**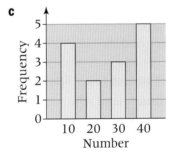

4 The weights, in kilograms, of 10 students are

  46 33 53 72 56 31 60 55 48 51

  Calculate the range of the weights. State the units of your answer.

5 The mean monthly temperature, in °F, is shown for Athens and Madrid.

	Jan	Feb	Mar	Apr	May	Jun	Jul	Aug	Sep	Oct	Nov	Dec
Athens	50	50	54	59	67	75	81	81	75	67	59	53
Madrid	42	45	49	53	60	69	76	76	69	58	49	44

  a Calculate the range for temperatures for Athens.

  b Calculate the range for temperatures for Madrid.

6 The range of these numbers is 17.
Find two possible values for the unknown number.

  | 34 | | 40 | | 25 | | ? |

This spread will show you how to:

● Calculate the mean, median, mode and range for sets of data

Keywords
Average
Mean
Median
Modal value
Mode
Representative
  value

The **average** 15-year-old boy in the UK is 172 cm tall.
This does not suggest that every boy's height is 172 cm, but that 172 cm is used to represent the height of all the 15-year-old boys in the UK.

● You can represent a set of data with one number, called the average.

There are three different ways to find a typical or **representative value** for a set of data.

● The **mean** of a set of data is the total of all the values divided by the number of values.
● The **mode** is the value that occurs most often.
● The **median** is the middle value when the data is arranged in order.

The mode is sometimes called the **modal value**.

Example

Calculate the mean, mode and median of

8, 3, 8, 7, 5

Mean = $(8 + 3 + 8 + 7 + 5) \div 5$
    = $31 \div 5$
    = 6.2

Mode = 8   as 8 occurs most often

For the median, first arrange the numbers in numerical order:

3   5   7   8   8
         ↑
      middle
Median = 7

To calculate the median of 7, 7, 8, 9, 10, 14: The middle numbers are 8 and 9.
Median = $(8 + 9) \div 2 = 8.5$

1 a Calculate the mean of these five numbers.

  3, 3, 8, 1, 5

  b Copy the bar chart to illustrate the five numbers.

  c Mark the mean on your diagram with a horizontal line.

  d Show how the rectangles above the mean can be moved to give five bars with equal heights.

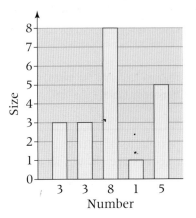

2 These 40 vehicles are recorded as they pass.

```
C  C  C  T  B  B  C  C  B  C
T  B  B  B  C  C  C  C  C  B
B  C  C  C  C  T  C  B  B  C
C  C  B  C  C  C  C  T  C  C
```

> B = Bus
> T = Tram
> C = Car

  a Copy and complete the frequency table for the vehicles.

Vehicle	Tally	Frequency
Bus (B)		
Tram (T)		
Car (C)		

  b State the modal vehicle.

> The mode is sometimes called the **modal value**.

3 Five men were asked to count the loose change in their pockets. The results were

  £2.47   £1.12   38p   £2.15   85p

  a Arrange the amounts in order, smallest first.

  b Find the median amount of money. State the units of your answer.

4 The seven-day weather forecast for a warm week in August is shown.

Thu	Fri	Sat	Sun	Mon	Tue	Wed
80°F	82°F	85°F	80°F	80°F	81°F	75°F

  Calculate

  a the mean temperature   **b** the modal temperature

  c the median temperature.

5 Six numbers are arranged in order. The median of these numbers is 5.5.

  | 3.2 | 4.5 | ? | 6.0 | 7.6 | 8.5 |

  a Calculate the unknown number.

  b Calculate the mean of the six numbers.

D4.3 Charts and tables

This spread will show you how to:

- Use frequency tables for discrete and grouped data

Keywords
Frequency table
Mean
Median
Mode
Range

- **You can calculate the mean, mode, median and range for discrete data from a frequency table.**

Example

Ten people took part in a golf competition.
Their scores are shown in the frequency table.

Calculate the mean, mode, median and range of the scores.

Score	Frequency
67	1
68	4
69	3
70	1
71	1

4 people scored 68.

1 person scored 71.

The results can be written in numerical order.

67, 68, 68, 68, 68, 69, 69, 69, 70, 71

Mean = 687 ÷ 10 = 68.7
Median = (68 + 69) ÷ 2 = 68.5
Mode = 68 (occurs 4 times)
Range = 71 − 67 = 4

Alternatively, you can calculate the mean, mode, median and range directly from the frequency table without rewriting the numbers.

Score	Frequency	Score × Frequency
67	1	67
68	4	272
69	3	207
70	1	70
71	1	71
	10	687

68 + 68 + 68 + 68 or 68 × 4.

The total of all the scores of the 10 golfers.

Mean = 687 ÷ 10 = 68.7
Median = (5th value + 6th value) ÷ 2 = (68 + 69) ÷ 2 = 68.5
Mode = 68 as the highest frequency is 4
Range = 71 − 67 = 4

The mode is 68, not 4.

1 The numbers of flowers on eight rose plants are shown in the frequency table.

  a List the eight numbers in order of size, smallest first.

  b Calculate the mean, mode, median and range of the eight numbers.

Number of flowers	Tally	Frequency
3	IIII	4
4	II	2
5	II	2

2 The number of days that 25 students were present at school in a week are shown in the frequency table.

  a List the 25 numbers in order of size, smallest first.

  b How many students were present for 5 days of the week?

  c Calculate the mean, mode, median and range of the 25 numbers.

Number of days	Tally	Frequency
0		0
1	IIII	4
2	JHT I	6
3	II	2
4	JHT	5
5	JHT III	8

3 Twenty people decide to buy some raffle tickets.
Some of the people buy more than one ticket.
The table gives the information.

Calculate the

  a mean   **b** mode   **c** median   **d** range.

Number of tickets	Tally	Number of people
1	JHT I	6
2	JHT	5
3	IIII	4
4	JHT	5

4 The tetrahedron dice is rolled 50 times.
The scores are shown in the frequency table.
Calculate the

  a mean   **b** mode

  c median   **d** range.

Score	Tally	Frequency
1	JHT JHT	10
2	JHT JHT I	11
3	JHT JHT III	13
4	JHT JHT JHT I	16

5 The test results are shown for a class of 20 students.

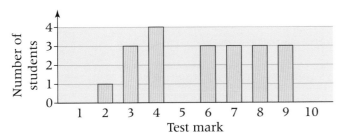

  a Copy and complete the frequency table to illustrate these results.

Mark	1	2	3	4	5	6	7	8	9	10
Number of students	0	1								

  b Calculate the mean, mode, median and range for the 20 marks.

This spread will show you how to:

- Compare distributions and make inferences

Keywords
Compare
Mean
Median
Mode
Range
Spread

- You can **compare** sets of data using the mean, mode, median and range.

Example

A team of 7 girls and a team of 8 boys do a sponsored run for charity. The distances the girls and boys ran are shown.

Girls

Distance (km)	Frequency
1	3
2	2
3	1
4	1
5	0

Boys

3, 5, 5, 3, 4, 4, 5, 5
all distances in kilometres

a Construct a similar frequency table for the boys' distance.
b By calculating the mean, median and range, compare each set of data.

a Boys

Distance (km)	Tally	Frequency	Distance × Frequency
1		0	0
2		0	0
3	||	2	6
4	||	2	8
5	||||	4	20
		8	34

b Girls

Mean = $(3 + 4 + 3 + 4 + 0) \div 7 = 14 \div 7 = 2$
Median = 2 (the 4th distance)
Range = $4 - 1 = 3$ (highest value − lowest value)

Boys

Mean = $34 \div 8 = 42.5$
Median = $(5 + 5) \div 2 = 10 \div 2 = 5$ (the mean of the 5th and 6th distances)
Range = $5 - 3 = 2$ (highest value − lowest value)

The mean and median show the boys ran further on average than the girls.
The range shows that the girls' distances were more **spread** out than the boys' distances.

1 The number of bottles of milk delivered to two houses is shown in the table.

	Sat	Sun	Mon	Tues	Wed	Thur	Fri
Number 45	2	0	1	1	1	1	1
Number 47	4	0	2	2	2	2	2

a Calculate the range for Number 45 and Number 47.

b Use your answers for the range to compare the number of bottles delivered to each house.

2 The number of cars at each house on Ullswater Drive are

2 4 1 0 1 2 1 2 3 2

a Copy and complete the frequency table.

Number of cars	Tally	Number of houses
0		
1		
2		
3		
4		

b Calculate the mean, mode and median number of cars for Ullswater Drive.

The mean, mode and median number of cars at each house on Ambleside Close are

Mean	Mode	Median
0.7	0	1

c Use the mean, mode and median to compare the number of cars on Ullswater Drive and Ambleside Close.

3 The number of days of rain each month in a particular year in Ireland and Spain is recorded.

	Jan	Feb	Mar	Apr	May	Jun	Jul	Aug	Sep	Oct	Nov	Dec
Ireland	27	22	27	24	23	24	25	24	26	26	26	28
Spain	11	10	10	11	10	7	2	5	6	11	11	12

a List each set of numbers in order, smallest first.

b Calculate the median days of rain for Ireland and for Spain.

c Using your answers for the median, compare the two sets of data.

d Calculate the range for each set of data.

e Using your answers for the range, compare the number of rainy days in Ireland and Spain.

This spread will show you how to:

- Estimate the mean, median and mode for grouped data

The number of students in a class and their absences are shown.

Absences	Frequency
0 to 4	9
5 to 9	8
10 to 14	5
15 to 19	6
20 to 24	2

5 students had either 10, 11, 12, 13 or 14 absences.

You cannot tell the **exact** number of absences in this frequency table.

Therefore you cannot calculate the exact mean, mode or median.

- For **grouped data** in a frequency table, you can calculate
  - the **estimated mean**
  - the **modal class**
  - the **class interval** in which the median lies.

Example

The times taken for 10 people to run a race are shown.

Use the frequency table to find
the estimated mean,
the modal class
and the class interval in which the median lies.

Time (t minutes)	Mid-value	Frequency	Mid-value × Frequency
$40 < t \leqslant 50$	45	1	45
$50 < t \leqslant 60$	55	2	110
$60 < t \leqslant 70$	65	5	325
$70 < t \leqslant 80$	75	2	150
Total		10	630

Use < ≤ for **continuous data**.
$40 < t \leqslant 50$ means more than 40, but less than or equal to 50.

By using the **mid-values**, the 10 times are taken as
45, 55, 55, 65, 65, 65, 65, 65, 75, 75.

$45 + 55 + 55 + 65 + 65 + 65 + 65 + 65 + 75 + 75 = 630$

Estimated mean = $630 \div 10$
  = 63 minutes
Modal class = $60 < t \leqslant 70$ as this class has the highest frequency

The median is given by the times of the 5th and 6th runners,
which are within the class interval $60 < t \leqslant 70$.

1 The weights, to the nearest kilogram, of 25 men are shown.

```
69  82  75  66  72
73  79  70  74  68
84  63  69  88  81
73  86  71  74  67
80  86  68  71  75
```

a Copy and complete the frequency table.

Weight (kg)	Tally	Number of men
60 to 64		
65 to 69		
70 to 74		
75 to 79		
80 to 84		
85 to 89		

b State the modal class.

c Find the class interval in which the median lies.

2 The speeds of 10 cars in a 30 mph zone are shown in the frequency table.

Speed (mph)	Mid-value	Number of cars	Mid-value × Number of cars
21 to 25		1	
26 to 30		6	
31 to 35		2	
36 to 40		1	

a Calculate the number of cars that are breaking the speed limit.

b Copy the frequency table and calculate the mid-values for each class interval.

c Complete the last column of your table and find an estimate of the mean speed.

3 The heights, in centimetres, of some students are shown in the frequency table.

Height (cm)	Number of students
$140 < h \leqslant 150$	3
$150 < h \leqslant 160$	9
$160 < h \leqslant 170$	8
$170 < h \leqslant 180$	10

a Calculate the total number of students shown in the table.

b Find the class interval in which the median lies.

c State the modal class.

d Find an estimate for the mean height.

D4 Exam review

Key objectives

- Calculate mean, range and median of small data sets with discrete data
- Identify the modal class for grouped data
- Calculate (and estimate) the mean for large data sets with grouped data
- Compare discrete distributions and make inferences, using the shapes of distributions and measures of average and range

1 The heights of students in a class are shown in this table:

Height (cm)	Frequency
$140 < h \leqslant 150$	6
$150 < h \leqslant 160$	15
$160 < h \leqslant 170$	9
$170 < h \leqslant 180$	2

a How many students are there in the class?

b What is the modal class for the data?

c Calculate the estimated mean for the data.

2 20 students scored goals for the school hockey team last month. The table gives information about the number of goals they scored:

Goals scored	Number of students
1	9
2	3
3	5
4	3

Copy the table.

a Write down the modal number of goals scored. (1)

b Work out the range of the number of goals scored. (1)

c Work out the mean number of goals scored. (3)

(Edexcel Ltd., 2004)

This unit will show you how to

- Understand angle measure using the associated language
- Construct triangles using a straight edge, protractor and compasses
- Use a straight edge and compasses to construct the perpendicular from a point to a line and the perpendicular from a point on the line
- Use straight edge and compasses to do standard constructions, including the bisector of an angle
- Find loci, both by reasoning and by using ICT to produce shapes and paths

Before you start ...

You should be able to answer these questions.

1 Using a protractor, measure these angles.

a   **b**

c

2 State the value of the marked angle.

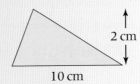

3 Using compasses, draw a circle with a diameter of 4.6 cm.

4 Calculate the area of this triangle, stating the units of your answer.

2 cm

10 cm

5 Measure this line

a in millimetres   **b** in centimetres.

Review

Key stage 3

Unit S2

Key stage 3

Unit S1

Key stage 3

This spread will show you how to:

● Understand angle measure using the associated language

Keywords
Bearing
Direction
Scale
Three-figure
  bearing

North, East, South or West are not enough to give an accurate direction on most occasions.

● A **bearing** is an angle measured clockwise from North.

To give a **direction** accurately, you need to find an angle measured on a 360° **scale**.

000° = North.

● To specify a direction with a bearing:
  ● measure from North
  ● measure clockwise
  ● use three figures.

The bearing of Scafell Pike from the Old Man of Coniston is 328°

Example

A boat is sinking.

The bearing of the boat from Dawlish Warren is 168°.

The bearing of the boat from Holcombe is 085°.

a Mark the position of the boat on the map.
b How far is the boat from Dawlish?
c What is the bearing of the boat from Dawlish?

From Dawlish Warren means centre the protactor **at** Dawlish Warren.

Do not rub out the construction lines.

a See map.
b 2 cm represents 1 km.
  5 cm represents 2.5 km.
  The boat is 2.5 km from Dawlish.
c 125°

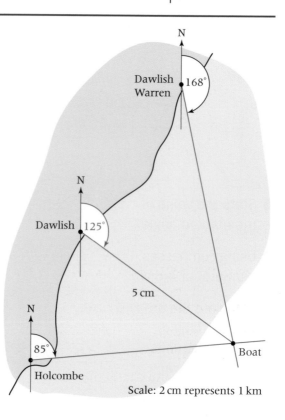

Scale: 2 cm represents 1 km

1 For each question, put a cross on your page.
Plot the points and join them to form a quadrilateral.
Name the shape, then measure and calculate the perimeter.

a

Bearing from the cross	060°	120°	240°	300°
Distance from the cross	5 cm	5 cm	5 cm	5 cm

b

Bearing from the cross	000°	090°	180°	270°
Distance from the cross	2.5 cm	5 cm	2.5 cm	5 cm

c

Bearing from the cross	035°	145°	215°	325°
Distance from the cross	5 cm	5 cm	5 cm	5 cm

2 Measure and write the bearing of

a Leeds from Manchester

b Sheffield from Leeds

c Manchester from Leeds

d Manchester from Sheffield

e Leeds from Sheffield.

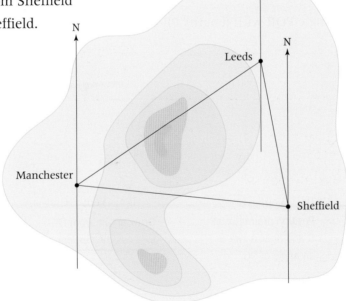

3 Copy the diagram.

The distance from Truro to Falmouth is 14 km.
The bearing of St. Mawes from Falmouth is 080°.
The bearing of St. Mawes from Truro is 170°.

a Mark the position of St. Mawes on your diagram.

b Calculate the distance from Falmouth to St. Mawes.

c Calculate the distance from Truro to St. Mawes.

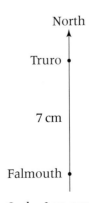

North

Truro

7 cm

Falmouth

Scale: 1cm represents 2 km

Constructing triangles

This spread will show you how to:

● Construct triangles using a straight edge, protractor and compasses

Keywords
Arc
Base
Compasses
Congruent
Construct
Construction
  lines
Hypotenuse
Protractor
Right-angled
Straight edge

You can **construct** a triangle when you know

Two sides and   or   Two angles   or   Right angle, the   or   Three sides
the angle   and a side   hypotenuse and   (SSS)
between them   (ASA)   a side (RHS)
(SAS)

5cm   5cm   6cm   R   8cm

30°   60°   30°   P

6cm   7cm   3cm   10cm

You will need a ruler and a protractor   You will need a ruler and compasses
for SAS, ASA and RHS triangles.   for SSS triangles.

The longest side of
a **right-angled**
triangle is called
the **hypotenuse**.

Example

a Construct the triangle ABC so that angle C = 90°, AB = 6 cm and
BC = 3 cm.

b Construct the triangle PQR with lengths PR = 6 cm, QR = 8 cm and
PQ = 10 cm.

a

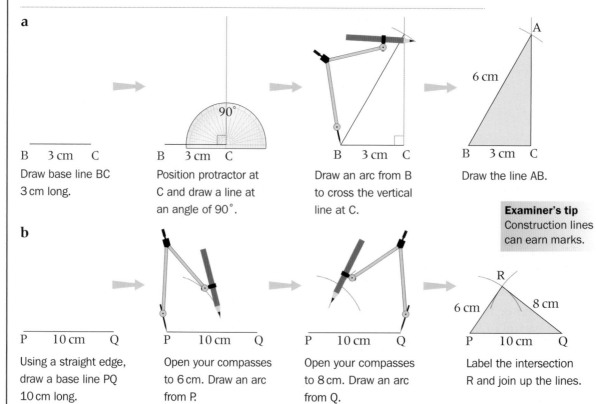

B   3 cm   C
Draw base line BC
3 cm long.

B   3 cm   C
Position protractor at
C and draw a line at
an angle of 90°.

B   3 cm   C
Draw an arc from B
to cross the vertical
line at C.

B   3 cm   C
Draw the line AB.

6 cm

Examiner's tip
Construction lines
can earn marks.

b

P   10 cm   Q
Using a straight edge,
draw a base line PQ
10 cm long.

P   10 cm   Q
Open your compasses
to 6 cm. Draw an arc
from P.

P   10 cm   Q
Open your compasses
to 8 cm. Draw an arc
from Q.

R   R
6 cm   8 cm
P   10 cm   Q
Label the intersection
R and join up the lines.

The triangles in this exercise have been sketched by hand.
Draw them accurately using the measurements given.

Leave your **construction lines** on your drawing to show your method.

1 Make accurate drawings of these triangles (SAS).
Measure the unknown length in each triangle.

a
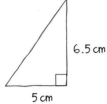
6.5 cm
5 cm

b
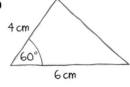
4 cm
60°
6 cm

c
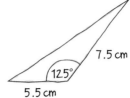
7.5 cm
125°
5.5 cm

2 Make accurate drawings of these triangles (ASA).
Measure the two unknown lengths in each triangle. State the units of your answers.

a
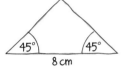
45°   45°
8 cm

b
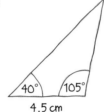
40° 105°
4.5 cm

c
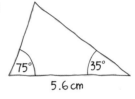
75°   35°
5.6 cm

3 Make accurate drawings of these triangles (SSS).
Measure the marked angle in each triangle.

a
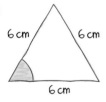
6 cm   6 cm
6 cm

b
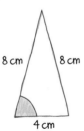
8 cm   8 cm
4 cm

c
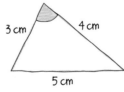
3 cm   4 cm
5 cm

4 Make accurate drawings of these triangles (RHS).
Measure the unknown length and the marked angle in each triangle.

a
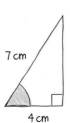
7 cm
4 cm

b
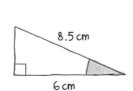
8.5 cm
6 cm

c
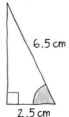
6.5 cm
2.5 cm

This spread will show you how to:

- Use a straight edge and compasses to construct the perpendicular from a point to a line and the perpendicular from a point on the line

Keywords
Arc
Compasses
Construct
Midpoint
Perpendicular
Perpendicular bisector

The shortest distance from a point to a line is the **perpendicular** distance.

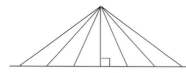

The perpendicular meets the line at right angles.

You construct a perpendicular from a point P to a line like this.

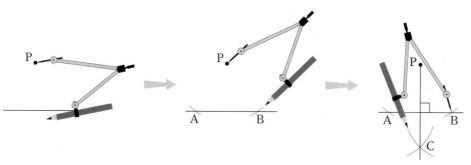

Construct means use compasses.

Open your compasses so that the distance is longer than the distance from the point to the line.

Construct two arcs from the point to the line.

Keep the compasses the same width and construct an arc from A and from B to meet at C. Join C to point P.

You construct the perpendicular from a point P on the line like this.

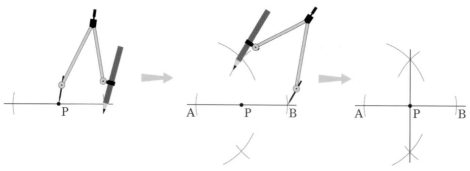

Construct two arcs on the line equidistant from point P.

Keep the compasses the same width apart. Construct arcs above and below the line from point A and from point B.

Draw the perpendicular bisector of AB.

P is the **midpoint** of AB.

- A **perpendicular bisector** divides a straight line into two equal parts at right angles.

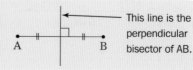

This line is the perpendicular bisector of AB.

For all constructions use a pencil and do not rub out your construction lines.

1 **a** Draw a line AB, so that AB = 8 cm.

b Using compasses, construct the perpendicular bisector of AB.

c Label the midpoint of AB as M.

d Measure the length AM.

2 **a** Draw a line of length 64 mm.

b Construct the perpendicular bisector of the line.

c Check by measuring that the perpendicular bisector passes through the midpoint of the line.

3 **a** Draw a line AB, so that AB = 10 cm.

b Mark the point P, so that AP = 7 cm.

c Construct the perpendicular to AB that passes through the point P.

4 **a** Draw a line AB, with a point P above the line.

b Using compasses, construct the perpendicular to AB that passes through the point P.

c Measure the angle between the line AB and the perpendicular from P.

5 Construct these rhombuses using compasses and ruler.

a
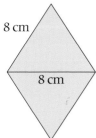
8 cm
8 cm

b
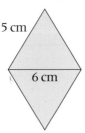
5 cm
6 cm

c
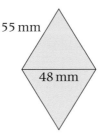
55 mm
48 mm

Draw the vertical diagonals on your diagrams.
For each rhombus, check that each diagonal is a perpendicular bisector of the other.

Angle bisectors

This spread will show you how to:

- Use straight edge and compasses to do standard constructions, including the bisector of an angle

Keywords
Angle bisector
Arc
Compasses
Construct

- To bisect an angle, you cut the angle exactly in half.

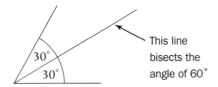

This line bisects the angle of 60°

You use **compasses** to construct an **angle bisector**.

| Use compasses to draw equal arcs on each arm. | Draw equal arcs from these arcs that intersect at C. | Join O to C, the vertex of the angle | OACB is a rhombus. |

Construct means use compasses, not a protractor.

Angle AOC = angle BOC

Example

Using compasses, construct

a an angle of 60°
b an angle of 30°.

a

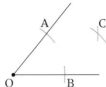 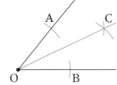 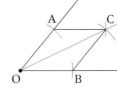

| Draw a line. | Draw an arc from A crossing the line at B. | Draw an arc from B crossing the first arc at C. | Draw a line from A to C. |

b

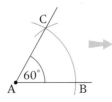 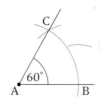 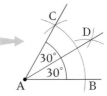

| Use the angle of 60°. | Draw an arc from B. | Draw an arc from C crossing the previous arc at D. | Draw a line from A to D. |

1 Use a protractor to draw these angles.

  a 70° **b** 110° **c** 90° **d** 130° **e** 50°

Using compasses, construct the angle bisectors for each angle.
Use a protractor to check each angle bisector.

2 a Using compasses, construct an angle of 60°.

  b Use a protractor to check the angle.

3 Construct a triangle that is similar to this equilateral
triangle.

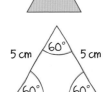

> Similar shapes are
> the same in shape
> but different in
> size.

4 a Using compasses and ruler, construct an
equilateral triangle with sides of length 5 cm.

  b Use a protractor to check the angles.

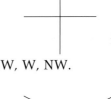

5 Using compasses, construct an angle of

  a 30°   **b** 120°.

Use a protractor to check your answers.

> Bisect a 60° angle.

6 a Use a protractor to draw two perpendicular lines
as shown.

  b Using compasses, construct the bisectors of the
right angles.

  c Label the eight points clockwise with N, NE, E, SE, S, SW, W, NW.

7 a Draw any two intersecting lines.

  b Construct the angle bisectors for the acute angles.

  c Construct the angle bisectors for the obtuse angles.

  d Copy and complete this sentence:

   The bisector of the acute angles is _____ to the bisector of the
obtuse angles.

  e Explain why the sentence is true for any two intersecting lines.

8 a Using compasses, construct the triangle PQR.

  b Construct the angle bisectors for angle P, angle Q and
angle R.

  c Label the point of intersection of the angle bisectors
as O.

  d Draw a circle, centre O, that just touches the lines PQ,
QR and PR.

  e State the radius of this circle.

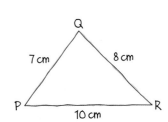

249

Loci

This spread will show you how to:

- Find loci, both by reasoning and by using ICT to produce shapes and paths

Keywords

Arc
Compasses
Construct
Equidistant
Loci
Locus
Perpendicular
 bisector

Loci is the plural of locus.

- The **locus** of an object is its path.
- A locus is a set of points that move according to a rule.

The red counters are all the same distance from the blue counter.

The red counters are the same distance from the two blue lines.

The red counters are the same distance from the two blue lines.

The red counters are the same distance from the two blue counters.

The locus is a circle.

The locus is a straight line.

The locus is the angle bisector of the angle between the two blue lines.

The locus is the perpendicular bisector of the line joining the two blue counters.

Example

Some treasure is positioned 2 m from C, but **equidistant** from A and B.
Using ruler and compasses only, mark the possible positions of the treasure.

×C

A×   ×B

Draw a circle, centre C, radius 2 m.
Join A and B.
Construct the perpendicular bisector of AB.
Mark where the line crosses the circle.

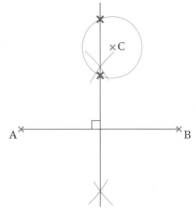

You can use LOGO to plot the path of a turtle.
You specify distance in mm and angles in degrees.

These commands ...   produce this path.

FORWARD 100
LEFT 90
FORWARD 100

The plan view is

100 mm

100 mm

1 a Using a protractor, draw and label an angle of 50°.

  b Draw the locus of the points that are the same distance from AB and BC.

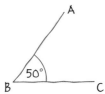

2 a Using compasses, construct and label an angle of 60°.

  b Construct the locus of the points that are equidistant from AB and BC.

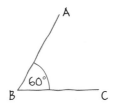

3 a Draw a line AB so that AB = 7 cm.

  b Construct the locus of the points that are equidistant from A and B.

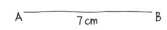

4 Draw a point and label it O.
Construct the locus of the points that are 3 cm from the point O.

5 Draw two parallel lines.
Draw the locus of the points that are equidistant from the two lines.

6 A 2 metre length of rope is used to tether a goat to a fixed point on a fence.

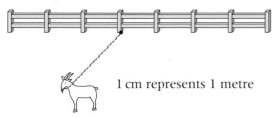

1 cm represents 1 metre

Draw a diagram to show the extent to which the goat can move while tethered.

7 a Draw a line AB so that AB = 8 cm.

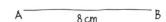

  b Construct the locus of the points that are equidistant from A and B.

  c On your diagram, indicate the region that has points that are nearer to A than B.

Key objectives

- Understand angle measure using the associated language
- Use straight edge and compasses to do standard constructions
- Find loci, both by reasoning and by using ICT to produce shapes and paths

1 Use a protractor to find the bearing of the following places from the house:
Give your answers to the nearest degree. (5)

Cinema

N

School

House

Café

Park

Church

2 The diagram represents a triangular garden ABC.
The scale of the diagram is 1 cm represents 1 m.
A tree is to be planted in the garden so that it is

nearer to AB than to AC,
within 2 m of point A.

Copy the diagram and shade the
region where the tree may be planted.

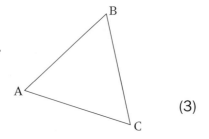

(3)

(Edexcel Ltd., 2003)

This unit will show you how to

- Express one number as a fraction (or proportion) of another number
- Use fractions and percentages as operators
- Use equivalent fractions and mental methods to calculate simple percentages
- Calculate a fraction and percentage of an amount using a variety of methods
- Calculate percentage increase and decrease using a range of methods
- Solve percentage problems
- Calculate simple and compound interest

Before you start ...

You should be able to answer these questions.

Review

1 Calculate

$\frac{3}{5}$ of £55.

Unit N3

2 Calculate

10% of $430.

Unit N3

3 Decrease 76 kg by 25%.

Unit N3

4 A shop increases all of its prices by 20%.
A cup normally costs £4.50.
What is the new price of the cup?

Unit N3

5 Increase £350 by 5%.

Unit N3

This spread will show you how to:

- Express one number as a fraction (or proportion) of another number
- Use fractions and percentages as operators

You can express one number as a **fraction** of another number.

Example

In a class there are 32 students. 20 of the students are girls. What fraction of the class are boys? Give your answer in its simplest form.

There are 32 students in the class altogether.
Number of boys = 32 − 20 = 12
Fraction who are boys = $\frac{12}{32} = \frac{3}{8}$

You can calculate a fraction of a quantity using a variety of methods.

Mental method
To calculate $\frac{3}{8}$ of 32 children:
$\frac{1}{8}$ of 32 children = 32 ÷ 8
$\qquad$ = 4 children
$\frac{3}{8}$ of 32 children = 3 × 4
$\qquad$ = 12 children

Written method
To calculate $\frac{3}{7}$ of 63 kg:
$\frac{3}{7}$ of 63 kg = $\frac{3}{7} \times 63$
$\qquad = 3 \times \frac{1}{7} \times 63$
$\qquad = \frac{3 \times 63}{7}$
$\qquad = \frac{189}{7}$
$\qquad = 27$ kg

Calculator method
To calculate $\frac{7}{11}$ of £90:
Decimal equivalent of $\frac{7}{11}$
$\qquad = 7 \div 11 = 0.636\,363\,...$
$\frac{7}{11}$ of £90 = $\frac{7}{11} \times$ £90
$\qquad = 0.636\,363\,... \times 90$
$\qquad =$ £57.2727
$\qquad =$ £57.27

Example

Meagan is 150 cm tall. Piper is $\frac{6}{5}$ of the height of Meagan.

a Calculate the height of Piper.
b What fraction of Piper's height is Meagan?

a Piper's height = $\frac{6}{5}$ of Meagan's height
$\qquad = \frac{6}{5} \times 150$ cm
$\qquad = 6 \times 150 \times \frac{1}{5}$
$\qquad = \frac{900}{5} = 180$ cm

b Meagan's height as a fraction of Piper's height = $\frac{150 \text{ cm}}{180 \text{ cm}}$
$\qquad = \frac{150}{180}$
$\qquad = \frac{5}{6}$

$\dfrac{\text{Piper's height}}{\text{Meagan's height}} = \dfrac{6}{5}$

$\dfrac{\text{Meagan's height}}{\text{Piper's height}} = \dfrac{5}{6}$

$\times \frac{6}{5}$

150 cm $\qquad$ 180 cm

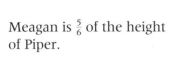

$\times \frac{5}{6}$

Meagan is $\frac{5}{6}$ of the height of Piper.

1 Calculate each of these, leaving your answer in its simplest form.

   a $5 \times \frac{1}{2}$ **b** $8 \times \frac{1}{4}$ **c** $8 \times \frac{1}{3}$ **d** $13 \times \frac{1}{7}$ **e** $\frac{1}{12} \times 24$ **f** $\frac{1}{3} \times 4$

2 Calculate each of these, leaving your answer in its simplest form.

   a $6 \times \frac{2}{3}$ **b** $5 \times \frac{3}{4}$ **c** $6 \times \frac{2}{3}$ **d** $4 \times \frac{7}{6}$

   e $5 \times \frac{9}{20}$ **f** $\frac{4}{5} \times 28$ **g** $\frac{4}{9} \times 30$ **h** $\frac{11}{18} \times 14$

   i $1\frac{2}{3} \times 6$

3 Calculate each of these, leaving your answer in its simplest form.

   a What is the total mass of four packets that each weigh $\frac{1}{5}$ kg?

   b A cake weighs $\frac{7}{20}$ of a kg. What is the mass of 10 cakes?

   c What is the total capacity of 12 jugs that each have a capacity of $\frac{3}{5}$ of a litre?

   d What is the total mass of 16 bags of flour that each weigh $\frac{9}{10}$ of a kilogram?

4 Use a mental or written method to work out these. Leave your answers as fractions in their simplest form where appropriate.

   a $\frac{3}{10}$ of €40   **b** $\frac{2}{5}$ of £70   **c** $\frac{3}{4}$ of 50 m   **d** $\frac{4}{7}$ of 64 km

   e $\frac{3}{8}$ of £1000   **f** $\frac{5}{6}$ of 70 mm   **g** $\frac{11}{12}$ of 1500 m   **h** $\frac{4}{13}$ of 60 g

5 Use a suitable method to calculate each of these. Where appropriate round your answer to 2 decimal places.

   a $\frac{8}{15}$ of 495 kg   **b** $\frac{9}{10}$ of $5000   **c** $\frac{5}{9}$ of 8 kg

   d $\frac{7}{9}$ of 1224 cups   **e** $\frac{13}{18}$ of 30 tonnes   **f** $\frac{4}{15}$ of 360°

   g $\frac{12}{31}$ of 360°   **h** $\frac{13}{15}$ of 1 hour   **i** $\frac{17}{15}$ of £230

   j $\frac{5}{6}$ of 24 hours

6 Express each of these as proportions. Give each answer as a fraction in its simplest form.

   a 40 kg as a fraction of 60 kg   **b** 15 m as a fraction of 25 m

   c 40 cm as a proportion of 2 m   **d** 55p as a fraction of £3

7 **a** A shirt normally costs £40. In a sale the price is reduced by $\frac{2}{5}$. What is the new price of the shirt?

   b Benito receives £20 a week pocket money. He saves $\frac{3}{8}$ of it. How much money does he save each week?

   c Karen rents out her holiday cottage to tourists for $\frac{4}{5}$ of the 365 day year. For how many days is her cottage empty?

This spread will show you how to:

- Use equivalent fractions and mental methods to calculate simple percentages
- Calculate a fraction and percentage of an amount using a variety of methods

Keywords

Percentage

You can calculate simple **percentages** of amounts in your head using equivalent fractions.

Calculate   **a** 10% of £83   **b** 5% of 164 m.

a 10% of £83 is the same as working out $\frac{1}{10}$ of £83 $= \frac{1}{10} \times 83$
$$= 83 \div 10$$
$$= £8.30$$

$10\% = \frac{10}{100} = \frac{1}{10}$

$\times \frac{1}{10}$ is the same as $\div 10$.

b 10% of 164 m $= \frac{1}{10}$ of 164 m
$$= \frac{1}{10} \times 164$$
$$= 164 \div 10$$
$$= 16.4 \text{ m}$$
5% of 164 m $= \frac{1}{2}$ of (10% of 164 m)
$$= 16.4 \div 2$$
$$= 8.2 \text{ m}$$

To find 5% of something:
- Find 10% of it.
- $\div 2$.

Harder percentages of amounts can be worked out using a written or calculator method.

Written method
Change the percentage to its equivalent fraction and multiply by the amount.

To calculate 9% of 24 m:
9% of 24 m $= \frac{9}{100} \times 24$
$$= \frac{9 \times 1 \times 24}{100}$$
$$= \frac{9 \times 24}{100}$$
$$= \frac{216}{100}$$
$$= 2.16 \text{ m}$$

9% of an amount
$= \frac{9}{100}$ of it
$= 9 \times \frac{1}{100}$ of it.
This is the same as $\times 9$ and $\div 100$, so you work out $9 \times 24 \div 100$.

Calculator method
Change the percentage to its equivalent decimal and multiply by the amount.

To calculate 37% of £58:
37% of £58 $= \frac{37}{100} \times 58$
$$= 0.37 \times 58$$
$$= £21.46$$

$37\% = \frac{37}{100} = 37 \div 100 = 0.37$
$2.7\% = \frac{2.7}{100} = 2.7 \div 100 = 0.027$

1 Calculate these percentages without using a calculator.

   a 50% of £300   **b** 50% of 4 kg   **c** 50% of £80

   d 50% of 37 kg   **e** 1% of £30   **f** 10% of 342.8 m

2 Calculate these percentages without using a calculator.

   a 5% of £180   **b** 20% of 410 kg   **c** 20% of $25

   d 25% of £3   **e** 75% of £42   **f** 5% of 3.8 m

3 Calculate these percentages using a mental or written method.

   a 15% of £340   **b** 60% of 120 Mb   **c** 60% of £75

   d 80% of £50   **e** 30% of 455 m   **f** 2.5% of £880

   g 70% of 1570 mm   **h** 15% of 42 kg   **i** 45% of 70 mm

4 Write the method you would use to calculate each of these without using a calculator.

   a 15% of anything   **b** 5% of anything   **c** 35% of anything

   d 17.5% of anything   **e** 95% of anything

5 **a** Paul downloads a file from the internet. The file is 16 Mb. After 2 minutes he has downloaded 70% of the file. How much of the file has Paul downloaded?

   b Winston has to move 24 tonnes of hardcore. In the morning he moves 55% of the hardcore. How many tonnes of hardcore has he moved?

   c A train journey is 395 km long. Lola is travelling on a train that has completed 23% of the journey. How many kilometres has Lola's train travelled?

   d At Herbie's school there is a charity race night. The evening raises £234. 58% of the money raised goes to charities and the rest is given to the school. How much money is given to the school?

6 Calculate these using a mental or written method. Show all the steps of your working out. Give your answers to 2 decimal places as appropriate.

   a 12% of £17   **b** 16% of 87 km   **c** 8% of £38

   d 32% of €340   **e** 17% of 65 m   **f** 73% of 46 cm

   g 85% of 148 m   **h** 2% of £76.40   **i** 25% of £85

Revise the work you have done previously on mental and written methods of multiplication:

- partitioning
- compensation
- doubling and halving
- grid method
- standard method.

This spread will show you how to:

● Calculate percentage increase and decrease using a range of methods

Keywords
Decrease
Increase
Percentage

Percentages are used in real life to show how much an amount has increased or decreased.

WORKERS DEMAND A 6% INCREAS

MARKET NEWS

● To calculate a **percentage increase**, work out the increase and add it to the original amount.

● To calculate a **percentage decrease**, work out the decrease and subtract it from the amount.

Example

a Alan is paid £940 a month. His employer increases his wage by 3%. Calculate the new wage Alan is paid each month.

b A new car costs £19 490. After one year the car depreciates in value by 8.7%. What is the new value of the car?

a Calculate 3% of the amount.
Add to the original amount.
Increase in wage = 3% of £940 = $\frac{3}{100} \times £940$
$$= \frac{3 \times 940}{100} = \frac{2820}{100}$$
Increase in wage = £28.20 per month
Alan's new wage = £940 + £28.20 = £968.20

The percentage calculation has been worked out using a written method.

b Calculate 8.7% of the amount.
Subtract from the original amount.
Depreciation $= 8.7\%$ of £19 490
$= \frac{8.7}{100} \times £19\ 490$
$= 0.087 \times £19\ 490$
Price reduction = £1695.63
New value of car = £19 490 − £1695.63 = £17 794.37

The percentage calculation has been worked out using a calculator.

You can calculate a percentage increase or decrease in a single calculation.

Example

a In a sale all prices are reduced by 16%. A pair of trousers normally costs £82. What is the sale price of the pair of trousers?

b Last year, Leanne's Council Tax bill was £968. This year the local council have raised the bill by 16%. How much is Leanne's new bill?

a Sale price $= (100 - 16)\%$
of the original price
$= 84\%$ of £82
$= \frac{84}{100} \times 82$
$= 0.84 \times 82$
$= 68.88$
$= £68.88$

b New bill $= (100 + 16)\%$
of the original bill
$= 116\%$ of £968
$= \frac{116}{100} \times £968$
$= 1.16 \times £968$
$= £1122.88$

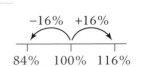

−16% +16%

84% 100% 116%

1 Calculate these amounts using an appropriate method.

a 25% of 18 kg   **b** 20% of 51 m   **c** 15% of 360°

d 2% of 37 cm   **e** 65% of 510 ml   **f** 17.5% of 360°

g 28% of 65 kg   **h** 31% of 277 kg   **i** 3.6% of 154 kg

j 0.3% of 1320 m^2

2 Calculate each of these using a mental or written method.

a Increase £350 by 10%   **b** Decrease 74 kg by 5%

c Increase £524 by 5%   **d** Decrease 756 km by 35%

e Increase 960 kg by 17.5%

3 Calculate these. Give your answers to 2 decimal places as appropriate.

a Increase £340 by 17%   **b** Decrease 905 kg by 42%

c Increase £1680 by 4.7%   **d** Decrease 605 km by 0.9%

e Increase $2990 by 14.5%

4 These are the weekly wages of five employees at Suits-U clothing store. The manager has decided to increase all the employees' wages by 4%. Calculate the new wage of each employee. Give your answers to 2 decimal places as appropriate.

Employee	Original wage	Increase	New wage
Hanif	£350	350 × 1.04 = ?	
Bonny	£285.50		
Wilf	£412.25		
Gary	£209.27		
Marielle	£198.64		

5 Use an appropriate method to work out each of these. Give your answers to 2 decimal places as appropriate.

a A drink can contains 440 ml. The size is increased by 12%. How much drink does it now contain?

b The price of a coat was £185. The price is reduced by 10% in a sale. What is the sale price of the coat?

c A house is bought for £195 000. During the next year, the house increases in price by 28.3%. What is the new value of the house?

d The number of students in a school is 940. Next year the school expects the number of students to increase by 15%. How many students does the school expect next year?

Percentage problems

This spread will show you how to:

- Calculate percentage increase and decrease using a range of methods
- Solve percentage problems

You will often encounter percentages in real life.

- VAT (Value Added Tax) is a tax which is added to bills for services and purchases. VAT is always given as a **percentage**.

Example

Helen has a contract for her home phone.
She pays £38.29 for calls and a quarterly charge of £19.60.
VAT has to be added at 17.5%.
Calculate the cost of Helen's bill + VAT.

Estimate:
Bill = £40 + £20 = £60

$\begin{aligned} \text{VAT} = 20\% \text{ of } £60 &= \frac{20}{100} \times 60 \\ &= 0.2 \times 60 \\ &= £12 \end{aligned}$

Bill + VAT = £60 + £12
$\qquad = £72$

Bill = £38.29 + £19.60
$\qquad = £57.89$

$\begin{aligned} \text{VAT} = 17.5\% \text{ of } £57.89 &= \frac{17.5}{100} \times 57.89 \\ &= 0.175 \times 57.89 \\ &= 10.130\,75 \\ &= £10.13 \end{aligned}$

Bill + VAT = £57.89 + £10.13
$\qquad = £68.02$

You should always estimate your answers when working with a calculator to solve percentage problems.

Calculate VAT at 17.5% of the amount.
Add this to the original amount.

When people buy and sell things they try to sell for more than they paid.

- The difference between the selling price and cost price is called the **profit**. A profit is normally written as a percentage of the cost price.

Example

Danii buys and sells protractors. She buys each protractor for 12p and sells them for 15p. What is her percentage profit?

Profit = 15p − 12p
$\qquad = 3p$

Calculate the profit.

$\begin{aligned} \text{Percentage profit} &= \frac{3p}{12p} \\ &= \frac{3}{12} \\ &= 0.25 \\ &= 25\% \end{aligned}$

Write the profit as a proportion of the cost price.

Express this fraction as a percentage.

1 Calculate the selling price of each of these items. In each case give the answer to 2 decimal places.

Item	Cost price	% profit or % loss	Selling price
DVD	£8.50	Profit 20%	
DVD player	£29.50	Loss 12%	
Pack 5 CD-RW	£4.60	Profit 73%	
USB hub 4-way	£21.30	Profit 32%	
TFT monitor	£185	Loss 4.6%	

2 Here are the prices of various objects without VAT. Calculate the real price of each item including VAT at a rate of 17.5%.

a

b

c

d

3 For each of these questions

   i   make an estimate

   ii work out your answer using a suitable method

   iii give your answer to an appropriate degree of accuracy.

   a A carton of milk contains 580 ml. The size of the carton is increased by 28%. How much milk does it now contain?

   b A piece of wood is 7.8 m long. It is reduced in length by 37%. What is the new length of the piece of wood?

   c A lorry carries a load of sand that weighs 2.8 tonnes. The lorry loses 2.3% of its load as it travels. What mass of sand does the lorry now carry?

   d A kitten weighs 300 g. After a month the kitten has grown by 73.2%. What is the new mass of the kitten?

4 Samir can buy a Games Console for one cash payment of £189, or pay a deposit of 24% and then 12 equal monthly payments of £12. Which is the better option?
Explain and justify your answer.

This spread will show you how to:

- Calculate percentage increase and decrease using a range of methods
- Calculate simple and compound interest

Keywords

Appreciation
Compound
  interest
Decrease
Depreciation
Increase
Percentage
Simple interest

When you borrow money from a bank or building society you have to pay interest. When you save money, you earn interest.

People sometimes choose to have the interest they earn at the end of each year taken out of their bank account. This is called **simple interest**.

- To calculate simple interest you multiply the interest earned at the end of the year by the number of years.

Example

Calculate the simple interest on investing £7650 for 3 years at an interest rate of 4.3%.

Interest each year = 4.3% of £7650 = $\frac{4.3}{100} \times 7650$
$= 0.043 \times 7650 = £328.95$

Total amount of simple interest after 3 years = $3 \times £328.95$
$= £986.85$

Don't forget to estimate:
4.3% of £7650
$\approx$ 5% of £7000
$= 10\%$ of £7000 $\div$ 2
$= £700 \div 2$
$= £350$

People usually choose to leave the interest in their bank account. This is called **compound interest**.

- To calculate compound interest you work out the amount of money in the bank account at the end of each year.

At the end of the next year the interest is paid on **all** the money.

Example

Ben puts £1200 into a bank account. Each year the bank pays a rate of interest of 10%. Work out the amount of money in Ben's bank account after 3 years.

Year 1 amount	Year 2 amount	Year 3 amount
= (100 + 10)% of £1200	= 110% of £1320	= 110% of £1452
= 110% × £1200	= 1.1 × £1320 = £1452	= 1.1 × £1452 = £1597.20
= 1.1 × £1200 = £1320		

- Some items grow in value over time. This is called **appreciation**.
- Other items reduce in value over time. This is called **depreciation**.

Example

A company buys a van at a cost of £15 000. Each year the van depreciates in value by 17%. Work out the value of the van after 2 years.

End of Year 1 amount	End of Year 2 amount
= (100 − 17)% of £15 000	= 83% of £12 450
= 83% × £15 000	= 0.83 × £12 450 = £10 333.50
= 0.83 × £15 000 = £12 450	

1 **a** Louise puts £8750 into a bank account. The bank pays interest of 7% on any money she keeps in the account for 1 year. Calculate the interest received by Louise at the end of the year.

   b Jermaine puts £45 800 into a savings account. The account pays interest of 5.1% on any money he keeps in the account for 1 year. Calculate the interest received by Jermaine at the end of the year.

   c Vicky takes out a loan of £24 800 for 1 year from a building society. The building society charges interest on the loan of 7.6% for 1 year. Calculate the total amount of money that Vicky must pay back at the end of the year.

2 Calculate the simple interest paid on £13 582

   a at an interest rate of 5% for 2 years

   b at an interest rate of 13% for 5 years

   c at an interest rate of 4.9% for 7 years

   d at an interest rate of 4.85% for 4 years.

3 Calculate the simple interest paid on

   a an amount of £3950 at an interest rate of 10% for 2 years

   b an amount of £6525 at an interest rate of 8.5% for 2 years

   c an amount of £325 at an interest rate of 2.4% for 7 years

   d an amount of £239.70 at an interest rate of 4.25% for 13 years.

4 **a** Nanette buys an antique wall covering for £430. At the end of the year the wall covering has risen in value by 11%. Calculate the new value of the wall covering.

   b A new car costs £15 500. After 1 year the car depreciates in value by 9%. What is the value of the car after 1 year?

   c A house is bought for £128 950. After 1 year, the house increases in value by 16%. What is the new value of the house?

5 **a** Patricia puts £8000 into a bank account. Each year the bank pays a compound interest rate of 5%. Work out the amount of money in Patricia's bank account after 2 years.

   b Simone puts £12 500 into a savings account. Each year the building society pays a compound interest rate of 6.5%. Work out the amount of money in Simone's bank account after 3 years.

   c Antonio invests £3400 into a Super Saver account. Each year the account pays a compound interest rate of 6.2%. Work out the amount of money in Antonio's account after 4 years.

Exam review

Key objectives

- Calculate a given fraction of a given quantity
- Select and use suitable strategies and techniques to solve problems and word problems, including those involving ratio, proportion, fractions and percentages

1 Courtney received £50 for his birthday.

He spent $\frac{1}{4}$ of this money on a CD.

He spent $\frac{2}{5}$ of this money on a new t-shirt.

He put the remaining money into his bank account.

a Work out the fraction of his birthday money that
Courtney saved. (3)

b Write the amount of money, in pounds, that Courtney put
into his bank account. (2)

2 Ben bought a car for £12 000.

Each year the value of the car depreciated by 10%.

Work out the value of the car two years after he bought it. (3)

(Edexcel Ltd., 2003)

This unit will show you how to

- Draw and produce, using paper and ICT, pie charts for categorical data, and diagrams for data, including line graphs for time series and frequency diagrams
- Interpret a wide range of graphs and diagrams and draw conclusions
- Compare distributions and make inferences
- Look at data to find patterns and exceptions
- Calculate the mean, median, mode and range of small sets of discrete data
- Have a basic understanding of correlation, including lines of best fit

Before you start ...

You should be able to answer these questions.

Review

1 Find the value of each angle x.

Unit S2

a   **b**   **c**

  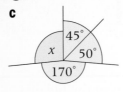

2 Calculate

Unit N2

  a $360 \div 12$ **b** $360 \div 18$
  c $360 \div 24$ **d** $360 \div 36$
  e $360 \div 120$

3 Find the mean, mode, median and range of

Unit D4

  a 4, 8, 10, 24, 24.
  b 2, 2, 8, 12.
  c 5, 3, 8, 16, 3.

4 Give the coordinates of

Key stage 3

  a point A
  b point B

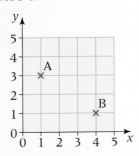

Diagrams and charts

This spread will show you how to:

● Interpret a wide range of graphs and diagrams and draw conclusions

Keywords
Bar chart
Bar-line chart
Pictogram
Pie chart
Sector

You can interpret data from a variety of diagrams.

Pictograms use symbols to represent the size of each category.

Food	◯ ◯ ◖
Heat	◯
Rent	◯ ◯ ◯ ◯ ◖

Key: ◯ represents £10

Bar charts use horizontal or vertical bars to represent the frequencies.

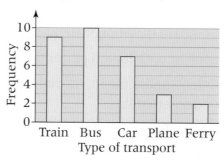

Notice the gaps between the bars.

Bar-line charts use vertical lines to represent numerical data.

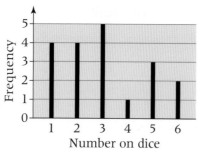

Pie charts use sectors of a circle to represent the size of each category.

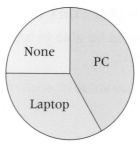

The size of the **sector** is proportional to the frequency.

The pie chart shows 24 hours in the life of a Y11 student. The student spends 8 hours sleeping.
Calculate

a the value of x
b the fraction of time spent sleeping
c the percentage of time spent watching TV
d the number of hours for each category.

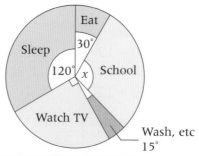

a $360° - (120° + 30° + 15° + 90°) = 105°$

b $\frac{120}{360} = \frac{1}{3}$

c $\frac{90}{360} = \frac{1}{4} = 25\%$

d 8 hours represent 120°
  1 hour represents 15°
  Eat $30 \div 15 = 2$ hours
  School $105 \div 15 = 7$ hours
  Wash etc $15 \div 15 = 1$ hour
  Watch TV $90 \div 15 = 6$ hours

The angles at a point add to 360°.

Check:
2 + 7 + 1 + 6 + 8
= 24 hours

1 A survey of the number of lorries passing through four villages each day is shown in the pictogram.

    a Calculate the number of lorries passing daily through

        i Abbey   **ii** Batty   **iii** Cotton   **iv** Ditty

        v all four villages taken together.

    b Which village should be considered for a bypass?

Abbey	🚚 🚚 🚚
Batty	🚚 🚚
Cotton	🚚 🚚 🚚 🚚 🚚
Ditty	🚚

Key: 🚚 represents 8 lorries

2 Travel insurance prices are shown on the bar chart.

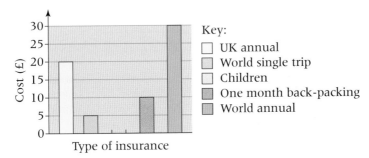

Key:
- ☐ UK annual
- ☐ World single trip
- ☐ Children
- ☐ One month back-packing
- ☐ World annual

    a State the cost of

        i annual insurance in the UK

        ii one month back-packing insurance.

    b Who is offered free travel insurance?

    c Suzie plans to make four trips abroad during the year.
She can either buy World Single Trip insurance each time or World Annual insurance.
Which is her cheaper option? Show your working.

3 The bar-line chart shows the number of tickets bought by 10 people.

    a State the number of people who bought

        i 5 tickets   **ii** 4 tickets.

    b Calculate the total number of tickets that were bought by the 10 people.

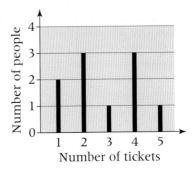

4 The pie chart shows the year groups for 120 children. Calculate

    a the value of x

    b the angle that represents one child

    c the number of children in

        i Year 4   **ii** Year 5   **iii** Year 6.

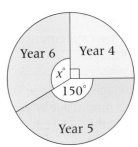

This spread will show you how to:

- Interpret a wide range of graphs and diagrams and draw conclusions
- Compare distributions and make inferences
- Look at data to find patterns and exceptions

Keywords
Comparative bar
 chart
Frequency
 polygon
Grouped
Histogram
Modal

You can interpret **grouped** continuous data from a **histogram** and a **frequency polygon**.

The lengths of eight pieces of string are shown in the histogram.

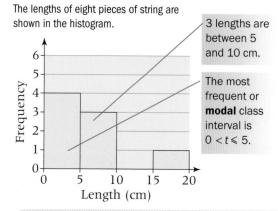

3 lengths are between 5 and 10 cm.

The most frequent or **modal** class interval is $0 < t \leqslant 5$.

The same eight lengths are shown in a frequency polygon.

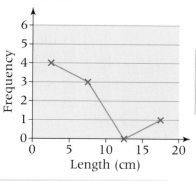

The points are plotted at the midpoints of the class intervals.

- You can interpret two sets of data from a **comparative bar chart**.

This shows the attendances of boys and girls on Wednesday and Friday.

- Overall attendance is the same on both days.
- Girls' attendance is better than boys'.

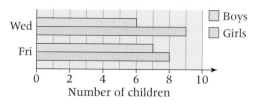

Boys
Girls

Example

The frequency polygons show the age distribution for the population of two villages.

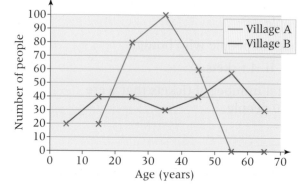

Village A
Village B

Make two statements to compare the distribution of ages in the two villages.

- The ages in village B are more spread out.
- The modal age is younger in village A than in village B.
  Village A: 35 years   Village B: 55 years

1   The bar chart shows the number of
    minutes per day that men and women
    spend on household chores.
    Which household chore do

    a men and   **b** women spend

    i the most time doing

    ii the least time doing?

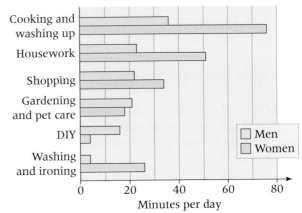

Division of household chores, 2000/01 UK

Source: www.statistics.gov.uk

2   The populations of four countries in 1994 and 2004
    are shown in the bar chart.

    a State the population of

    i Bangladesh in 1994

    ii India in 2004.

    b Which country shows the largest increase from
    1994 to 2004?

    c Which country's population is approximately the
    same in 1994 and 2004?

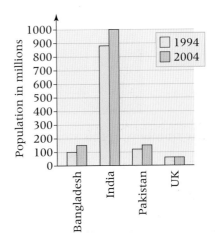

3   The histogram shows the best distances, in metres, that
    athletes threw a javelin in a competition.

    a State the number of athletes who threw the javelin

    i between 65 and 70 metres

    ii between 80 and 85 metres.

    b In which class interval was the winner?

    c What is the modal class interval?

    d Calculate the total number of athletes who threw a javelin.

4   The lengths of the long jumps for men and
    women are shown in the frequency polygon.
    Make two statements to compare the
    distributions of the length of long jumps for
    the men and women.

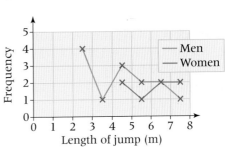

More stem-and-leaf diagrams

This spread will show you how to:

- Interpret a wide range of graphs and diagrams and draw conclusions
- Calculate the mean, median, mode and range of small sets of discrete data.

- You can interpret numerical data from a **stem-and-leaf diagram**.

Maggie used a stem-and-leaf diagram to record the number of minutes she spent reading each day for two weeks.

This stem-and-leaf diagram is **ordered** as the data is in numerical order.

90	7		
80	3	4	9
70	0	4	8
60	3	3	6
50	6	9	
40	3	8	

stem   leaf

Key: | 80 | 7 | means 87

This means 97.

This means 70.

Always give the key.

The numbers in this stem-and-leaf diagram are

43, 48, 56, 59, 63, 63, 66, 70, 74, 78, 83, 84, 89, 97.

- You can calculate the mean, mode, median and range from a stem-and-leaf diagram.

The weights to the nearest tenth of a kilogram, of eight parcels are shown in the diagram. Calculate

3.0	0		
2.0	5		
1.0	3	4	9
0.0	7	8	8

Key:

| 1.0 | 3 | means 1.3 kg

a the mean
b the mode
c the median
d the range.

a Mean = $(0.7 + 0.8 + 0.8 + 1.3 + 1.4 + 1.9 + 2.5 + 3.0) \div 8$
       = 1.55 kg

b Mode = 0.8 kg, the most common weight

c Median = $(1.3 + 1.4) \div 2$ (2 middle numbers)
         = 1.35 kg

d Range = 3.0 − 0.7   (highest value − lowest value)
       = 2.3

1 The attendances of the nine Year 11 classes one Friday afternoon are shown in the stem-and-leaf diagram.

10	0 6
20	2 2 4 6 8 9
30	0

Key:

| 20 | 4 | means 24 students |

a Write out the nine attendances in numerical order, smallest first.

b Calculate

    i the mean   **ii** the mode   **iii** the median   **iv** the range.

2 The test marks of 20 students are shown.

31 17 43 19 25 12   7 40 25 21
11 32 37 25 15   9 18 41 23 17

0	
10	
20	
30	
40	

Key:

| 20 | 5 | means 25 marks |

a Copy and complete the stem-and-leaf diagram.

b Redraw the diagram to give an ordered stem-and-leaf diagram.

c Calculate

    i the mean   **ii** the mode   **iii** the median   **iv** the range.

3 The times, to the nearest second, for 15 athletes to run 800 m are shown in the stem-and-leaf diagram. Calculate

110	4 6 9
120	0 0 4 5 6 7
130	1 5 6
140	0 2 5

Key:

| 120 | 5 | means 125 seconds |

a the mean

b the mode

c the median

d the range.

4 The speedway scores of a team during one season are shown in the stem-and-leaf diagram.

30	3 4
40	1 1 4 4 5 6 7 9 9 9
50	0 2 7
60	0

Key:

| 40 | 5 | means 45 points |

a Calculate the modal score.

b Calculate the number of scores shown in the diagram.

c If one score is chosen at random, calculate the probability that it is 50 or over.

5 Ten competitors achieve the following distances, measured in centimetres, in the High Jump and the Long Jump.

High Jump

180	1 3 2 5
190	1 6 7 7
200	3 7

Key:

| 190 | 6 | means 196 cm |

Long Jump

730	7 8
740	0 3 6 7 9
750	0 2

Key:

| 740 | 3 | means 743 cm |

a One competitor was injured and could not take part in one of the events. Which event did he miss?

b By calculating the range for each event, make a comparison between the two different events.

More time series graphs

This spread will show you how to:

● Interpret a wide range of graphs and diagrams and draw conclusions

Keywords

Horizontal
Line graph
Time series
   graph
Trend

● You can interpret data as it changes with time from a **time series graph**.

The percentage of adults who smoke cigarettes is shown by the **line graph**.

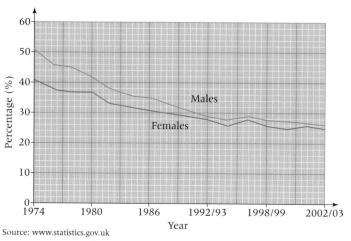

Source: www.statistics.gov.uk

Time is always the **horizontal** axis.

You can see the **trend** from the graphs.

● The percentage of males who smoke is always greater than the percentage of females who smoke.

● The percentages of males and females who smoke are decreasing.

Example

The monthly average temperatures in Madrid and Grand Canaria are shown in the line graphs.

a Which place is usually hotter in April?

b What is the average temperature in Madrid in October?

c In which three months is it colder in Grand Canaria than in Madrid?

d Calculate the range of the temperatures for Grand Canaria.

e Calculate the range of the temperatures for Madrid.

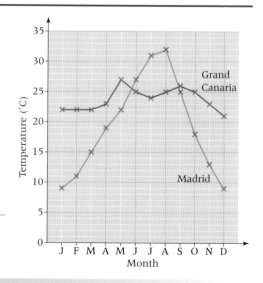

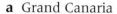

a Grand Canaria

b 18 °C

c June, July, August

d 27 − 21 = 6 °C

e 32 − 9 = 23 °C.

The answers to parts **d** and **e** show that the temperature is more variable in Madrid than in Grand Canaria.

1 The line graph shows the temperature, in °C, over 24 hours.

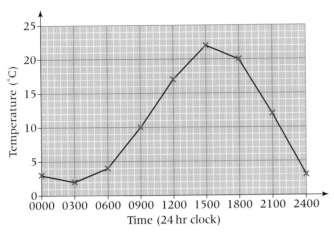

a What time in the morning was the temperature 10 °C recorded?

b What was the maximum temperature recorded? When was the maximum temperature recorded?

c What was the minimum temperature recorded? When was the minimum temperature recorded?

d Calculate the range of the recorded temperatures.

2 The number of passengers, in billions, for local buses and for trains is shown on the line graphs.
Give two observations about the trend shown on the graphs.

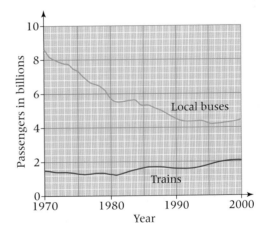

3 The graphs show the expected demand for energy and the supply of fossil fuels for the world.

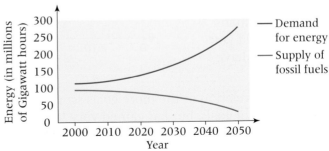

a Describe the trend for the demand for energy.

b Describe the trend for the supply of fossil fuels.

c What will be needed by 2050 to solve this problem?

This spread will show you how to:

● Have a basic understanding of correlation, including lines of best fit

Keywords

Correlation
Line of best fit
Relationship
Scatter graph
Variable

● You can interpret two sets of data that have been drawn on a **scatter graph**.

If the points are roughly in a straight line, there is a **relationship** or **correlation** between the two **variables**.

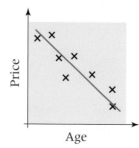

Positive correlation

Height / Weight

As height increases, weight also increases.

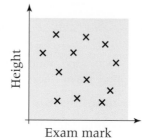

Negative correlation

Price / Age

As the age of a car increases, the price decreases.

No correlation

Height / Exam mark

There is no relationship between height and exam mark.

The red straight line is the **line of best fit**.

You cannot draw a line of best fit for no correlation.

Example

The scatter graph shows the number of goals scored by 21 football teams in a season plotted against the number of points gained.

a Describe the relationship between the goals scored and the number of points.

b Describe the goals and points for team A.

c If a team scored 45 goals, how many points would you expect it to have?

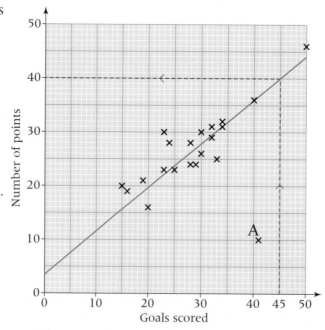

A line of best fit does not have to pass through (0, 0).

a Positive correlation or the more goals scored the more points gained.

b Scored lots of goals, but has gained very few points.

c See the graph: 45 goals gives 40 points.

1 Describe the type of correlation for each scatter graph.

a

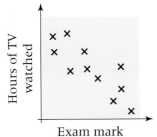

b

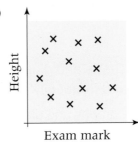

c

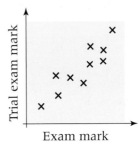

2 Describe the points A, B, C, D and E on each scatter graph.

a

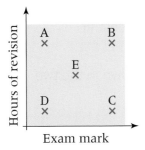

b

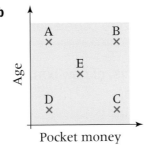

c

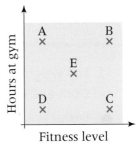

3 The graph shows the marks in two papers achieved by nine students.

Use the line of best fit to estimate

a the Paper 2 mark for a student who scored 13 in Paper 1

b the Paper 1 mark for a student who scored 23 in Paper 2.

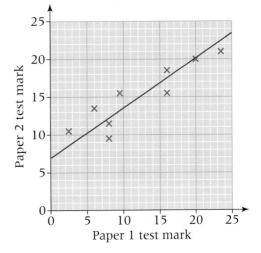

4 The table shows the age and diameter, in centimetres, of trees in a forest.

Age (years)	10	27	6	22	15	25	11	16	21	19
Diameter (cm)	20	78	9	65	38	74	25	44	59	50

Use 2 cm to represent 10 centimetres on the horizontal axis, numbered 0 to 80. Use 2 cm to represent 5 years on the vertical axis, numbered 0 to 30.

a Draw a scatter diagram to show the information.

b State the type of correlation between the age and diameter of the trees.

c Draw a line of best fit.

d If the diameter of a tree is 55 cm, estimate the age of the tree.

D5

Exam review

Key objectives

- Draw and produce pie charts and diagrams for data, including line graphs for time series and frequency diagrams
- Interpret a wide range of graphs and diagrams and draw conclusions
- Calculate the mean, range and median of small discrete data sets
- Appreciate that correlation is a measure of the strength of the association between two variables and distinguish between positive, negative and zero correlation using lines of best fit

1 The weights, in kilograms, of new-born babies are shown in the two stem-and-leaf diagrams:

Boys

1.0	
2.0	1 3 4 4 5 6
3.0	0 1 2

Girls

1.0	9
2.0	0 3 3 6 6
3.0	0

Key:

1.0	1

means 1.1 kg

a Calculate the median and range for   (4)

i the boys   **ii** the girls.

b Make two comparisons between the distributions.   (2)

2 The table shows the number of pages and the weight, in grams, for 10 books:

Number of pages	80	130	100	140	115	90	160	140	105	150
Weight (g)	160	270	180	290	230	180	320	270	210	300

a Copy and complete the scatter graph to show the information in the table.
The first six points have been done for you.   (1)

b For these books, describe the relationship between the number of pages and the weight of a book.   (1)

c Draw a line of best fit on the scatter diagram.   (1)

d Use your line of best fit to estimate

i the number of pages in a book of weight 280 g.

ii the weight of a book with 120 pages.   (2)

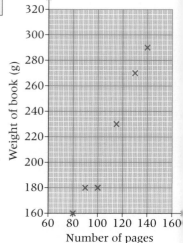

(Edexcel Ltd., 2004)

This unit will show you how to

- Find the surface area of simple shapes using the area formulae for triangles and rectangles
- Calculate the volume of right prisms
- Convert between length measures, area measures including cm^2 and m^2, and volume measures including cm^3 and m^3
- Understand and use compound measures including speed
- Use formulae from Mathematics and other subjects
- Understand the difference between formulae for perimeter, area and volume, considering dimensions

Before you start ...

You should be able to answer these questions.

Review

1 Calculate the area of each shape.

Unit S1

a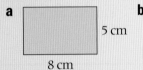
5 cm
8 cm

b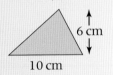
6 cm
10 cm

c
6 cm $\pi = 3.14$

2 Calculate the volume of the cuboid, stating the units of your answer.

Unit S1

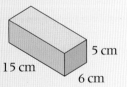
5 cm
15 cm
6 cm

3 Evaluate.

Unit N1

a 25×10 **b** 63×100

c 4.1×10 **d** 2.5×100

e 3.5×1000 **f** $40 \div 10$

g $56 \div 10$ **h** $4000 \div 100$

i $410 \div 100$ **j** $5200 \div 1000$

4 Match the quantity with the units.

Unit S1

a length   **b** area   **c** volume

i cm^3 **ii** cm   **iii** cm^2

This spread will show you how to:
- Find the surface area of simple shapes using the area formulae for triangles and rectangles

Keywords
Faces
Net
Surface area

When you unfold a shape its **net** is formed.

 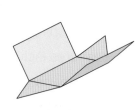 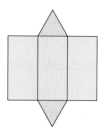

The area of the net is called the surface area.

- The **surface area** of a 3-D shape is the total area of its **faces**.

Units of area are cm².

A cuboid has 6 faces. They are in pairs.

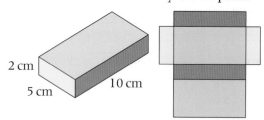

The surface area is

$2 \times$ red $= 2 \times 2 \times 10 = 40$ cm²
$2 \times$ green $= 2 \times 10 \times 5 = 100$ cm²
$2 \times$ yellow $= 2 \times 5 \times 2 = 20$ cm²
surface area $= 160$ cm²

Example

A tin of tomato soup is shown. The diameter of the circle is 8 cm and the height is 10 cm. The label fits exactly round the tin.

Calculate the area of the label.
Give your answer to a suitable degree of accuracy.

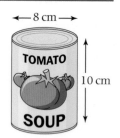

←8 cm→

10 cm

$\pi = 3.14...$

If the label is unfurled, the length is the same as the circumference.

The label is a rectangle.

Circumference of a circle $= \pi \times d$

←— $\pi \times 8$ cm —→

10 cm

Area of label $= \pi \times 8 \times 10$
$= 251.327\ 41$
$= 251$ cm² (to nearest whole number)

1 A 4 cm by 6 cm by 8 cm cuboid is shown. Calculate

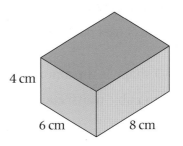

 a the area of the red rectangle

 b the area of the orange rectangle

 c the area of the green rectangle

 d the surface area of the cuboid.

2 Calculate the surface area of these cuboids.

> State the units of your answer.

a

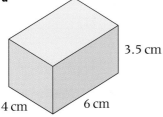

3 cm
8 cm
4 cm

b

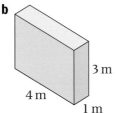

3 m
4 m
1 m

c

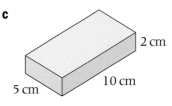

2 cm
10 cm
5 cm

d

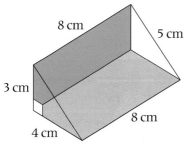

3.5 cm
4 cm
6 cm

e

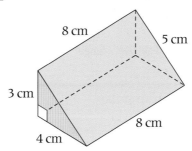

6 cm
7 cm
4 cm

3 Two views of the same triangular prism are shown.

8 cm
5 cm
3 cm
8 cm
4 cm

8 cm
5 cm
3 cm
8 cm
4 cm

Calculate the area of the

 a red rectangle   **b** grey rectangle   **c** green rectangle

 d orange triangle   **e** the surface area of the triangular prism.

4 Calculate the surface area of these shapes.

a

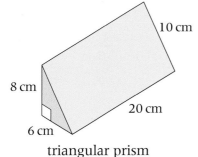

10 cm
8 cm
20 cm
6 cm

triangular prism

b

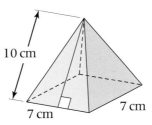

10 cm
7 cm
7 cm

square-based pyramid

DID YOU KNOW?

The Great Pyramid of Giza was 145.75 m tall with four 229 m long bases when it was built. That's a surface area of 66 753.5 m^2!

This spread will show you how to:

- Calculate the volume of right prisms

Keywords
Cross-section
Cubic centimetre (cm³)
Cubic metre (m³)
Prism
Volume

The **volume** of a 3-D shape is the amount of space it takes up.

Volume is measured in cubic units: cubic centimetres (cm³), cubic metres (m³).

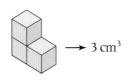 → 3 cm³

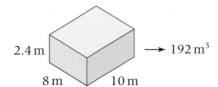 → 192 m³

8 m · 10 m

The ³ in cm³ shows there are 3 dimensions in a cube: length, width and height.

- **Volume of a cuboid = length × width × height**

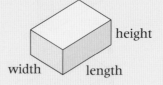

height / width / length

A **prism** is a 3-D shape with the same **cross-section** throughout its length.

cross section 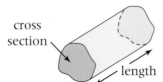 length

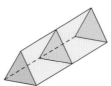

A cuboid is a prism.

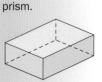

- **Volume of a prism = area of cross-section × length**

Example

Calculate the volume of this triangular prism. State the units of your answer.

Area of triangle $= \frac{1}{2} \times 4 \times 2 = 4$ m²
Volume of prism $=$ area of triangle $\times 8$
$\qquad = 4 \times 8 = 32$ m³

2 m / 4 m / 8 m

- **Volume of cylinder = area of circle × height**

A cylinder is a prism with a circular cross-section.

Example

Calculate the volume of this cylinder.

$\leftarrow$ 10 cm $\rightarrow$

4 cm

Do not round intermediate workings.

Area of circle $= \pi \times r^2$
$\qquad = \pi \times 5^2$
$\qquad = 78.539\ 816$

Volume of cylinder $= 78.539\ 816 \times 4$
$\qquad\qquad = 314.159\ 265$
$\qquad\qquad = 314$ cm³ (to nearest whole number)

1 Calculate the volume of these cuboids.

Give the units of your answers.

a 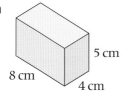 5 cm, 8 cm, 4 cm

b 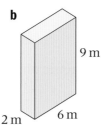 9 m, 2 m, 6 m

c 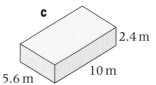 2.4 m, 10 m, 5.6 m

2 Calculate the volume of these cuboids.

a 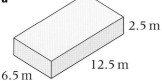 2.5 m, 12.5 m, 6.5 m

b 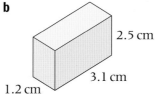 2.5 cm, 3.1 cm, 1.2 cm

c 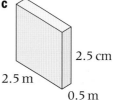 2.5 cm, 2.5 m, 0.5 m

3 Calculate the area of cross-section and the volume for each prism.

a 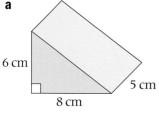 6 cm, 5 cm, 8 cm

b 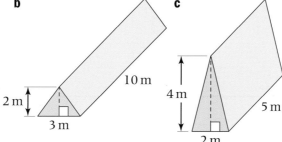 10 m, 2 m, 3 m

c 4 m, 5 m, 2 m

d 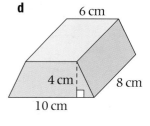 6 cm, 4 cm, 8 cm, 10 cm

4 Calculate the areas of these circles. State the units of your answers.

In questions 4 and 5, give your answers to a suitable degree of accuracy.

a 4 cm

b 3 cm

c 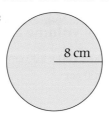 8 cm

d 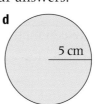 5 cm

5 Calculate the volumes of these cylinders.

a 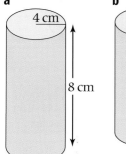 4 cm, 8 cm

b 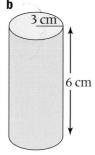 3 cm, 6 cm

c 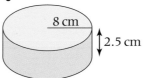 8 cm, 2.5 cm

d 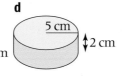 5 cm, 2 cm

2-D and 3-D measures

This spread will show you how to:

- Convert between length measures, area measures including cm² and m², and volume measures including cm³ and m³

Keywords
Area
Cubic centimetre
Cubic metre
Litre
Square centimetre
Square metre
Volume

You should know these relationships between the metric units of length:

- 1 cm = 10 mm

$$\times 10$$
cm $\rightarrow$ cm
$$\div 10$$

0   10
mm |++++++++|

cm |————|
0   1

- 1 m = 100 cm

$$\times 100$$
m $\rightarrow$ cm
$$\div 100$$

←100 cm→
←1 m→

- 1 km = 1000 m

$$\times 1000$$
km $\rightarrow$ cm
$$\div 1000$$

The relationships between the metric units of area are:

- 1 cm² = 10 × 10 mm²
  = 100 mm²

$$\times 10^2$$
cm² $\rightarrow$ mm²
$$\div 10^2$$

- 1 m² = 100 × 100 cm²
  = 10 000 cm²

$$\times 100^2$$
m² $\rightarrow$ cm²
$$\div 100^2$$

- 1 km² = 1000 × 1000 m²
  = 1 000 000 m²

$$\times 1000^2$$
km² $\rightarrow$ m²
$$\div 1000^2$$

Example

Change 5 m² to cm².

$5 \text{ m}^2 = 5 \times 10\,000 \text{ cm}^2$
$= 50\,000 \text{ cm}^2$

You expect a larger number, so multiply.

The relationship between metric units of **volume** are

- 1 cm³ = 10 × 10 × 10 mm³
  = 1000 mm³

- 1 m³ = 100 × 100 × 100 cm³
  = 1 000 000 cm³

$$\times 10^3$$
cm³ $\rightarrow$ mm³
$$\div 10^3$$

$$\times 100^3$$
m³ $\rightarrow$ cm³
$$\div 100^3$$

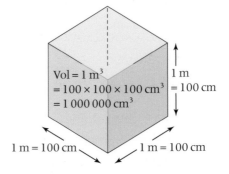

Vol = 1 m³
= 100 × 100 × 100 cm³
= 1 000 000 cm³

1 m = 100 cm

1 m = 100 cm   1 m = 100 cm

Example

Change 6 000 000 cm³ to cubic metres (m³).

$6\,000\,000 \text{ cm}^3 = 6\,000\,000 \div 1\,000\,000 \text{ m}^3$
$= 6 \text{ m}^3$

You expect a smaller number, so divide.

1 Convert these metric measurements of length.

  a 180 cm to mm   **b** 45 mm to cm   **c** 350 cm to m

  d 2000 m to km   **e** 3500 m to km   **f** 4500 mm to m

  g 85 cm to m   **h** 2500 mm to cm   **i** 2500 mm to m

  j 800 m to km

2 Here are two identical rectangles, A and B.

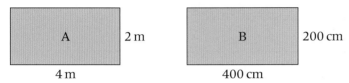

  A 2 m   B 200 cm

  4 m   400 cm

  a Calculate the area of rectangle A in m².

  b Calculate the area of rectangle B in cm².

3 **a** Calculate the area of this rectangle in m².

  b Convert your answer to cm².

  3 m

  8 m

4 Convert these areas to mm².

  a 4 cm²   **b** 7.3 cm²   **c** 10.9 cm²

  d 2.5 cm²   **e** 400 cm²

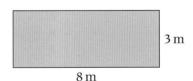

cm² $\xrightarrow{\times 10^2}$ mm²

$\xleftarrow{\div 10^2}$

$10^2 = 100$

5 Convert these areas to cm².

  a 600 mm²   **b** 1200 mm²   **c** 850 mm²

  d 6500 mm²   **e** 10 000 mm²

6 Convert these areas to m².

  a 40 000 cm²   **b** 85 000 cm²   **c** 1 000 000 cm²

  d 125 000 cm²   **e** 5000 cm²

m² $\xrightarrow{\times 100^2}$ cm²

$\xleftarrow{\div 100^2}$

$100^2 = 10\ 000$

7 Convert these areas to cm².

  a 5 m²   **b** 10 m²   **c** 6.5 m²

  d 7.75 m²   **e** 0.6 m²

8 Convert these areas to km².

  a 4 000 000 m²   **b** 18 000 000 m²

  c 500 000 m²   **d** 1 500 000 m²

km² $\xrightarrow{\times 1000^2}$ m²

$\xleftarrow{\div 1000^2}$

$1000^2 = 1$ million

9 Convert these volumes to litres.

  a 1 m³   **b** 6 m³   **c** 7.5 m³

1 m³ = 1000 litres

Compound measures

This spread will show you how to:

● Understand and use compound measures including speed

Keywords
Density
Distance
Mass
Speed
Time
Volume

Speed measures how fast something is moving.

Speed can be measured in metres per second (m/s), miles per hour (mph) or kilometres per hour (km/h).

● Speed $(S) = \dfrac{\text{Distance travelled } (D)}{\text{Time taken } (T)}$

Example

Calculate the average speed of a car that travels 50 miles in 2 hours. State the units of your answer.

$$\text{Speed} = \frac{\text{Distance travelled}}{\text{Time taken}} = \frac{50}{2} = 25 \text{ mph}$$

25 mph is the average speed of the car.

You can use this triangle to calculate speed, distance or time.

$\text{Speed} = \dfrac{\text{Distance}}{\text{Time}}$ $\text{Distance} = \text{Speed} \times \text{Time}$ $\text{Time} = \dfrac{\text{Distance}}{\text{Speed}}$

Cover up the quantity you want to calculate.

Example

James walks at 4 km per hour for 30 minutes. How far does he walk? State the units of your answer.

$\text{Distance} = \text{Speed} \times \text{Time}$
$\qquad\quad = 4 \times \tfrac{1}{2} = 2 \text{ km}$

Notice the different units of minutes and hours.

30 minutes $= \tfrac{1}{2}$ hour

Density is another compound measure.

A cubic metre of concrete is heavier than a cubic metre of feathers.

Density measures how heavy something is 'per unit volume'.

Density can be measured in grams per cubic centimetre, g/cm^3, kilograms per cubic metre, kg/m^3.

● Density $(D) = \dfrac{\text{Mass } (M)}{\text{Volume } (V)}$

You can also write:

$\text{Mass} = \text{Density} \times \text{Volume}$ $\text{Volume} = \dfrac{\text{Mass}}{\text{Density}}$

1 Cheryl takes 4 hours to walk 10 miles. Calculate her average speed, giving the units of your answer.

2 Copy and complete this table.

	Distance (m)	Time (s)	Speed (m/s)
a	40	5	
b	120	8	
c	3000	20	
d	480	12	
e	12.5	5	

3 A cyclist travels at 15 mph for $2\frac{1}{2}$ hours. How many miles is the journey?

4 Copy and complete this table.

	Distance (miles)	Time (hours)	Speed (mph)
a		4	80
b		7	25
c		6	45
d		2.5	20
e		2hr 30mins	50

5 I can usually drive at an average speed of 60 mph on the motorway. How long will a 150-mile journey take?

6 Copy and complete this table.

	Distance (km)	Time (h)	Speed (km/h)
a	160		80
b	20		8
c	70		20
d	27		6
e	100		30

7 A 420-km journey by car takes 6 hours and uses 30 litres of petrol. Calculate

a the average speed   **b** the petrol consumption in km per litre.

8 An athlete runs 1500 m in 4.5 mins. Calculate the athlete's speed in

a metres per minute   **b** metres per second.

9 The density of tin is 7.3 g/cm³.
Calculate the mass of a 5 cm cube of tin.

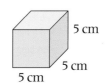

285

This spread will show you how to:

● Understand the difference between formulae for perimeter, area and volume, considering dimensions

Keywords
Area
Dimensions
Formula
Length
Volume

A **length** has 1 **dimension**: length (L).

● You measure a distance in units of length, such as 1 centimetre (1 cm).

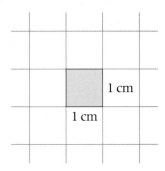

Area has 2 dimensions: length × length (L^2).

● You measure area in squares, such as 1 square centimetre (1 cm^2).

● You measure volume in cubes, such as 1 cubic centimetre (1 cm^3).

Volume has 3 dimensions: length × length × length (L^3).

Numbers such as 2 and π have no dimensions.

You can use dimensions to check **formulae**.

For a rectangle, with sides of length a and b,

Perimeter $= a + b + a + b$
$= 2a + 2b$

Dimensions: number × length + number × length = L + L = 2L = length

Area $= a \times b$

Dimensions: length × length = L^2 = area

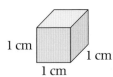

Example

David cannot remember the formula for the volume of a cylinder. He thinks it might be

$2\pi r$ or $\pi(r + h)$ or πr^2 or $\pi r^2 h$

How can he work out which one it might be?

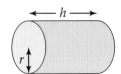

$2\pi r$	number × number × length = L = a length	NO
$\pi(r + h)$	number × (length + length) = L = a length	NO
πr^2	number × length × length = L^2 = an area	NO

π is just a number and has no dimensions.

Exercise S6.5

1 Choose one of length (L), area (L^2), volume (L^3) or none of these (N) for the dimensions of each of these.

   a The surface of a cube   **b** The space inside a sports hall

   c The distance from London to Paris   **d** 6

   e The amount of liquid in a mug   **f** The mass of a guinea pig

   g The height of a mountain   **h** 90 litres

   i The surface covered by a lawn   **j** 45°

   k The perimeter of an airport   **l** 3 metres

   m Your weight   **n** £10

   o 80 kilograms   **p** The surface covered by a wall

   q 4 m^2 **r** π

   s The amount of space inside a car   **t** 9 m^3

2 State whether these expressions represent length (L), area (L^2) or volume (L^3).

   a length × width   **b** length + width + length + width

   c length × width × height   **d** base length × height

   e $\frac{1}{2}$ × base × height   **f** diameter

   g π × diameter   **h** radius

3 One of these formulae gives the volume of a sphere. Which one?

   a $\frac{4}{3} \times \pi \times r$

   b $\frac{4}{3} \times \pi \times r^2$

   c $\frac{4}{3} \times \pi \times r^3$

4 One of these formulae gives the surface area of a cylinder. Which one?

   a $2\pi r + 2\pi h$

   b $2\pi r^2 h$

   c $2\pi r^2 + 2\pi rh$

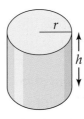

5 One of these formulae gives the volume of a cone. Which one?

   a $\frac{1}{3} rh$

   b $\frac{1}{3} r^2 h$

   c $\frac{1}{3} r + \frac{1}{3} h$

Exam review

Key objectives

- Solve problems involving surface areas and volumes
- Convert between area measures, including square centimetres and square metres, and volume measures, including cubic centimetres and cubic metres
- Understand and use compound measures, including speed and density

1 The letters x, y and z represent lengths.

Choose whether each of the following expressions represent a length, an area or a volume:

a $x + y$ **b** x^3 **c** yz **d** $3x^2 + z^2$ **e** $y(x^2 + yz)$ (5)

2

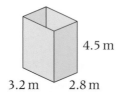

Not drawn to scale

4.5 m

3.2 m   2.8 m

The diagram represents a large tank in the shape of a cuboid.
The tank has a base.
It does not have a top.
The width of the tank is 2.8 metres.
The length of the tank is 3.2 metres.
The height of the tank is 4.5 metres.

The outside of the tank is going to be painted.
1 litre of paint will cover 2.5 m² of the tank.
The cost of paint is £2.99 per litre.

Calculate the cost of the paint needed to paint the outside of the tank.   (5)

(Edexcel Ltd., 2003)

Graphical solutions

This unit will show you how to

- Plot straight line graphs
- Change the subject of an equation
- Recognise the general equation forms of horizontal, vertical and diagonal line graphs
- Understand that parallel lines have the same gradient
- Read x and y values from a graph
- Use graphs to find solutions to equations
- Recognise the form of and plot simple quadratic graphs

Before you start ...

You should be able to answer these questions.

Review

1 Plot these points on a coordinate grid.

  a $(3, 6)$ **b** $(-4, 2)$

  c $(5, -3)$ **d** $(-3, -1)$

Unit A4

2 Copy and complete this table of values for the equation

$$y = 2x + 5$$

x	-2	-1	0	1	2
y					

Unit A4

3 Write the letters of the parallel lines.

  a $y = x$

  b $y = x + 2$

  c $y = 2x$

  d $y = -x$

  e $y = x - 2$

  f $y = x + 4$

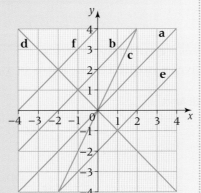

Unit A6

4 Which line in question 3 is the steepest?

Unit A6

5 Rearrange these equations to make y the subject.

  a $2x - y = 5$ **b** $4x + 2y = 8$

Unit A6

This spread will show you how to:
● Plot straight line graphs

Keywords
Explicit
Implicit

● To plot a graph of a function:
  ● Draw up a table of values
  ● Calculate the value of y for each value of x
  ● Draw a suitable grid
  ● Plot the (x, y) pairs and join them with a straight line.

Draw the graph of $y = 3x - 4$.

First construct a table of values.

x	-2	-1	0	1	2
y	-10	-7	-4	-1	2

Then plot the points and draw the line.

Choose four or five values, including negative values and zero.

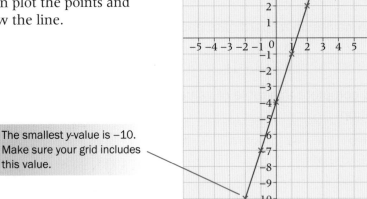

The smallest y-value is -10. Make sure your grid includes this value.

The equation $y = 3x - 4$ gives y **explicitly** in terms of x.
The equation $2x + 3y = 6$ gives y **implicitly** in terms of x.

An **explicit** function has the variables separated by the $=$ sign.
An **implicit** function can have the variables on the same side of the $=$ sign.

● To draw a graph of an implicit function:
  ● Draw up a table of values for $x = 0$ and $y = 0$.

or

  ● Rearrange the equation to make y the subject.

For $2x + 3y = 6$:

x	0	$2x = 6$ $x = 3$
y	$3y = 6$ $y = 2$	0

For $2x + 3y = 6$:

$3y = 6 - 2x$

$y = \dfrac{6 - 2x}{3}$

x	-2	-1	0	1	2
y	$\frac{10}{3}$	$\frac{8}{3}$	2	$\frac{4}{3}$	$\frac{2}{3}$

1 **a** Copy and complete the table of values for $y = 2x + 5$.

x	-3	-1	0	1	3
y	-1			7	

b Draw the graph of $y = 2x + 5$ on a copy of the grid.

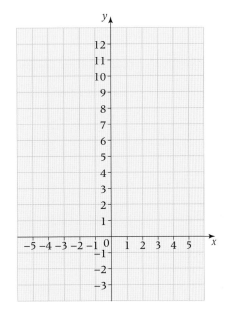

2 Draw the graphs of these functions.

a $y = 3x - 2$ **b** $y = -2x + 4$ **c** $y = \frac{1}{2}x + 3$ **d** $y = 5 - x$

3 Draw the graphs of these functions.

a $x + y = 4$ **b** $2x - y = 3$ **c** $2y + x = 4$ **d** $3y + 6x = 9$

4 Draw the graphs of these functions.

a $y = 5x - 3$ **b** $4y - x = 2$ **c** $y = 3 - 4x$ **d** $2x - 3y = 6$

5 Rearrange these equations to make y the subject. Which is the odd one out?

$y = 2x + \frac{1}{2}$ $2y - 4x = 1$

$4x + 2y = 1$ $8x - 4y = -2$

6 **a** Draw the graph of $y = 3x + 4$.

b Use your graph to find

i the value of y when $x = \frac{1}{2}$ **ii** the value of x when $y = -\frac{1}{2}$.

7 Draw the graphs of these functions on the same axes.

a $y = 2x + 1$ **b** $y = 2x - 2$ **c** $y = 2x + 5$ **d** $y = 2x$

What do you notice?

8 Draw the graphs of these functions on the same axes.

a $y = -x$ **b** $y = -x + 3$ **c** $y = -x - 2$

What do you notice?
Where do you think the graph of $y = -x + 1$ would be on your grid?

The equation of a straight line

This spread will show you how to:

- Recognise the general equation forms of horizontal, vertical and diagonal line graphs

Keywords
Gradient
Intercept
Parallel

Straight lines can be vertical, horizontal or diagonal.

$x = 2$ is a vertical line

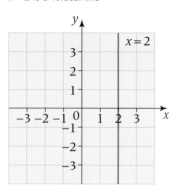

$y = -1$ is a horizontal line

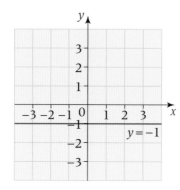

$y = x + 4$ is a diagonal line

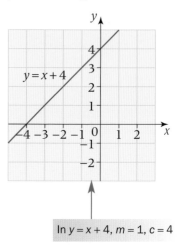

In $y = x + 4$, $m = 1$, $c = 4$

- The general equation for a diagonal line is
  $$y = mx + c$$
  where m and c are numbers.
  m is the **gradient**.
  c is the y-**intercept**.
- The greater the value of m, the steeper the gradient.
- **Parallel** lines have the same gradient.

Example

Match each graph to its equation.

a $x = -2$ **b** $y = 3$
c $y = x + 1$ **d** $y = 2x + 1$
e $y = 2x - 2$

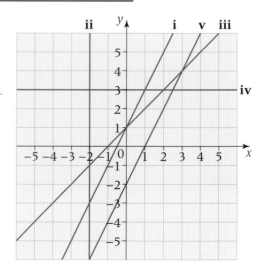

a $x = -2$ is a vertical line, so graph **ii**.
b $y = 3$ is a horizontal line, so graph **iv**.
c $y = x + 1$ has y-intercept $+1$, so could be graph **i** or graph **iii**.
   $y = x + 1$ is less steep than $y = 2x + 1$, so must be graph **iii**.
d $y = 2x + 1$ is the steeper of the graphs with y-intercept 1, so graph **i**.
e $y = 2x - 2$ has y-intercept -2 and is parallel to $y = 2x + 1$, so graph **v**.

Exercise A7.2

1 Match these graphs to their equations.

a $x = 3$

b $y = -1$

c $y = 3x - 1$

d $y = 4x + 3$

e $y = x - 1$

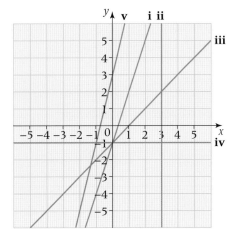

2 Rearrange these equations into the form $y = mx + c$.

a $y - 2x = 3$ **b** $3x + y = 1$ **c** $3x - y = 1$

d $2y - 6x = 10$ **e** $y - 3x - 2 = 0$ **f** $2y + 4x = -3$

3 Write the equations of the parallel lines from question **3**.

4 Which line is steeper:

$$4y - 12x = 16 \qquad \text{or} \qquad 12x - 3y = 9?$$

5 Write these equations of straight lines in order of steepness, starting with the least steep.

a $2x - y + 1 = 0$ **b** $2y - x = 4$ **c** $y - x = 2$

d $2y = 3x + 2$ **e** $3x - y - 1 = 0$.

> First rearrange into the form $y = mx + c$.

6 a Draw the graph of $y = 4x - 3$ on square grid paper.

b Label the point P (1, 1) on your graph.

c Label the point Q (2, 5) on your graph.

d Draw a horizontal line across from P and a vertical line down from Q, until the two lines cross. Label the point where they cross R.

e Work out the ratio $\dfrac{\text{distance QR}}{\text{distance PR}} =$

What do you notice?

f Label the point S (0, −3) on your graph.

g Draw a horizontal line across from S and a vertical line down from Q, until the two lines cross. Label this point T.

h What can you say about the ratio: $\dfrac{\text{distance QT}}{\text{distance PR}}$?

i What is the gradient of the graph?

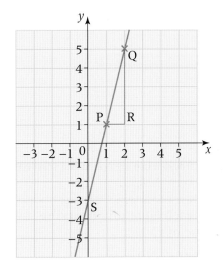

293

Finding solutions from graphs

This spread will show you how to:

- Plot straight line graphs
- Use graphs to find solutions to equations

Keywords

Solution

- All the points on a graph line fit the equation of the line.

  You could extend the graph an infinite distance.

You draw the graph line right to the edge of the grid, to show it continues.

- You can read x and y values from a graph.

Example

Here is the graph of $y = 3x - 2$.

a Find the value of y when $x = \frac{1}{2}$.

b Find the value of x when $y = 7$.

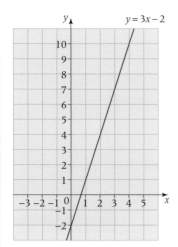

a Draw a horizontal line from $y = 7$ to the graph.
Draw a vertical line from the graph to the x-axis.
Read off the value of x.
When $x = \frac{1}{2}$, $y = -\frac{1}{2}$.

b Draw a vertical line from $x = \frac{1}{2}$ up to the graph.
Draw a horizontal line from the graph to the y-axis.
Read off the value of y.
When $y = 7$, $x = 3$.

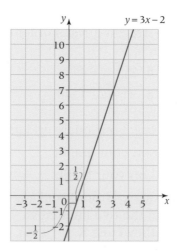

- You can use a graph to find **solutions** to equations.

Example

For each equation, **describe** how you could draw a graph to find the value of x.

You do not need to draw the graph.

a $2x + 6 = 10$

b $-5x + 1 = 11$

a Draw the graph of $y = 2x + 6$.
Read off the x-value when $y = 10$.

b Draw the graph of $y = -5x + 1$.
Read off the x-value when $y = 11$.

1 Here is the graph of $y = -2x + 3$.
Use the graph to find

a the value of y when $x = \frac{1}{2}$

b the value of y when $x = -2\frac{1}{2}$

c the value of x when $y = -1$

d the value of x when $y = 9$.

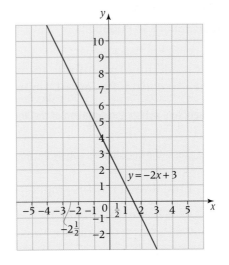

2 a Draw the graph of $y = \frac{1}{2}x + 3$.

b Point P on this line has y-coordinate 7.
Use your line to find the x-coordinate of point P.

c Which of these points lie on the line?
$(2, 4)$ $(3, 7)$ $(-3, 1\frac{1}{2})$ $(-4, 2)$

3 a What graph would you draw to find the solution to the equation
$4x - 7 = -15$?

b Draw the graph and use it to find the value of x.

4 Write down three equations that you could solve using the graph in
question **1**.
Use the graph to find a solution to each of your equations.

5 Draw the graph of $y = 3x + 2$.

a Use your graph to solve

    i $3x + 2 = 6.5$ **ii** $3x + 2 = 17$ **iii** $3x + 2 = -7$.

b You can rewrite the equation
$$3x + 6 = 5$$
as $\qquad\qquad 3x + 2 + 4 = 5$
Subtract 4 from each side: $3x + 2 = 5 - 4 = 1$
So $3x + 2 = 1$ is equivalent to $3x + 6 = 5$.
You can use your graph from part **a** to solve $3x + 2 = 1$.
Rewrite the equation $3x + 7 = 16$
as $3x + 2 = ?$
Find the value of x from your graph.

6 a Draw a graph to solve the equation $2x + 6 = 10$.
What is the value of x?

b Use your graph from **a** to solve
    i $2x + 6 = 14$ **ii** $2x + 6 = -3$ **iii** $2x + 9 = 12$.

This spread will show you how to:

- Use graphs to find solutions to equations

Keywords

Solution

A straight line graph is made up of an infinite number of points.
You normally only need to consider a few of them.

- All the points on a straight line **satisfy** the equation of the line.

- Where two straight lines cross, the coordinates satisfy the equations of both lines.

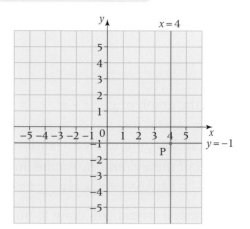

The lines $x = 4$ and $y = -1$ are drawn on this graph.

Every point on the line $x = 4$ has x-coordinate 4.
Every point on the line $y = -1$ has y-coordinate -1.

So the point where they cross is $(4, -1)$.

The point P satisfies both equations: $x = 4$ **and**
$y = -1$. It has coordinates $(4, -1)$.

P is the **solution** to the equations $x = 4$ and $y = -1$.

Example

a Draw the graphs of $y = x + 6$ and $y = 2x$ on the
same pair of axes.
b Write the coordinates of the point where they
cross.
c What can you say about this point?

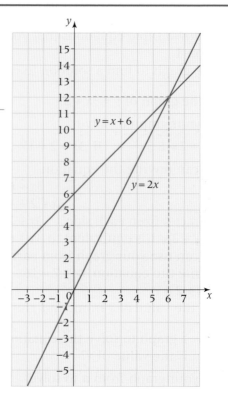

a $y = x + 6$

x	−2	−1	0	1	2
y	4	5	6	7	8

$y = 2x$

x	−2	−1	0	1	2
y	−4	−2	0	2	4

b Graphs cross at $(6, 12)$

c $(6, 12)$ satisfies both equations.

$x = 6$ is the solution to $x + 6 = 12$ **and** $2x = 12$.

1 Write the coordinates of the points where these lines cross.
Draw graphs to check your answers.

   a $x = 2$ and $y = 3$ **b** $x = -1$ and $y = -4$ **c** $x = 3$ and $y = 7$

   d $x = -2$ and $y = -4$ **e** $x = 7$ and $y = -2$ **f** $y = 1$ and $x = 4$

2 For each pair of equations, decide whether the lines will cross.

   a $y = 2x + 1$ and $y = 4x + 2$ **b** $y = 3$ and $y = x + 1$

   c $y = 3x + 2$ and $y = 3x - 1$ **d** $y = x$ and $y = -x$

> Consider the gradient of each line.

3 **a** Draw graphs of the pairs of lines from question **2** that cross.

   b For each pair, write the coordinates of the point where the lines cross.

4 **a** Draw the graphs of $y = -x + 2$ and $y = 2x - 1$ on the same axes.

   b Write the coordinates of the point where the two lines cross.

   c Does the point $(1, 2)$ satisfy both of these equations? Explain how you know.

5 **a** Draw the graphs of $y = 2x - 4$ and $y = x - 1$ on the same axes.

   b Write the coordinates of the point where they cross.

6 **a** Draw the graphs of these two equations on the same axes:

      $x + 2y = 8$ $x - y = 2$

   b Where the two lines cross, the x and y values satisfy both these equations.
Write these x and y values.

7 Jenny buys 2 cakes and 3 sandwiches. The total cost is £8.
She writes this as an equation:

      $2x + 3y = 8$

where x is the cost of a cake and y is the cost of a sandwich.
Tim buys 5 cakes and 2 sandwiches. The total cost is £9.

   a Copy and complete this equation for Tim:

      $5\square + \square y = \square$

   b Draw the graph of $2x + 3y = 8$.

   c Draw the graph for Tim's equation on the same axes.

   d Write the coordinates of the point where the two lines cross.

   e The x-coordinate of the point where the two lines cross gives the cost of a cake in pounds (£). How much does a cake cost?

   f How much does a sandwich cost?

Graphs of quadratic functions

This spread will show you how to:

● Recognise the form of and plot simple quadratic graphs

Keywords

Quadratic
Solution

A **quadratic** function includes a 'squared' term, for example x^2.

These are all quadratic functions:

x^2 $\qquad$ $x^2 + 3$ $\qquad$ $x^2 + 3x - 1$ $\qquad$ $2x - x^2$

● To draw a graph of a quadratic function:
  ● Draw a table of values
  ● Calculate the value of y for each value of x
  ● Draw a suitable grid
  ● Plot the (x, y) pairs and join them with a smooth curve.

Example

Draw the graph of $y = x^2 + 1$.

Draw a table of values.

$y = x^2 + 1$

x	−3	−1	0	1	3
y	10	2	1	2	10

Draw a suitable grid.
Then plot the coordinate pairs
and join the points.

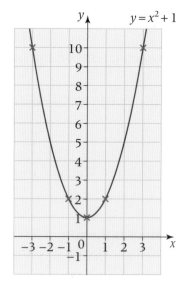

Graphs of quadratic functions have a distinctive shape.

● The graph of a quadratic function
  ● is always a U-shaped curve
  ● is symmetrical about a vertical line
  ● always has a maximum point or a minimum point.

Quadratic graphs can be
upside down:

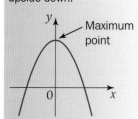

1 a Copy and complete the table of values for $y = x^2$.

x	−3	−1	0	1	3
y					

  b Draw a pair of axes from 0 to 10 on the y-axis and from −5 to +5 on the x-axis.

  c Plot the coordinate pairs on the grid.

  d Join the points with a smooth curve.

2 Draw the graphs of $y = x^2 + 2$ and $y = x^2 + 3$ on the same axes as your graph from question **1**.
What do you notice?

3 Draw the graphs of $y = x^2 - 1$ and $y = x^2 - 3$ on the same pair of axes.
What do you notice?

4 Match these graphs to their equations.

  a $y = x^2 + 1$

  b $y = x^2 - 2$

  c $y = 2 + x^2$

  d $y = x^2 - 1$

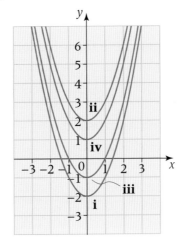

5 a Draw the graph of $y = x^2$ on square grid paper.

  b Draw the line $y = 9$ on your graph.
Write down the coordinates of the points where the graphs cross.

  c Your two pairs of coordinates from part **b** both give **solutions** to the equation $x^2 = 9$.
What are the two x-values that satisfy this equation?

  d Draw the line $y = 6$ on your graph.

  e Use the line $y = 6$ to help you to find two solutions to the equation $x^2 = 6$.

  f What horizontal line would you draw on the graph of $y = x^2$ to find the solutions to $x^2 = 3$?

  g Can you find a solution to the equation $x^2 = -9$?
Explain your answer.

You can use the table of values you drew up in question **1**.

Key objectives

- Plot graphs of functions in which y is given explicitly in terms of x or implicitly

- Recognise that equations of the form $y = mx + c$ correspond to straight-line graphs in the coordinate plane

- Generate points and plot graphs of simple quadratic functions

1 a State the gradient and y-intercept of the graphs to the corresponding equations:

    i $y = 3x + 2$ **ii** $y = x - 1$ **iii** $2y = 2x$ (4)

   b Which of the two graphs from part **a** will never intersect? (2)
    Explain your answer.

2 a Copy and complete the table for $y = x^2 - 3x + 1$:

x	-2	-1	0	1	2	3	4
y	11		1	-1		1	5

   b Copy the grid and draw the graph of $y = x^2 - 3x + 1$. (2)

   c Use your graph to find an estimate for the minimum value of y. (2)

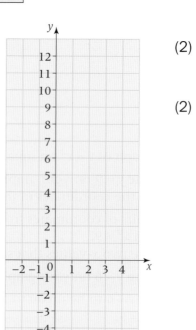

(Edexcel Ltd., 2003)

This unit will show you how to

- Simplify a ratio and express it in the form $1 : n$
- Solve problems involving ratio and proportion
- Divide an amount in a given ratio
- Express a ratio as a fraction, a decimal or a percentage
- Calculate rates
- Calculate missing amounts when two quantities are in direct proportion

Before you start ...

You should be able to answer these questions.

Review

1 Simplify the ratio $10 : 15$.

Unit N4

2 The ratio of boys to girls in a class is $3 : 2$.
There are 18 boys in the class.
How many girls are there?

Unit N4

3 Divide £30 in the ratio $3 : 7$.

Unit N4

4 A car has a fuel consumption of 30 miles per gallon.
How many miles will it travel on 8 gallons of petrol?

Unit N4

5 Gavin is running at 5 mph.
He runs for 3 hours.
How far does he travel?

Unit N4

6 Convert

a 23 cm into metres.

b 2.4 km into centimetres.

Unit S6

This spread will show you how to:

Keywords
Ratio
Scale
Simplest form
Unitary form

- Simplify a ratio and express it in the form 1 : n
- Solve simple problems involving ratio

You can compare the size of two quantities using a **ratio**.

- You can simplify a ratio by dividing both parts by the same number.
  When a ratio cannot be simplified any further it is in its **simplest form**.

Example

Express each of these ratios in its simplest form.

a 55 : 65   **b** 3 m : 120 cm   **c** 2.5 : 4.5

In part **b**, convert the measurements to the same unit.

a 55 : 65   **b** 3 m : 120 cm   **c** 2.5 : 4.5

$\div 5 \left(\begin{array}{c} 55 : 65 \\ 11 : 13 \end{array} \right) \div 5$

$\div 10 \left(\begin{array}{c} 300 : 120 \\ 30 : 12 \end{array} \right) \div 10$
$\div 6 \left(\begin{array}{c} 30 : 12 \\ 5 : 2 \end{array} \right) \div 6$

$\times 10 \left(\begin{array}{c} 2.5 : 4.5 \\ 25 : 45 \end{array} \right) \times 10$
$\div 5 \left(\begin{array}{c} 25 : 45 \\ 5 : 9 \end{array} \right) \div 5$

Answer 11 : 13   Answer 5 : 2   Answer 5 : 9

Convert decimals to whole numbers by multiplying everything by the same number.

- A ratio can be expressed in the form 1 : n. This is called the **unitary form**.

Example

Write these ratios in the form 1 : n.

a 6 cm : 9 cm   **b** 4 cm : 2 m

a 6 cm : 9 cm   **b** 4 cm : 2 m   Change 2 m into 200 cm

$\div 6 \left(\begin{array}{c} 6 : 9 \\ 1 : 1.5 \end{array} \right) \div 6$

$\div 4 \left(\begin{array}{c} 4 : 200 \\ 1 : 50 \end{array} \right) \div 4$

Answer 1 : 1.5   Answer 1 : 50

Maps and plans are drawn to **scale**.

Example

On a plan, a real-life measurement of 4 m is drawn as a length of 25 cm.
What is the scale of the plan?

Ratio of plan : real life   Change 4 m into 400 cm
    = 25 cm : 4 m

$\div 25 \left(\begin{array}{c} 25 : 400 \\ 1 : 16 \end{array} \right) \div 25$

The scale of the plan is 1 : 16.

1 Write each of these ratios in its simplest form.

   a 4 : 8   **b** 16 : 10   **c** 40 : 25   **d** 36 : 24

   e 95 : 45   **f** 28 : 168   **g** 4 : 8 : 6   **h** 20 : 25 : 40

2 Write each of these ratios in its simplest form.

   a 40 cm : 1 m   **b** 55 mm : 8 cm   **c** 3 km : 1200 m

   d 4 m : 240 cm   **e** 700 mm : 42 cm   **f** 12 mins : 450 secs

3 Express each of these pairs of measurements as a ratio in its simplest form.

   a A table width of 40 cm to a table length of 1.2 m. What is the ratio of width to length?

   b A lorry is 8.4 m long. A van is 360 cm long. What is the ratio of the lorry length to the van length?

   c An alloy contains 24 kg of tin and 3.2 kg of zinc. What is the ratio of tin to zinc in the alloy?

   d A bag of newly dug potatoes contains 6.4 kg of potatoes and 576 g of earth. What is the ratio of earth to potatoes in the bag?

4 Write each of these ratios in its simplest form.

   a 1.5 : 4.5   **b** 2.25 : 1.5   **c** $\frac{1}{2} : \frac{1}{4}$ **d** $\frac{3}{8} : \frac{1}{2}$

5 Write each of these ratios in the form 1 : n.

   a 4 : 10   **b** 39 : 150   **c** 30 : 125   **d** 720 g : 30 kg

   e 95p : £22.50   **f** 3.2 : 480   **g** 0.36 : 4.5

6 In each of these questions, work out the scale of the map, plan or model. This is a ratio expressed in the form 1 : n.

   a On a plan, a length of 4 cm represents a real-life measurement of 2 m. What is the scale of the plan?

   b On a map, a length of 3.2 cm represents a real-life measurement of 640 m. What is the scale of the map?

   c On a plan, a length of 7.2 cm represents a real-life measurement of 2.592 m. What is the scale of the plan?

7 Solve each of these problems.

   a In a batch of concrete the ratio of sand to cement is 5 : 3. How much sand is needed to mix with 21 kg of cement?

   b In a metal alloy the ratio of aluminium to zinc is 7 : 2.5. How much aluminium is needed to mix with 10 kg of zinc?

This spread will show you how to:

- Solve problems involving ratio and proportion
- Divide an amount in a given ratio

Keywords

Ratio
Scale

A **ratio** tells you how many times bigger one number is compared to another number.

Example

a A pencil is 150 mm long. A pen is 165 mm long. How many times longer than the pencil is the pen?
b An alloy is made from zinc and copper in the ratio 3 : 8. How much zinc would you need to mix with 43 kg of copper? Give your answer to an appropriate degree of accuracy.

a Pencil length : Pen length
$$150 : 165 = 10 : 11$$
Pen = $\frac{11}{10}$ of length of pencil
Pen = $\frac{11}{10}$ × length of pencil

b Amount of zinc = $\frac{3}{8}$ × amount of copper
$$= \frac{3}{8} \times 43 \text{ kg} = 0.375 \times 43 \text{ kg}$$
$$= 16.125 \text{ kg} = 16 \text{ kg (nearest kg)}$$

Example

A map has a **scale** of 1 : 2500. A distance in real life is 50 m.
What is this distance on the map?

Distance on map = $\frac{1}{2500}$ × distance in real life
$$= \frac{1}{2500} \times 50 \text{ m}$$
$$= \frac{1 \times 5000}{2500} \text{ cm}$$
$$= 2 \text{ cm}$$

50 m = 50 × 100 cm
= 5000 cm

You can divide a quantity in a given ratio.

Example

Sean and Patrick share £355 in the ratio 3 : 7.
How much money do they each receive?

Sean receives 3 parts for every 7 parts that Patrick receives.

Total number of parts = 3 + 7 = 10 parts
Each part = £355 ÷ 10 = £35.50

Sean will receive 3 parts = 3 × £35.50 = £106.50
Patrick will receive 7 parts = 7 × £35.50 = £248.50

Check your answer by adding up the two parts.
They should add up to the amount being shared!
£106.50 + £248.50 = £355

1 In each question, simplify the ratio, draw a diagram and write two statements. The first one is done for you.

a A length of 50 cm : length of 80 cm

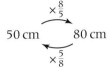

50 : 80

5 : 8

a length of 80 cm = $\frac{8}{5}$ × a length of 50 cm

a length of 50 cm = $\frac{5}{8}$ × a length of 80 cm

b Andrew's height of 144 cm : Andrew's width of 48 cm

c A limousine of length 6.4 m : a car of length 280 cm

d A can containing 330 ml : a can containing 0.44 litres

2 Solve each of these problems.

a The ratio of boys to girls in a class is 4 : 5. There are 12 boys in the class. How many girls are there?

b In a metal alloy the ratio of aluminium to tin is 8 : 5. How much aluminium is needed to mix with 55 kg of tin?

c The ratio of the number of purple flowers to the number of white flowers in a garden is 5 : 11. There are 132 white flowers. How many purple flowers are there?

d The ratio of KS3 students to KS4 students in a school is 7 : 6. There are 588 KS3 students. How many KS4 students are there at the school?

3 a A map has a scale of 1 : 400. A distance in real life is 4.8 m. What is this distance on the map?

b In a school the ratio of teachers to students is 1 : 22.5. If there are 990 students at the school, how many teachers are there?

c The model of an aircraft is in the scale 1 : 32. If the real aircraft is 12.48 m long, how long is the model?

4 A map has a scale of 1 : 5000.

a What is the distance in real life of a measurement of 6.5 cm on the map?

b What is the distance on the map of a measurement of 30 m in real life?

5 Solve each of these problems.

a Divide £90 in the ratio 3 : 7.

b Divide 369 kg in the ratio 7 : 2.

c Divide 103.2 tonnes in the ratio 5 : 3.

d Divide 35.1 litres in the ratio 5 : 4.

e Divide £36 in the ratio 1 : 2 : 3.

This spread will show you how to:

- Express a ratio as a fraction, a decimal or a percentage
- Divide an amount in a given ratio

Keywords

Ratio
Scale

A **ratio** compares the size of two or more objects. You can express a ratio as a fraction, a decimal or a percentage.

Wing span of model : Wing span of enlargement
2 : 5

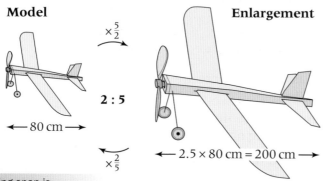

Model

$\times \frac{5}{2}$

2 : 5

← 80 cm →

$\times \frac{2}{5}$

Enlargement

← 2.5 × 80 cm = 200 cm →

Enlargement wing span is
$\frac{5}{2}$ of model wing span
$\frac{5}{2}$ × model wing span
2.5 × model wing span
250% of model wing span

Model wing span is
$\frac{2}{5}$ of enlargement wing span
$\frac{2}{5}$ × enlargement wing span
0.4 × enlargement wing span
40% of enlargement wing span

Some calculations involving ratio and **scale** need to be broken down into smaller steps.

Example

A model is made of a truck. The length of the model is 28 centimetres. The length of the real truck is 6.3 metres. Work out the ratio of the length of the model to the length of the real truck. Write your answer in the form 1 : n.

Step 1
Express the ratio in equal units.

Length of model : length of truck
28 cm : 6.3 m
28 cm : 630 cm
28 : 630

Step 2
Express the ratio in the form 1 : n.

The scale is 1 : 22.5.

$\div 28 \left(\begin{array}{c} 28 : 630 \\ 1 : 22.5 \end{array} \right) \div 28$

When a ratio is expressed in different units, convert the measurements to the same unit.

1 **a** The ratio of men to women in a club is 3 : 7. There are 18 men who are members of the club. How many women are members of the club?

   b In a recipe the ratio of butter to flour is 3 : 2. How much flour is needed to mix with 360 g of butter?

   c The heights of two buildings are in the ratio 8 : 9. The smaller building has a height of 56 feet. What is the height of the larger building?

   d Marlene reads two books on holiday. The first book is a travel book with 258 pages. The second book is a science fiction novel, with more pages than the travel book. The number of pages in the two books is in the ratio 3 : 5. How many pages are there in the science fiction novel?

2 Solve each of these problems. Give your answers to 2 decimal places where appropriate.

   a Divide £75 in the ratio 8 : 7.   **b** Divide £1000 in the ratio 7 : 13.

   c Divide 364 days in the ratio 5 : 2.   **d** Divide 500 g in the ratio 2 : 5.

   e Divide 600 m in the ratio 5 : 9.

3 **a** The ratio of the length of a car to the length of a van is 2 : 3. The car has a length of 240 cm.

   i Express the length of the car as a percentage of the length of the van.

   ii Calculate the length of the van.

   b The ratio of the weight of Dave to Morgan is 6 : 5. Morgan has a weight of 85 kg.

   i Express the weight of Dave as a percentage of the weight of Morgan.

   ii Calculate the weight of Dave.

4 Work out these. For each problem show all the steps in your working out.

   a A metal alloy is made from copper and aluminium. The ratio of the weight of copper to the weight of aluminium is 5 : 3.

   i What weight of the metal alloy contains 45 grams of copper?

   ii Work out the weight of copper and the weight of aluminium in 184 grams of the metal alloy.

   b Siobhan and Ralph shared £700 in the ratio 2 : 3. Siobhan gave a quarter of her share to Karen. Ralph gave a fifth of his share to Karen. What fraction of the £700 did Karen receive?

This spread will show you how to:

- Express a ratio as a fraction, a decimal or a percentage
- Calculate rates

Keywords

Compound
measure
Ratio
Rate

You can use **ratios** written as fractions to solve problems.

Example

The ratio of girls to boys in a year group is 7 : 5. There are 45 boys in the year group. How many girls are there?

The number of girls = y

You can say that girls : boys = 7 : 5 = y : 45

Writing as fractions: $\frac{girls}{boys} = \frac{7}{5} = \frac{y}{45}$

× 9: $\frac{63}{45} = \frac{y}{45}$

                                 $63 = y$

y = number of girls = 63

These are
equivalent ratios.

The ratio 7 : 5 can
be written as $\frac{7}{5}$.

These are
equivalent
fractions.

- **A rate** tells you how many units of one quantity there are compared to one unit of another quantity. You can calculate a rate using division.

Example

Wang drives his car for 3 hours on the motorway. He travels a distance of 180 miles. What is his average speed for the journey?

The rate of travel = Speed = $\dfrac{\text{distance travelled}}{\text{time taken}}$

$= \dfrac{180 \text{ miles}}{3 \text{ hours}}$

$= 60$ miles per hour

This means that in every 1 hour Wang travels 60 miles.

Rates are always written using two units, for example the **density** of a substance is expressed in terms of mass (kg) and volume (m³).
These are called **compound measures**.

Write the rate as
an arrow diagram.
Write the unit you
are trying to find
first.
Multiply the
amount you are
given by the
multiplier.

Example

a A batch of aluminium has a mass of 1350 kg and a volume of 0.5 m³. What is the density of aluminium?
b Magnesium has a density of 174 kg/m³. What is the mass of a piece of magnesium with a volume of 0.25 m³?

a Density = $\dfrac{\text{Mass of the object}}{\text{Volume of the object}}$

$= \dfrac{1350}{0.5} = 2700 \text{ kg/m}^3$

b Express the density as a rate:

Density = 174 kg/m³

0.25 m³ = 0.25 × 174 m³

$= 43.5 \text{ m}^3$

$1 \text{ m}^3 \xrightarrow[\times \frac{1}{174}]{\times 174} 174 \text{ kg}$

1 Find the value of y in each of these pairs of equivalent ratios.

a $\dfrac{3}{4} = \dfrac{y}{12}$ **b** $\dfrac{12}{15} = \dfrac{y}{5}$ **c** $4 : 5 = y : 10$ **d** $y : 10 = 13 : 5$ **e** $4 : 7 = 12 : y$

2 **a** Sandra and Steve share £507 in the ratio $4 : 9$.

  i How much money does each person receive?

  ii What proportion of the £507 does Sandra receive?

  iii How many times more money than Sandra does Steve receive?

  b Kirsty and Steve share the cost of buying a house at £84 000 in the ratio $5 : 2$.

  i How much does each person spend on the house?

  ii What proportion of the house does Kirsty buy?

  iii What fraction of the amount Kirsty spends does Steve spend?

3 **a** The length of a rectangle is 9 cm. The rectangle is enlarged. The length of the enlarged rectangle is 22.5 cm.

  i What is the ratio of the enlarged length to the original length?

  ii How many times longer is the enlargement compared to the original?

  b Frank's height is 165 cm. Safraz's height is 180 cm.

  i What is the ratio of Frank's height to Safraz's height?

  ii What fraction of Safraz's height is Frank?

4 Solve each of these problems.

  a The ratio of boys to girls in a class is $3 : 2$. There are 15 boys in the class. How many girls are there?

  b The ratio of the number of MP3 players to the number of ipods owned by students in Year 11 is $6 : 5$. There are 45 ipods. How many MP3 players are there?

  c Antifreeze is put into the cooling system of a car in the ratio 3 parts antifreeze to 25 parts of water. Jerry puts 27 cl of antifreeze into his car. How much water does he need to add?

5 **a** Gerome travels at an average speed of 48 miles per hour.

  i How far does he travel in 3 hours?

  ii How long will it take him to travel 168 miles?

  b Tin has a density of 7310 kg/m^3.

  i What is the mass of 2.5 m^3 of tin?

  ii What is the volume of 500 kg of tin?

This spread will show you how to:

- Calculate missing amounts when two quantities are in direct proportion

You can use **ratio** and **direct proportion** to solve many problems.

Example

Here are the results of a survey to show the favourite colours chosen by students in a Reception class.

Draw a pie chart to show this information.

Colour	Frequency
Green	5
Red	6
Blue	7

The total number of people in the survey = 5 + 6 + 7 = 18 students.

$360 \div 18 = 20$

One person is represented by 20° on the pie chart.
The angle for green = $20 \times 5 = 100°$
The angle for red $\quad = 20 \times 6 = 120°$
The angle for blue $\quad = 20 \times 7 = 140°$

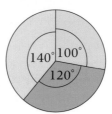

- You can calculate missing lengths when two objects are similar.

This means one object is an enlargement of the other object.

Example

These two triangles are similar. Calculate the length of XY.

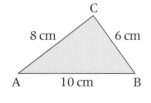

The corresponding sides of similar triangles are in direct proportion.
This means that the ratio of the corresponding sides is the same.

So

$XY = AB \times \frac{11.2}{8}$

$\quad = AB \times 1.4$

$\quad = 10 \text{ cm} \times 1.4$

$\quad = 14 \text{ cm}$

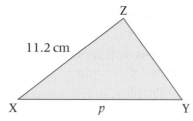

1 Work out each of these direct proportion problems.

a Alain buys 8 kg of apples for £4.40. Bernice buys 13 kg of the same apples. How much does Bernice have to pay for her apples?

b Material for stair carpets costs £45.16 for 4 metres. How much would 11 metres cost?

c 12 pencils cost £7.08. What is the cost of 18 pencils?

d 9 litres of super unleaded petrol cost £8.64. What is the cost of 35 litres of the petrol?

2 **a** Here are the results of a survey to show the favourite bands chosen by students in a class.

Draw a pie chart to show this information.

Colour	Frequency
Green Day	8
Red Hot Chili Peppers	3
Blue	13

b Here are the results of a class survey to find how students in Class 11B travel to school.

Draw a pie chart to show this information.

Transport	Frequency
Walk	18
Bus	5
Cycle	2
Taxi/minibus	4
Car	1

3 **a** Change 360 cm into metres.

b Change 20 km into miles.

c Use the facts that 1 hour = 60 minutes; 1 minute = 60 seconds; 1 km = 1000 m; to change 50 km/h into metres per second.

d Use the facts that 1 hour = 60 minutes; 1 minute = 60 seconds; 1 km = 1000 m; 1 mile = 1.6 km; to change a speed of 8 m/s (metres per second) into miles per hour.

e Change 140 cm^2 into m^2.

4 For this pair of similar triangles, calculate the length of XY and YZ.

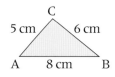
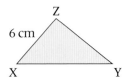

5 **a** In a sale all prices are reduced by 20%. Germaine buys a book for £5.60 in the sale. What was the original price of the book?

b Monique has a pay rise of 6%. Her new wage is £371 per week. What was her original wage before the pay rise?

Find the percentage of the original price, then the value of 1%, then the value of 100%.

Exam review

Key objectives

● Divide a quantity in a given ratio

● Solve problems and word problems, including those involving ratio and proportion, fractions, percentages and measures

1 A youth club has an annual budget of £150 to spend on their Christmas party.

They decide to spend 50% of this budget on food and drink.

They spend a further £25 on decorations.

Work out the ratio

Money spent on food and drink : Money spent on decorations

expressing your answer in its simplest form. (3)

2 Brass is made up of copper and zinc.

Every 100 grams of brass contains 20 grams of zinc.

a Work out the weight of zinc in 60 grams of brass. (2)

Brass contains 4 parts by weight of copper to 1 part by weight of zinc.

b Work out the weight of copper in 350 grams of brass. (2)

(Edexcel Ltd., 2003)

This unit will show you how to

- Use and interpret maps and scale drawings
- Understand that enlargements are specified by a centre and positive scale factor
- Recognise, visualise and construct enlargements of objects
- Identify the scale factor of an enlargement as the ratio of the lengths of any two corresponding line segments
- Understand that any two circles and any two squares are mathematically similar, while in general, two rectangles are not
- Understand the effects of enlargement on the angles, perimeter, area and volume of shapes and solids

Before you start ...

You should be able to answer these questions.

Review

1 Use a protractor to measure these angles.

a   **b**

Key stage 3

2 Using compasses and protractor, construct these triangles.

Key stage 3

a
7 cm
60°
5 cm

b
40° 50°
5 cm

c
6 cm   7 cm
5 cm

3 Calculate the perimeter and the area of these shapes.
State the units of your answers.

Unit S5

a
5 cm
15 cm

b
5 cm   3 cm
4 cm

4 Calculate the volume of this cuboid, stating the units of your answer.

Unit S1

10 cm
5 cm   4 cm

Maps and scale drawings

This spread will show you how to:

● Use and interpret maps and scale drawings

Keywords

Enlarged
Reduced
Scale drawing
Scale factor

In **scale drawings**, lines and shapes are **reduced** or **enlarged**.

Corresponding lengths are multiplied by the same **scale factor**.
You can write the scale factor as a ratio.

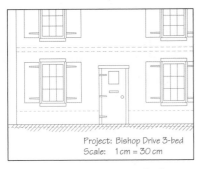

1 cm on the architect's plan = 30 cm of the actual house.

You can write this scale factor as 1 cm represents 30 cm
or 1 : 30.

Maps are scale drawings.

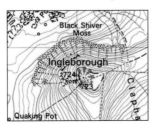

This is an enlargement of scale factor 50 000.

The map scale can be written 1 : 50 000.

You write the scale as 1 cm represents 50 000 cm
or 1 cm represents 500 m.

Example

In this scale drawing 1 cm represents 3 m.

a Calculate the height of the building.
b Calculate the length of the building.
c Calculate the area of the front.
   State your units.
d There are 26 windows in the scale drawing.
   How many windows are there on the front of the real house?

3 cm

7 cm

a 1 cm represents 3 m
   3 cm represents 3 × 3 = 9 m
   Height of building = 9 m

b 7 cm represents 7 × 3 = 21 m
   Length of building = 21 m

c Area of front = 9 m × 21 m = 189 m^2

d 26 windows

The number of windows is the same on the scale drawing as on the real house.

1 The scale on a drawing is 1 cm represents 10 cm.
Calculate the distance represented by

a 4 cm   **b** 10 cm   **c** 0.5 cm

d 6.5 cm   **e** 12.5 cm

0   10   20   cm

2 This is an accurate scale drawing of a Dalek.
For the real Dalek, calculate

a the height

b the width of the base.

Scale: 1 cm represents 20 cm

3 On the plan of a house, a door measures 3 cm by 8 cm.
If the plan scale is 1 cm represents 25 cm, calculate the dimensions of
the real door.

4 This is a scale
drawing of a
volleyball court.

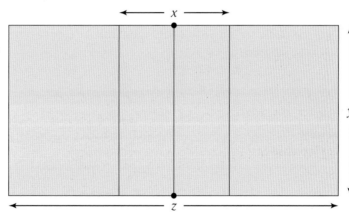

Scale 1 : 200
or 1 cm
represents 2 m

Calculate

a the actual distances marked *x*, *y* and *z*

b the area of the court. State the units of your answer.

5 A map has a scale of 1 : 50 000 or 1 cm represents 50 000 cm.
Calculate in metres the actual distance represent on the map by

a 2 cm   **b** 8 cm   **c** 10 cm

d 0.5 cm   **e** 14.5 cm.

Enlargements

This spread will show you how to:

● Recognise, visualise and construct enlargements of objects

Keywords
Enlargement
Multiplier
Scale factor
Similar
Transformation

To enlarge a shape, multiply corresponding lengths by the same scale factor.

● The scale factor is the **multiplier** in the **enlargement**.

The green trapezium is an enlargement of the yellow trapezium.

Corresponding lengths are multiplied by 2, $1 \times 2 = 2$, $2 \times 2 = 4$.

The scale factor of this enlargement is 2.

The two trapeziums are **similar** – same shape but different size.

Example

The green shape is an enlargement of the yellow shape.
Calculate the scale factor for each enlargement.

a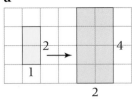

b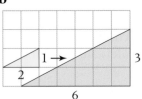

c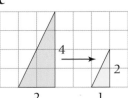

a Scale factor = $4 \div 2 = 2$
Check: $1 \times 2 = 2$

b Scale factor = $6 \div 2 = 3$
Check: $1 \times 3 = 3$

c Scale factor = $2 \div 4 = \frac{1}{2}$
Check: $2 \times \frac{1}{2} = 1$

The scale factor is less than 1 as the shape actually reduces during the enlargement.

● In an enlargement
  ● the angles stay the same
  ● the lengths increase in proportion.

Example

The green kite is an enlargement of the yellow kite by scale factor 2.
The smallest angle in the yellow kite is 53°.
What is the smallest angle in the enlargement?

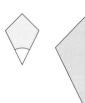

Each length is multiplied by 2.

53°, as angles stay the same in enlargements.

1 Calculate the scale factor of these enlargements.

a

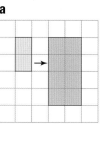

b

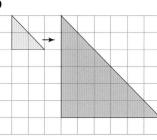

c

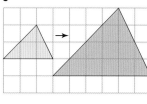

d

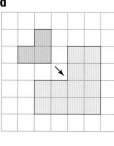

e

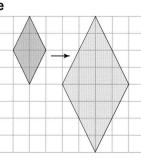

f

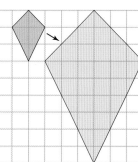

g

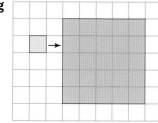

h

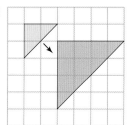

2 a Decide if these rectangles are enlargements of the yellow rectangle.
   If so, calculate the scale factor.

   b List the rectangles that are similar to the yellow rectangle.

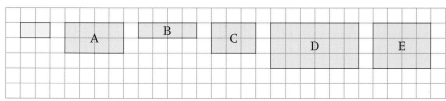

3 a Decide if these triangles are enlargements of the yellow triangle.
   If so, calculate the scale factor.

   b List the triangles that are similar to the yellow triangle.

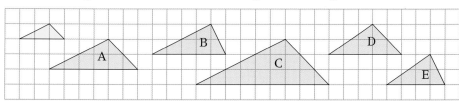

More enlargements

This spread will show you how to:

- Understand that enlargements are specified by a centre and positive scale factor

Keywords
Centre of enlargement
Enlargement
Scale factor
Vertices

- In an **enlargement**
  - the angles stay the same
  - the lengths increase in proportion.

The position of an enlargement is fixed by the **centre of enlargement**.

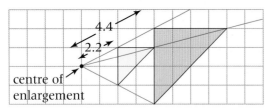

You multiply the distance from the centre to the object by the **scale factor**.
This gives the distance to the image along the same extended line.

The scale factor of the enlargement is 2.

The red lines start from the centre and pass through corresponding **vertices** of the two shapes.

- To describe an enlargement, you give
  - the scale factor
  - the centre of enlargement.

Example

Find the centre of enlargement and calculate the scale factor of the enlargement from A to B.

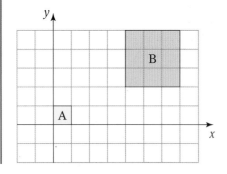

Draw the red lines to find the centre of enlargement.
Centre of enlargement is (−2, −1)
Scale factor = 3 ÷ 1 = 3

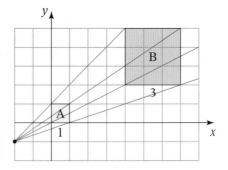

Example

Draw the enlargement of the yellow shape, using scale factor 2 and P as the centre of enlargement.

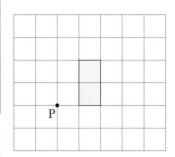

Draw lines from P to each vertex. Multiply the distances from the centre by 2.

$$2 \times 2 = 4 \qquad 2.2 \times 2 = 4.4$$

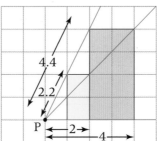

1 Copy each diagram on square grid paper. Find the centre of enlargement and calculate the scale factor for these enlargements.

a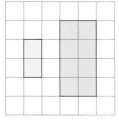

b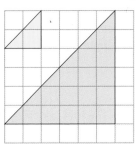

c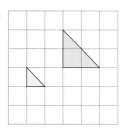

d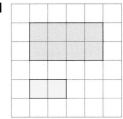

2 Copy each diagram on square grid paper.
Enlarge each shape by the given scale factor using the given centre of enlargement.

a

Scale factor 3

b

Scale factor 2

c

Scale factor 2

d

Scale factor 3

e

Scale factor 3

f

Scale factor 2

g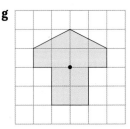

Scale factor 2

h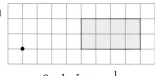

Scale factor $\frac{1}{2}$

i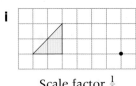

Scale factor $\frac{1}{2}$

j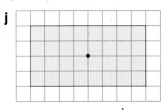

Scale factor $\frac{1}{2}$

Similar shapes

This spread will show you how to:

- Identify the scale factor of an enlargement as the ratio of the lengths of any two corresponding line segments and apply this to triangles
- Understand that any two circles and any two squares are mathematically similar, while in general, two rectangles are not

Keywords

Enlargement
Scale factor
Similar

- In an **enlargement**, the object and the image are **similar**,
  - the angles stay the same
  - the lengths increase in proportion.

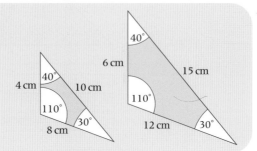

You use corresponding lengths to find the **scale factor**.

- Scale factor $= \dfrac{\text{length of image}}{\text{length of object}}$.

Example

These triangles are similar.
Find the length x.

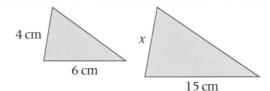

The scale factor is $\frac{15}{6} = 15 \div 6 = 2.5$
$x = 4 \text{ cm} \times 2.5 = 10 \text{ cm}$

Example

a Show that triangle ABE is similar to triangle ACD.
b Calculate the value of x.

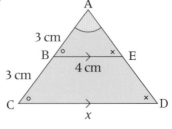

a Angle B = angle C (corresponding angles are equal)
Angle E = angle D (corresponding angles are equal)
Angle A is common to both triangles.
So △ABE and △ACD are similar.

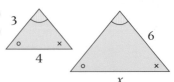

b The scale factor is $6 \div 3 = 2$
$x = 4 \text{ cm} \times 2 = 8 \text{ cm}$

See S2.4 or S8.2 for corresponding angles for parallel lines.

1 In each question, the two triangles are similar.
Find the value of the unknown angles.

a

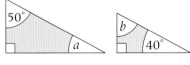

b

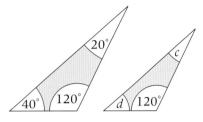

Angles in a triangle add to 180°.

c

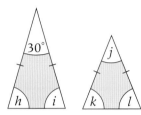

d

2 Which of these rectangles are similar to the green rectangle?
For the ones that are similar, give the scale factor of the enlargement.

2 cm

3 cm

a

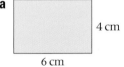

4 cm

6 cm

b

10 cm

15 cm

c

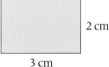

4 cm

5 cm

d

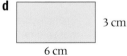

3 cm

6 cm

e

8 cm

12 cm

f

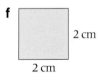

2 cm

2 cm

3 In each question, the two triangles are similar. Calculate the scale factor of the enlargement and the unknown length.

a

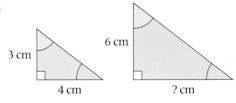

3 cm

4 cm

6 cm

? cm

b

3 cm

4 cm

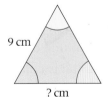

9 cm

? cm

4 Calculate the value of each unknown length.

a

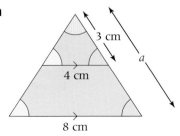

3 cm

4 cm

8 cm

a

b

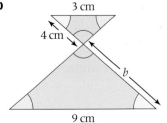

3 cm

4 cm

9 cm

b

Relationships

This spread will show you how to:

● Understand the effects of enlargement on the angles, perimeter, area and volume of shapes and solids

Keywords
Area
Enlargement
Multiplier
Perimeter
Scale factor
Volume

In this **enlargement**, corresponding lengths are multiplied by 2, so the **scale factor** is 2.

 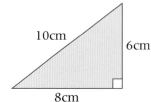

5cm · 3cm
4cm
Perimeter=12cm
Area=6cm^2

10cm · 6cm
8cm
Perimeter=24cm
Area=24cm^2

Area of a triangle = $\frac{1}{2}$ × base × height.

If scale factor for length is 2 then scale factor for **area** is 2 × 2 = 4.

Scale factor is 2 but area is ×4.

In this enlargement, corresponding lengths are multiplied by 2, so the scale factor is 2.

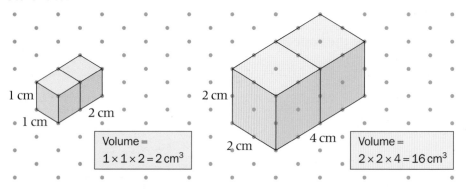

Volume of a cuboid = length × width × height.

1 cm
1 cm
2 cm
Volume = 1 × 1 × 2 = 2 cm^3

2 cm
2 cm
4 cm
Volume = 2 × 2 × 4 = 16 cm^3

Scale factor is 2 but volume is ×8.

If scale factor for length is 2 then scale factor for **volume** is 2 × 2 × 2 = 8.

● If scale factor for length is L then scale factor for area is $L \times L = L^2$ and scale factor for volume is $L \times L \times L = L^3$.

Example

A 2 cm by 3 cm by 4 cm cuboid is shown. Calculate

a the area of the base rectangle
b the volume of the cuboid.

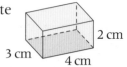

2 cm
3 cm
4 cm

The cuboid is enlarged by scale factor 3.

c Calculate the area of the new base rectangle.

a Area = 3 × 4 = 12 cm^2
b Volume = 2 × 3 × 4 = 24 cm^3
c Scale factor is 3, so new lengths are
3 × 3 = 9 cm, 4 × 3 = 12 cm, 2 × 3 = 6 cm
Area = 9 × 12 = 108 cm^2

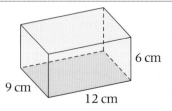

6 cm
9 cm
12 cm

Note that enlarged volume = 6 × 9 × 12
= 648 cm^3

Scale factor is 3 but area is ×9.

Scale factor is 3 but volume is ×27.

1 a Calculate the perimeter of this rectangle. State the units of your answer.

2 cm

6 cm

b Find the area of the rectangle. State the units of your answer.

The rectangle is enlarged by scale factor 5.

c Calculate the length and width of the enlarged rectangle.

d Calculate the perimeter of the enlarged rectangle.

e Calculate the area of the enlarged rectangle.

f Copy and complete this sentence:

For an enlargement scale factor 5, the perimeter increases by multiplying by ___ and the area increases by multiplying by ___.

2 a Calculate the volume of this cuboid.
State the units of your answer.

The cuboid is enlarged by scale factor 3.

b Calculate the dimensions of the new cuboid.

c Calculate the volume of the new cuboid.

d Copy and complete this sentence:
For an enlargement scale factor 3, the volume increase by multiplying by ___.

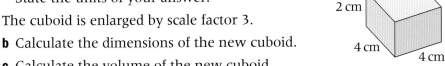

2 cm

4 cm

4 cm

3 a Calculate the area of this triangle.
State the units of your answer.

The triangle is enlarged by scale factor 2.

b Calculate the area of the enlarged triangle.

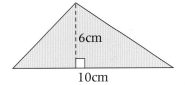

6cm

10cm

4 a Calculate the volume of this cuboid.
State the units of your answer.

The cuboid is enlarged by scale factor 2.

b Calculate the volume of the enlarged cuboid.

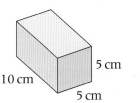

5 cm

10 cm

5 cm

5 Copy and complete this table for enlargements.

Scale factor	Multiplier for length	Multiplier for area	Multiplier for volume
2	2	4	8
3	3	9	27
4			
5			
6			
7			

6 A shape has a perimeter of 14 cm and an area of 10 cm^2.
Calculate the perimeter and area of the shape after an enlargement of scale factor 4.

Key objectives

- Recognise, visualise and construct enlargements of objects using positive fractional scale factors
- Identify the scale factor of an enlargement as the ratio of the lengths of any two corresponding line segments
- Understand similarity of triangles and other plane figures and use this to make geometric inferences

1 Enlarge the triangle by a scale factor 3, centre O.

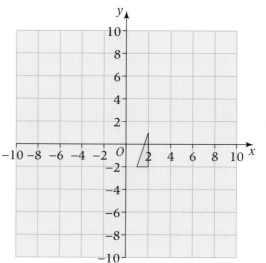

(3)

2 BE is parallel to CD.
ABC and AED are straight lines.
AB = 4 cm
BC = 6 cm
BE = 5 cm
AE = 4.8 cm.

Diagram **not** accurately drawn

a Calculate the length of CD. (2)

b Calculate the length of ED. (2)

(Edexcel Ltd., 2004)

This unit will show you how to

● Understand and use the probability scale
● Understand and use estimates or measures of probability
● Identify different mutually exclusive outcomes
● Know that the sum of the probabilities of all the outcomes is 1
● Gather data from secondary sources
● Use effective methods for random sampling
● Identify sources of bias and plan to minimise it
● List all of the outcomes for two successive events in a systematic way

Before you start ...

You should be able to answer these questions.

Review

1 State the numbers from the rectangle that are

   a prime
   b square
   c triangular
   d multiples of 4
   e factors of 100

> 12 20 14
>   19
> 15 11 13
>   17 18 16

Unit N5

2 Cancel these fractions to their simplest form.

   a $\frac{3}{9}$ **b** $\frac{8}{12}$
   c $\frac{18}{20}$ **d** $\frac{25}{100}$
   e $\frac{13}{52}$

Unit N3

3 Calculate.

   a $\frac{3}{5} + \frac{2}{5}$ **b** $\frac{3}{5} + \frac{1}{5}$
   c $1 - \frac{4}{5}$ **d** $1 - \frac{3}{10}$

Unit N3

4 Calculate.

   a $\frac{1}{5} \times 200$ **b** $\frac{4}{5} \times 200$
   c 0.7×50 **d** 0.8×20
   e 0.15×20

Unit N2, N3

5 Order these numbers in size, smallest first.

   a 1.8, 1.3, 1.1, 1.0, 0.9, 2.1.
   b £1450, £540, £1300, £450, £1540.

Unit N1

This spread will show you how to:

- Understand and use the probability scale
- Understand and use estimates or measures of probability
- Identify different mutually exclusive outcomes

Keywords
Equally likely
Event
Expected
   frequency
Mutually
   exclusive
Outcome
Probability
Trial

An **event** is an activity, for example spinning a coin.

The possible **outcomes** are 'Heads' or 'Tails'.

For the spinning coin:

- Each outcome is **equally likely**.
  The two sides of the coin are identical in size and shape.

- The outcomes are **mutually exclusive**.
  If you get one outcome you cannot get the other one.

The **probability** of an outcome is a measure of how likely it is that an outcome will happen.

0 means
impossible.
1 means certain.

- You can calculate probability using

  Probability of an outcome happening = $\dfrac{\text{number of ways the outcome can happen}}{\text{total number of all possible outcomes}}$

The probability of
an outcome can be
written as
P(outcome).

- The probabilities of mutually exclusive outcomes add up to 1.

- Probability of an outcome **not** happening = 1 − probability of the outcome happening

- The **expected frequency** is the number of times you expect the outcome to happen.

- Expected frequency = probability × number of trials

Each spin of the
coin is called a
trial.

Example

40 red and 10 yellow balls are put into a bag.
One ball is taken out at random and then replaced.

a Decide whether the following statement is true or false. Give a reason for your answer.
'The balls are either red or yellow, so the probability of picking a red is $\frac{1}{2}$.'

b How many red balls would you expect to have picked after picking and replacing a ball 20 times?

a False. There are 40 red balls out of a total of 50, so P(red) = $\frac{40}{50}$
$$= 0.8.$$

b Expected number of red balls = 0.8 × 20 = 16

1 a Give an example of an outcome with a probability of 0.

  b Give an example of an outcome with a probability of 1.

2 There are 12 boys and 18 girls in a class. One student is chosen at random. Calculate the probability that the student is

  a a boy   **b** a girl.

3 a Arrange these probabilities in order of likelihood of happening, with the least likely first.

$$\frac{2}{5} \qquad \frac{3}{8} \qquad 0.35 \qquad \frac{3}{10} \qquad 45\%$$

  b Draw a 10 cm line. Put a mark at every centimetre. Label the marks 0, 0.1, 0.2, ..., 0.9, 1 as shown.

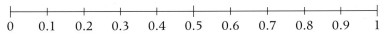

    0   0.1   0.2   0.3   0.4   0.5   0.6   0.7   0.8   0.9   1

  On your probability scale, mark the positions of the probabilities in part **a**.

4 Red, blue and green cubes are put in a bag. The probability of taking out each colour of cube is shown in the table.

Red	Blue	Green
$\frac{1}{2}$	$\frac{1}{8}$	

  a Calculate the probability of taking out a green cube.

  b What colour is most likely to be taken out?

  c What colour is least likely to be taken out?

  d If a cube is taken out and then replaced 16 times, how many red, blue and green cubes would you expect to take out?

5 A spinner is made from a square. The spinner is spun 100 times. The results are shown in the table.

Colour	Green	Red	Blue	Yellow
Frequency	20	27	25	28

  a Calculate an estimate for the probability of each colour occurring.

  b How many times would you expect each colour to occur if the spinner is fair?

Mutually exclusive outcomes

This spread will show you how to:

- Identify different mutually exclusive outcomes
- Know that the sum of the probabilities of all the outcomes is 1

Keywords

Mutually
   exclusive
Or
Outcomes

The possible **outcomes** when a dice is rolled are 1, 2, 3, 4, 5, 6.

These outcomes are **mutually exclusive** because if you get one outcome, you cannot get another one.

The probability of rolling a 4 = $\frac{1}{6}$

The probability of rolling a 5 = $\frac{1}{6}$

The probability of rolling a 4 **or** a 5 = $\frac{2}{6}$

Notice that

$$P(4 \text{ or } 5) = P(4) + P(5)$$
$$\frac{2}{6} = \frac{1}{6} + \frac{1}{6}$$

$P(4) = \frac{1}{6}$

$P(5) = \frac{1}{6}$

Or means either of the outcomes 4 or 5.

- In general, if outcomes A and B are mutually exclusive,

  P(A or B) = P(A) + P(B)

Example

A spinner is made from a regular pentagon and numbered from 1 to 5. Calculate

a P(3)   **b** P(3 or 4)   **c** P(3 or an odd number)

a There is one 3. There are 5 possible outcomes. P(3) = $\frac{1}{5}$

b P(3) = $\frac{1}{5}$ P(4) = $\frac{1}{5}$

The outcomes are mutually exclusive and so

$$P(3 \text{ or } 4) = P(3) + P(4)$$
$$= \frac{1}{5} + \frac{1}{5}$$
$$= \frac{2}{5}$$

c P(3) = $\frac{1}{5}$ P(odd) = $\frac{3}{5}$

The outcomes are not mutually exclusive so P(A or B) = P(A) + P(B) cannot be used.

A list of the 5 possible outcomes is

$$\begin{pmatrix} 1 \\ \text{odd} \end{pmatrix} \begin{pmatrix} 2 \\ \text{even} \end{pmatrix} \begin{pmatrix} 3 \\ \text{odd} \end{pmatrix} \begin{pmatrix} 4 \\ \text{even} \end{pmatrix} \begin{pmatrix} 5 \\ \text{odd} \end{pmatrix}$$

P(3 or an odd number) = $\frac{3}{5}$

There are 3 outcomes that are OK.

1 Outcomes are mutually exclusive if they cannot occur at the same time. State if these outcomes are mutually exclusive.

a spinning a Head and spinning a Tail with a coin

b rolling a 2 and rolling a 3 with a dice

c rolling a 2 and rolling an even number with a dice

d rolling a 2 and rolling an odd number with a dice

e rolling a 2 and rolling a prime number with a dice

f winning and losing a game of chess

g sunny and rainy weather

h taking out a red ball and taking out a blue ball, when taking out one ball from a bag.

2 This is a net of a tetrahedral dice. The dice is made and rolled. What is the probability of rolling

a a 3   **b** a 2   **c** a 2 or a 3?

3 A bag contains 4 red discs, 5 blue discs and 1 white disc. One disc is taken out.
Calculate the probability that the disc is

a red   **b** blue   **c** white

d red or white   **e** blue or white **f** red or blue or white

4 Five names are written on cards and placed in a bag. One name is taken out of the bag at random. Calculate the probability that

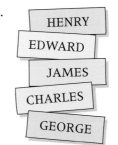

HENRY

EDWARD

JAMES

CHARLES

GEORGE

a the first letter on the card is H

b the first letter on the card is G

c the first letter on the card is H or G

d the card has 5 letters written on it

e the card has 5 or 6 letters written on it.

5 A survey of vehicles passing the school gate is taken.

```
C    C    C    C    V    L    C    C    V    B
C    L    C    C    C    C    B    C    C    V
V    V    C    C    L    C    C    B    C    C
L    B    C    C    C    V    L    C    C    C
B    V    C    V    C    C    V    C    C    V
```

C = Car
L = Lorry
B = Bus
V = Van

a Copy and complete the frequency table.

b Calculate the estimated probability that the next vehicle that passes will be

  i a car   **ii** a lorry   **iii** a bus or a van.

Vehicle	Tally	Frequency
Car (C)		
Lorry (L)		
Bus (B)		
Van (V)		

This spread will show you how to:
- Gather data from secondary sources
- Use effective methods for random sampling
- Identify sources of bias and plan to minimise it

- A **database** is an organised collection of data, especially in a form that can be used by a computer.

An example might be the records of the Year 11 students in a school.

You can sort a computer database
- alphabetically
- numerically.

You can sort using any or several of the columns (fields).

Number	Surname	Forename	Form	Gender
0001	Smith	Thomas	10E	Male
0002	Jones	Michaela	10B	Female
0003	Chapham	Leah	10A	Female
0004	Clark	Alan	10B	Male

This database has been sorted by number.

Sometimes there is too much data in a database to process all the data, and so a **random sample** is used.

- In a random sample, each person or item must be **equally likely** to be chosen.

If each person is not equally likely to be chosen, the sample is **biased**.

Example

Describe a method to choose a random sample of 30 students from a year group of 120 students.

- Number each student from 1 to 120.
- Generate 30 random numbers, by either
  - picking 30 numbers from a bag of 120, numbered 1 to 120, or
  - using the RAN# key on a calculator.

- You can generate random numbers on a calculator using the random function. RAN# generates random numbers from 0.000 to 0.999.

- You can generate a random number from, say, 1 to 120 by using 120 × RAN#.

Use the first three digits of the display.

1 Sanjit wants to buy a laptop. He creates a database of the 10 laptops he is considering buying.

Laptop number	Speed of processor	RAM memory	Size of hard drive	Screen size	Warranty	Cost
1	1.2 GHz	128 MB	8 GB	14.1"	No	£250
2	1.3 GHz	256 MB	20 GB	14.1"	1 year	£300
3	1.8 GHz	256 MB	40 GB	15"	1 year	£450
4	1.2 GHz	512 MB	60 GB	12.1"	1 year	£1300
5	1.7 GHz	512 MB	80 GB	15.4"	3 years	£1400
6	2.4 GHz	1024 MB	100 GB	17"	2 years	£1500
7	2.0 GHz	512 MB	60 GB	14.1"	3 years	£1200
8	2.3 GHz	512 MB	80 GB	14.1"	3 years	£1400
9	1.6 GHz	512 MB	60 GB	14.1"	1 year	£700
10	1.6 GHz	256 MB	60 GB	15.1"	No	£600

a Write down the costs of the laptops in order of price, smallest first.

b Write down the speeds of the processors in order of size, smallest first.

c Which laptop has the smallest RAM memory?

d Which laptop has the largest RAM memory?

e List the laptops that have

   i a screen size of 15" or more

   ii at least 60 GB of hard drive memory

   iii a 2-year or 3-year warranty.

f Sanjit wants a laptop with a screen size of 15" or more, at least 60 GB of hard drive memory and one with a 2- or 3-year warranty. Which laptop is the cheapest option?

2 A class of 30 students decide to elect a class representative by a random process. State whether these methods of selection are random or biased. Give a reason for each answer.

a Arrange the class list into alphabetical order and select the first name on the list.

b Arrange the class list into alphabetical order and select the last name on the list.

c Put the names of the students on cards of equal size. Put the cards into a bag and pick out one card.

d Arrange the students in order of height and select the smallest student.

e Hide a gold star in the classroom, and select the student who finds the star.

f Number the students from 1 to 30. Roll a dice and select the student with that number.

g Number the students from 1 to 30. Use a calculator to find 30 × RAN# and take the first two digits on the display.

This spread will show you how to:

● List all of the outcomes for two successive events in a systematic way

Keywords
Event
Outcome
Successive
Systematic
Tree diagram

● You can list the possible **outcomes** for two successive **events**.

Successive means following on, such as 3, 4, 5.

Example

A spinner has colours red, yellow and green.
A coin has Heads or Tails.
Julie spins the spinner and flips the coin.

a List all the possible outcomes.
b What is the probability that Julie gets yellow and a Tail?
c If the spinner is spun and coin is flipped 60 times, how many times would you expect to get a yellow and a Tail?

a There are several ways to illustrate the outcome.
  ● You could produce a list:

    Red – Head
    Red – Tail
    Yellow – Head
    Yellow – Tail
    Green – Head
    Green – Tail

This list is **systematic** because it is in order.

  ● You could draw a **tree diagram**.

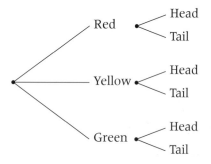

  ● Or you could produce a table.

Colour on spinner	Red	Red	Yellow	Yellow	Green	Green
Head/Tail on coin	Head	Tail	Head	Tail	Head	Tail

b Yellow and Tail occurs once. There are 6 possible outcomes.

  $P(\text{Yellow and Tail}) = \frac{1}{6}$

c Expected outcomes = P(Yellow and Tail) × 60

  $= \frac{1}{6} \times 60$

  $= 10$

1 Tamsin is going to hire a different DVD on Wednesday and Thursday.
She has a choice of 3 films: A, B or C.
Copy and complete the table to show her 6 possible choices.

Wednesday	Thursday
A	B
A	

2 A fair spinner is labelled A, B, C.
Another spinner is labelled D, E, F.
Both spinners are spun.

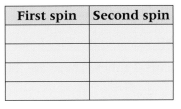

a List the 9 possible outcomes.

b Calculate the probability of getting an A and an E.

c Calculate the probability of not getting either an A or an E.

3 A coin has Heads or Tails. The coin is spun and then spun again.

a Copy and complete the table to show the four possible outcomes.

b Copy and complete the tree diagram to show the four outcomes.

First spin	Second spin

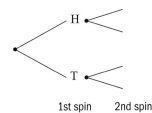

1st spin   2nd spin

c Calculate the probability of getting a Head and then a Head.

d Calculate the probability of not getting a Head and then a Head.

e If both coins are spun 100 times, how many times would you expect to get a Head and then a Head?

4 A pack of cards contains 26 red cards and 26 black cards. A card is taken out of the pack and replaced. Another card is taken out.

a Copy and complete the table to show the outcomes.

b Draw a tree diagram to show the same outcomes.

First selection	Second selection
Red	

c Calculate the probability of getting a red card and a black card in any order.

Two events again

This spread will show you how to:

● List all of the outcomes for two successive events in a systematic way

Keywords

Equally likely
Sample space
diagram

You can use a systematic list or a tree diagram if the number of outcomes is small.

You can use a **sample space diagram** if the number of outcomes is large.

Example

A dice is numbered 1, 2, 3, 4, 5, 6. A spinner has colours red, blue, yellow and green.
Stephanie rolls the dice and spins the spinner.

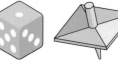

a Draw a sample space diagram to show the possible outcomes.
b What is the probability that she gets an even number and blue?

a

		Score on the dice					
		1	**2**	**3**	**4**	**5**	**6**
Colour on the spinner	**Red**	(1, R)	(2, R)	(3, R)	(4, R)	(5, R)	(6, R)
	Blue	(1, B)	(2, B)	(3, B)	(4, B)	(5, B)	(6, B)
	Yellow	(1, Y)	(2, Y)	(3, Y)	(4, Y)	(5, Y)	(6, Y)
	Green	(1, G)	(2, G)	(3, G)	(4, G)	(5, G)	(6, G)

b Even and Blue occurs 3 times. There are 24 possible outcomes.

$$P(\text{Even and Blue}) = \frac{3}{24} = \frac{1}{8}$$

The 24 outcomes could be shown in a long list or a complicated tree diagram.

● **The sample space diagram shows the outcome of two successive events clearly and concisely.**

The sample space diagram can only be used for **equally likely** outcomes.

Example

Two spinners are numbered 1, 3, 5 and 2, 4, 6.
Each spinner is spun and the scores are added.

a Draw a sample space diagram to show the possible totals.
b What is the probability of getting a total of 7?

a

	1	**3**	**5**
2	3	5	7
4	5	7	9
6	7	9	11

b 7 occurs 3 times. There are 9 possible outcomes.

$$P(\text{total of 7}) = \frac{3}{9} = \frac{1}{3}$$

1 A spinner is made from a square and coloured red (R), yellow (Y), green (G) and pink (P). Another spinner is made from a regular pentagon and labelled A, B, C, D, E. Both spinners are spun.

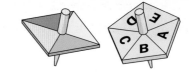

a List the 20 possible outcomes.

b Copy and complete the sample space diagram to show the outcomes.

Colour spinner

		R	Y	G	P
	A	(R, A)			
	B				
Letter spinner	**C**				
	D				
	E				

c Calculate the probability of getting Green and a C.

2 A dice is made from a tetrahedron, and numbered 1, 2, 3, 4. A coin has Heads or Tails. The dice is rolled and the coin is spun.

a Copy and complete the sample space diagram to show the possible outcomes.

Dice

		1	2	3	4
Coin	**Heads**	(1, H)			
	Tails				

b Calculate the probability of getting

i a 3 and a Head

ii an even number and a Head.

3 A 'fruit machine' has only two windows. Each window can show a Club (♣), a Diamond (♦), a Spade (♠) or a Heart (♥).

a Draw a sample space diagram to show the 16 possible outcomes.

b Calculate the probability of getting two of the same symbols.

4 Two fair dice each numbered 1 to 6 are rolled.

List all the possible outcomes.

Calculate the probability of getting a double six.

D6

Exam review

Key objectives

- Understand and use the probability scale
- Identify different mutually exclusive outcomes and know that the sum of the probabilities of all these outcomes is 1
- Understand and use estimates or measures of probability from theoretical models, or from relative frequency
- List all outcomes for single events, and for two successive events, in a systematic way

1 a Amy chooses balls at random from the bag.
Calculate the probability that she picks the following balls:

   i   a red ball.

   ii   a ball that is not red.

   iii a red ball or a white ball.   (3)

 b Write the probability that Amy picks a purple ball.   (2)
Explain your answer.

2 Julie does a statistical experiment. She throws a dice 600 times.
She scores six 200 times.

 a Is the dice fair? Explain your answer.   (1)

Julie then throws a fair red dice once and a fair blue dice once.

 b Copy and complete the probability tree diagram to show the outcomes.
Label clearly the branches of the probability tree diagram.   (3)

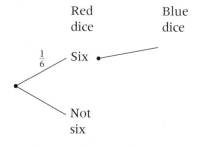

(Edexcel Ltd., 2003)

This unit will show you how to

- Draw and use conversion graphs
- Draw a straight-line graph by plotting and joining three points
- Draw, discuss and interpret graphs arising from real-life situations
- Understand and use compound measures, including speed
- Work out an average speed from a distance–time graph
- Understand the trend shown by a graph
- Read values off graphs and scales

Before you start ...

You should be able to answer these questions.

Review

1 Copy and complete, by following the pattern

  5 miles = 8 km

  10 miles = __ km

  20 miles = __ km.

Unit N4

2 Copy and complete, by following the pattern

  1 m = 100 cm

  __ m = 1000 cm

  20 m = __ cm.

Unit N4

3 Write the value shown on this scale.

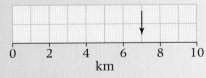

Key stage 3

4 Write the value shown on this scale.

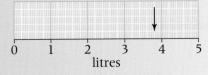

Key stage 3

5 Write the value shown on this scale.

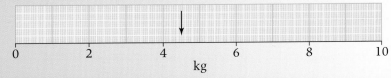

Key stage 3

This spread will show you how to:

● Draw and use conversion graphs

Keywords

Convert
Scale
Units

You can use a conversion graph to **convert**
● a distance in miles to a distance in kilometres
● a distance in kilometres to a distance in miles.

Example

Use the conversion graph to convert these distances.

a 2.5 miles to kilometres
b 6 km to miles

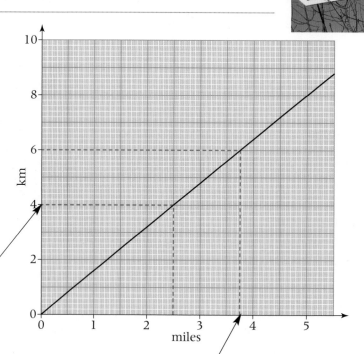

Read the **scale** on the axes carefully. The vertical axis goes up in 2s.

a To convert 2.5 miles to kilometres:
● Find 2.5 miles on the 'miles' axis
● Draw a vertical line up to the graph
● Draw a horizontal line across to the 'kilometres' axis
● Read off the value: 4 km.

b To convert 6 km to miles:
● Find 6 km on the 'kilometres' axis
● Draw a horizontal line across to the graph
● Draw a vertical line down to the 'miles' axis
● Read off the value: 3.75 miles.

● You can use a conversion graph to convert between **units**:

● distance (miles ↔ km)
● weight (pounds ↔ kg)
● temperature (°C ↔ °F)
● currency (£ ↔ €)

1 Use the conversion graph on page 338 to convert

  a 3 miles to kilometres   **b** 10 km to miles

  c 4.5 miles to km   **d** 2 km to miles.

  Which is longer: 1 mile or 1 km?

> Use the conversion graph to help you decide.

2 Use this kilograms to pounds (lb) conversion graph to convert

  a 6 lbs to kg

  b 10 lbs to kg

  c 4 kg to lbs

  d 1.8 kg to lbs

  e 7 lbs to kg

  f 2.2 kg to lbs

  g 12 lbs to kg

  h 5 kg to lbs.

  Which is heavier: 1 kg or 1 lb?
Explain your reasons.

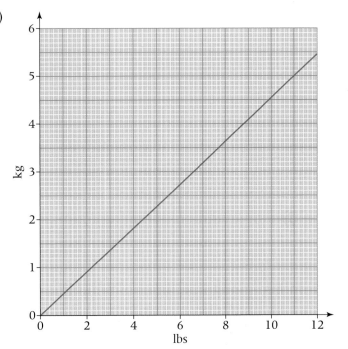

3 **a** Use this °C to °F conversion graph to convert these temperatures.

    i 20 °C to °F

    ii 58 °F to °C

    iii 30 °C to °F

    iv 20 °F to °C

  b The freezing point of water is 0 °C.
What is the freezing point of water in °F?

  c Copy this table.
Use the graph to convert the temperatures in this table to °F.

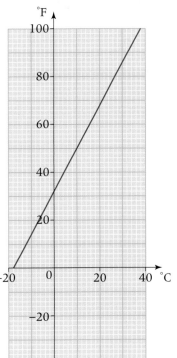

Reykjavik	Oslo	Paris	Madrid	Sydney
−2 °C	2 °C	6 °C	12 °C	24 °C
☐ °F	☐ °F	☐ °F	☐ °F	☐ °F

This spread will show you how to:

● Draw, discuss and interpret graphs arising from real-life situations

Keywords

Conversions
Exchange rate

Davina buys some euros for a trip to France.
The **exchange rate** is £1 = €1.60.

She draws a conversion graph to help her convert prices.

First she works out some simple **conversions** to plot on the graph:

£1 = €1.60   £0 = €0
              £10 = €16
              £20 = €32

Two points is enough to plot a straight line. The third point checks the line is accurate.

She wants to include prices up to £40.
£20 = €32, so £40 = €64.
The euros scale needs to go up to at least €64.

She chooses the scale so her graph fits her paper.

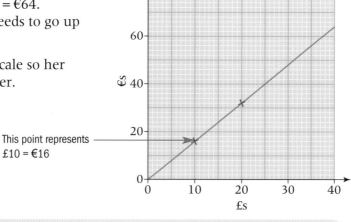

This point represents £10 = €16

The graph has £s on the horizontal axis and euros on the vertical axis. You could use either axis for either currency.

● To draw a conversion graph:
  ● Work out three simple conversions
  ● Decide on a suitable scale
  ● Plot your three points
  ● Join the points with a straight line, right to the edge of the grid.

Example

The conversion rate for miles to kilometres is

    5 miles = 8 kilometres

a Work out two simple conversions you could plot for a miles to kilometres conversion graph.

b The graph needs to convert distances up to 50 miles. What is the highest value needed on the km scale?

a You know: 5 miles = 8 km
    Try the zero value
              0 miles = 0 km
    Use doubling: 10 miles = 16 km

b   5 miles = 8 km
    So 5 × 10 miles = 8 × 10 km
         50 miles = 80 km
    The highest value needed on the km scale is 80 km.

Try the zero value – what is 0 miles in km?

Use doubling.

1 The conversion rate for millimetres to centimetres is

    1 cm = 10 mm

  a Work out two simple conversions you could plot for a millimetres to centimetres conversion graph.

  b The graph needs to convert distances up to 10 cm.
    What is the highest value needed on the mm scale?

2 The conversion rate for pounds (lb) to kilograms (kg) is

    1 kg = 2.2 lbs

  a Copy and complete these conversions.

    0 kg = _____ lbs

    10 kg = _____ lbs

    5 kg = _____ lbs

  b Copy the axes on to graph paper.

  c Complete the labelling of the axes.

  d Use your conversions from part **a** to draw a conversion graph from pounds to kilograms on your grid.

  e Use your graph to convert

    i 10 lbs to kg   **ii** 5 lbs to kg

    iii 3 kg to lbs   **iv** 2.5 kg to lbs.

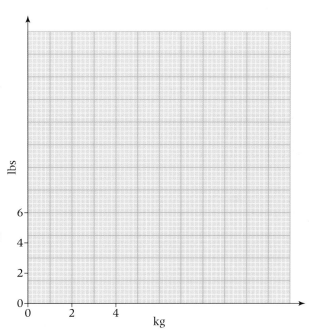

3 One day the exchange rate for pounds (£) to US dollars ($) is

    £1 = $1.70

  a Work out three simple conversions you could plot for a pounds to dollars conversion graph.

  b Max needs a graph to convert amounts up to £30 to dollars.
    What is the highest value needed on the dollars scale?

  c Draw a conversion graph for pounds to dollars.

  d Use your graph to find

    i £5 in dollars   **ii** $30 in pounds.

4 The exchange rate for pounds to New Zealand dollars (NZ$) is

    £1 = NZ$2.40

  a Draw a conversion graph to convert amounts up to £20 to New Zealand dollars.

  b Use your graph to decide which cap is cheapest.

This spread will show you how to:
- Draw, discuss and interpret graphs arising from real-life situations

- A distance–time graph represents a journey.
- It shows how the **distance** from the starting point changes over **time**.

This distance–time graph illustrates Ayesha's shopping trip to Birmingham.

The vertical axis represents the distance from home.

The horizontal axis represents the time from when the trip starts.

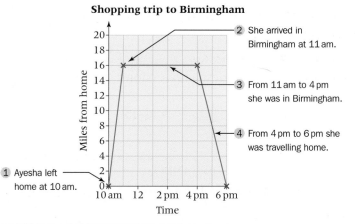

Shopping trip to Birmingham

1 Ayesha left home at 10 am.

2 She arrived in Birmingham at 11 am.

3 From 11 am to 4 pm she was in Birmingham.

4 From 4 pm to 6 pm she was travelling home.

- On a distance–time graph, a horizontal line represents a stay in one place.

Example

The Smith family were going on holiday. The distance–time graph shows the first part of their journey.

a What time did they set off?
b How far did they drive before they stopped for a break?
c How long did they stop for?
d The journey to Sunshine-on-Sea is 240 km. The Smiths arrived at 4 pm. Copy and complete the graph to show the last part of their journey.

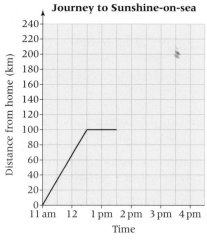

Journey to Sunshine-on-sea

a They set off at 11 am.
b They drove 100 km before stopping.
c 12.30 to 1.30 = 1 hour
d Journey ends at 4 pm, 240 km.

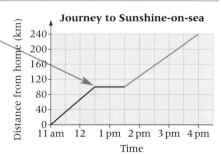

Journey to Sunshine-on-sea

1 The distance–time graph illustrates the first part of a coach tour.

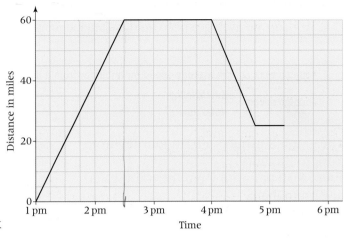

a What time did the coach tour set off?

b The coach arrived at Kinross Castle at 2.30 pm.
How many miles did the coach drive to the castle?

c How long did the coach stop at the castle?

d The tour stopped for a tea break at 4.45 pm.
How far from home were they?

e The tea break lasted $\frac{1}{2}$ hour. Then the coach drove home, arriving at 6 pm.
Copy the graph and complete it to show the whole tour.

2 The graph illustrates a cycle ride.
Match each section of the graph to a part of the description below.

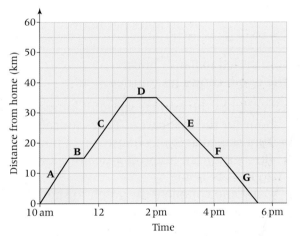

a 15 minute tea break

b Cycle 20 km in $1\frac{1}{2}$ hours

c 1 hour lunch break

d Cycle 15 km in 1 hour

e Cycle 15 km in $1\frac{1}{4}$ hours

f $\frac{1}{2}$ hour rest

g Cycle 20 km in 2 hours

3 The graph represents Karim's car journey to Cornwall.

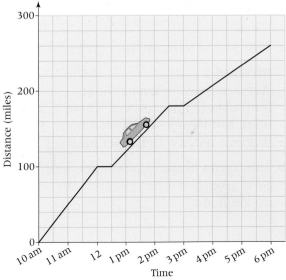

a How long did the journey take him altogether?

b How many miles was the journey altogether?

c How long did it take him to drive the first 100 miles?

d How long did he stop for at 12 pm?

e After his break at 12 pm, he drove another 80 miles before he stopped again.

How long did it take him to drive this 80 miles?

This spread will show you how to:

● Work out an average speed from a distance–time graph

Keywords

Average speed
Steady speed

● You can work out the **average speed** for a journey from a distance–time graph.

Average speed = $\dfrac{\text{total distance}}{\text{total time}}$

The graph illustrates a train journey from York to Banbury.
From 8.30 pm until 9 pm the train waits at Birmingham.
The whole journey is 200 miles.
The whole journey takes 4 hours.

The average speed for the whole journey is

Average speed = $\dfrac{\text{total distance}}{\text{total time}}$

$= \dfrac{200}{4} = 200 \div 4$

$= 50$ miles per hour

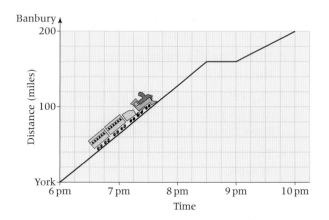

Example

Tom cycled to Sam's house.
The graph shows his journey.

a Work out the average speed in km per hour for the first part of Tom's journey.

b Tom stayed at Sam's house for $1\frac{1}{2}$ hours. He then cycled home at a steady speed of 20 km per hour.
Copy and complete the graph to show this information.

a First part of journey, Tom cycles 8 km in $\frac{1}{2}$ hour.

Method 1
Average speed in km per hour
= number of km cycled in 1 hour
8 km in $\frac{1}{2}$ hour → 16 km in 1 hour
Average speed = 16 km per hour

Method 2
Using the formula:
Average speed = $8 \div \frac{1}{2}$
$= 16$ km per hour

For speeds in km per hour, use distances in km and times in hours.

b Tom cycles home at 20 km per hour.
So it takes him 1 hour to cycle the 20 km home.

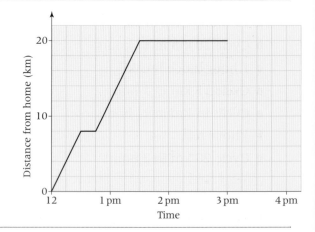

Steady speed
means no stops or change in speed.

1 The graph shows Shani's journey to her grandmother's house.

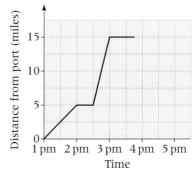

  a What was the total distance she travelled?

  b What was the total time for the journey?

  c Work out the average speed for the complete journey using the formula

  $$\text{Average speed} = \frac{\text{total distance}}{\text{total time}}$$

  d Copy and complete:

  Average speed for first part of journey $= \frac{}{2} = $ _____ km per hour

  e Work out the average speed for the second part of her journey.

  f Which part of the journey was fastest: first or second?

  g Copy and complete:

  The steeper the graph, the _____ the speed.

2 The graph illustrates a boat trip to two islands and then back to port.

  a How far from port was the first island?

  b How long did the boat stop at the first island?

  c From the graph, on which part of the trip was the boat travelling fastest?
  Explain how you know.

  d Work out the average speed for the trip to the first island.

  e How many miles is it from the first island to the second?

  f How long did it take to travel from the first island to the second?

  g Work out the average speed for the second part of the trip, to the second island.

  Use your answers to parts **e** and **f**.

  h How far is the second island from the port?

  i The boat waited for $\frac{3}{4}$ hour at the second island and then sailed back to port at a steady speed of 15 miles per hour.
  Copy and complete the graph for the trip.

  j What time did the boat arrive back in port?

3 Here is a graph showing part of Dave's trip to the dentist.

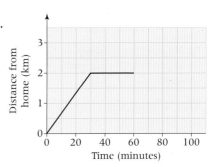

  a How far is the dentist's from Dave's home?

  b Dave took 30 minutes to walk to the dentist's.
  Work out his walking speed in km/h.

  c Dave was at the dentist's for 30 minutes.
  Then he jogged home at 6 km/h.
  Copy and complete the travel graph.

Real-life graphs

This spread will show you how to:

● Understand the trend shown by a graph

Keywords
Decrease
Increase
Trend

● The shape of a graph shows the **trend**.

The graph shows the numbers of video recorders sold over the past 10 years.

The trend is that the number of video recorders sold is **decreasing**.

You can read information from a graph, but read the axis labels and scale carefully.

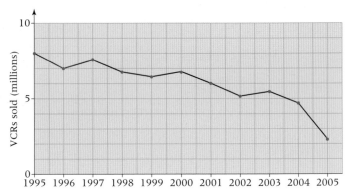

Example

The graph shows the amount of rainwater in a barrel over a few days.

a On day 1 it rained heavily. What happened to the amount of water in the barrel?
b On which day was 25 litres poured out of the barrel?
c What happened to the amount of water on day 2? Suggest a reason for this.

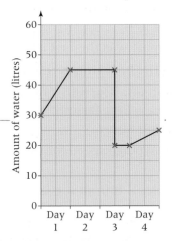

a The amount of water increased.
b Day 3, as the amount suddenly reduced by 25 litres.
c Amount of water stayed the same. It probably did not rain on day 2 and no water was poured out.

Think what could affect the amount of water.

● A straight line shows that a quantity is changing at a steady rate.
The steeper the slope, the faster the change.

quantity **increasing**   no change   quantity **decreasing**

The graphs show the water level as two tanks fill with water.

Water is poured into both tanks at a steady rate.
The first tank fills more slowly, as it is wider.
The second tank fills more quickly, as it is narrower.

The steeper the slope, the faster the change in water level.

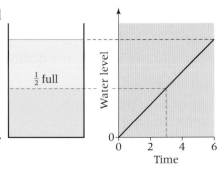

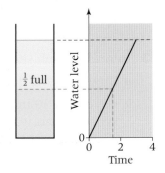

Exercise A8.5

1 The graph shows sales of 'Time 2 Chat' mobile phones.

a How many phones were sold in March?

b How many phones were sold in June?

c How many more phones were sold in June than in January?

d Here are the sales figures for the next three months.

Month	October	November	December
Number of phones sold	250	325	400

Copy the graph and complete it for this information.

e What happened to sales in November and December? Suggest a reason for this.

f What overall trend does the graph show?

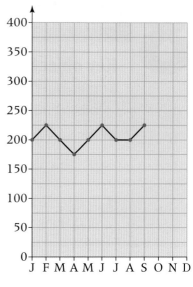

2 The graph shows how a bean plant grew from a seed over several weeks.

a How tall was the plant after 6 weeks?

b How much did the plant grow between weeks 8 and 10?

c How tall did the plant grow in total?

d How much did the plant grow between 15 and 20 weeks.

e Is the plant likely to reach a height of 3 metres? Explain your answer.

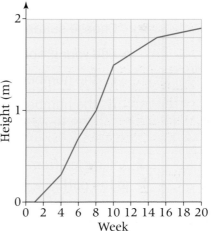

3 Rain rushes into these rain barrels at a steady rate. The graphs show how the water level changes. Match each graph to a rain barrel.

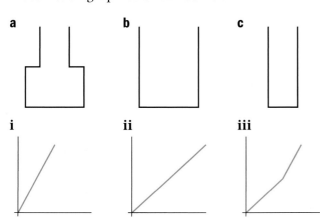

Key objectives

- Construct linear functions and plot the corresponding graphs arising from real-life problems
- Discuss and interpret graphs arising from real situations

1 The table shows the conversion rate between UK pounds sterling and Hong Kong dollars.

UK pounds sterling £	5	10		20
Hong Kong dollars $	70		210	

    a Copy and complete the table. (2)

    b Draw a conversion graph for this data.
       Choose suitable axes and a suitable scale (3)

    c Use your graph to find:

      i the number of Hong Kong dollars equivalent to £12 sterling

      ii the number of UK pounds sterling equivalent to 238 Hong Kong dollars. (2)

2 Anil cycled from his home to the park.

Anil waited in the park.

Then he cycled back home.

Here is a distance–time graph for Anil's complete journey:

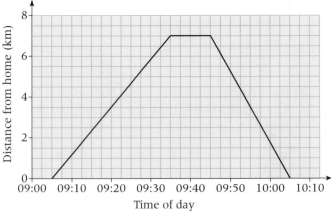

    a At what time did Anil leave home? (1)

    b What is the distance from Anil's home to the park? (1)

    c How many minutes did Anil wait in the park? (1)

    d Work out Anil's average speed on his journey home. (3)
       Give your answer in kilometres per hour.

(Edexcel Ltd., 2004)

S8

This unit will show you how to

- Use rotations and translations to make tessellations
- Recognise congruent polygons
- Understand and use angle properties
- Understand, recall and use Pythagoras' theorem
- Calculate the length and midpoint of the line AB

Before you start ...

You should be able to answer these questions.

1 State the sum of the three angles a, b, c.

a

b

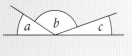

Unit S2

2 Copy the triangles and rotate them through 180° about the pivot (•).

a

b

Unit S3

3 Copy the diagram to squared paper and translate the shape by $\begin{pmatrix} 4 \\ -1 \end{pmatrix}$.

Unit S3

4 Calculate the area of the square, stating the units of your answer.

10 cm

10 cm

Unit S1

5 Round these numbers to 1 decimal place.

a 3.74   b 3.87

c 8.75   d 13.55

Unit N2

Review

Polygons and Pythagoras

S8.1 Tessellations

This spread will show you how to:

- Use rotations and translations to make tessellations
- Recognise congruent polygons

Keywords
Congruent
Regular
Rotate
Tessellation
Translate

A **tessellation** is a tiling pattern with no gaps or overlaps.
You can **rotate**, **translate** and repeat shapes to make a tessellation.

Example

a Give the mathematical name of this shape.
b Show how the shape tessellates.

a It has 6 sides. It is a hexagon.   **b**

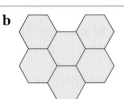

These shapes are
congruent – they
are the same size
and shape.

- Any triangle tessellates.
  Rotate the triangle about the midpoint of a side.

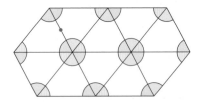

The six angles add
to 360°.

- Any quadrilateral tessellates.
  Rotate the quadrilateral about the midpoint of a side.

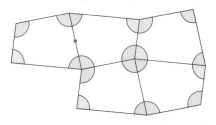 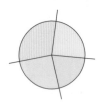

The four angles
add to 360°.

- Only three regular shapes tessellate.

Equilateral triangles   Squares   Hexagons

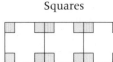

  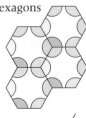

A **regular** shape
has equal sides
and equal angles.

The angles at a
point add to 360°.

1 a Calculate the interior angle of a regular hexagon.

   b Explain why a regular hexagon tessellates.

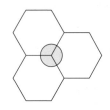

2 Calculate the interior angle of a regular octagon. Show your working.

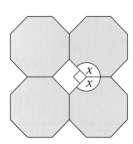

See page 90 to remind yourself about interior angles.

3 Six kites fit together as shown. Calculate the values of *a* and *b*.

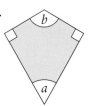

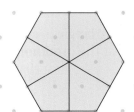

4 Twelve right-angled triangles fit together as shown. Calculate the values of *a* and *b*.

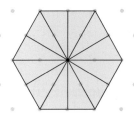

5 This pattern uses congruent equilateral triangles, rectangles and a hexagon.

   a Calculate the interior angle of the hexagon.

   b Show that the hexagon is regular.

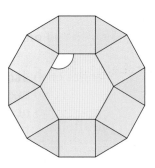

6 Does a regular pentagon tessellate? Explain your answer.

Using parallel lines

This spread will show you how to:

- Understand and use angle properties

Keywords
Alternate angle
Corresponding
   angles
Exterior angle
Interior angle
Parallel
Parallelogram
Proof

When a line crosses **parallel** lines, eight angles are formed.

- **Alternate angles** are equal

- **Corresponding angles** are equal

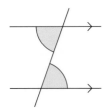

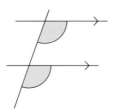

These are Z angles   These are F angles

You can use these parallel line angle properties for three **proofs**.

Proof 1

The **exterior angle** of a triangle is equal to the sum of the **interior angles** at the other two vertices.

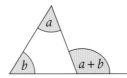

For exterior angles you extend each side in the same direction.

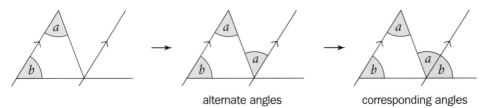

alternate angles   corresponding angles

Proof 2

The sum of the interior angles of a triangle is 180°.

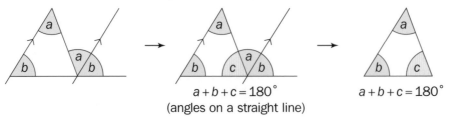

$a + b + c = 180°$
(angles on a straight line)

$a + b + c = 180°$

Proof 3

The opposite angles of a **parallelogram** are equal.

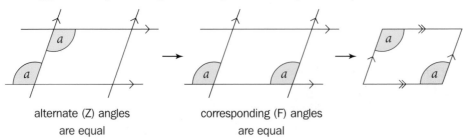

alternate (Z) angles   corresponding (F) angles
are equal   are equal

1 Find the value of the angles marked by a letter. Give a reason for each answer.

a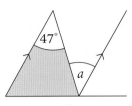

b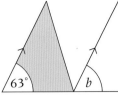

c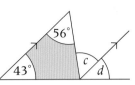

d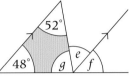

e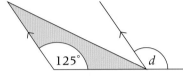

2 Find the value of the angles marked by a letter.

a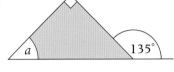

b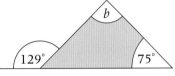

c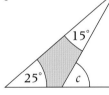

d

e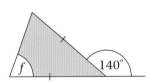

3 Find the value of the angles marked by a letter.

a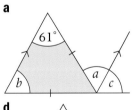

b

c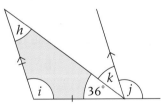

d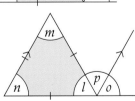

e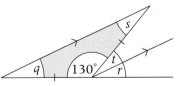

4 Find the value of the angles marked by a letter.

a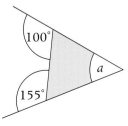

b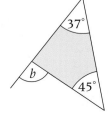

c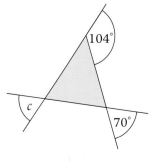

Pythagoras' theorem

This spread will show you how to:

● Understand, recall and use Pythagoras' theorem

Keywords

Hypotenuse
Pythagoras'
  theorem
Right-angled
  triangle
Square
Square root

The longest side of a **right-angled triangle** is
called the **hypotenuse**.
The hypotenuse is always opposite the right angle.

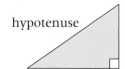

hypotenuse

This is a right-angled triangle.

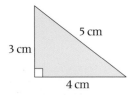

Draw the **squares** on each side.

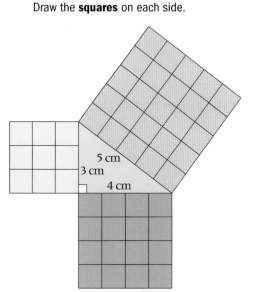

Calculate the areas of the squares.

Area of yellow square $= 3 \times 3 = 9$ cm^2
Area of red square $= 4 \times 4 = 16$ cm^2
Area of orange square $= 5 \times 5 = 25$ cm^2

Area of orange square = area of yellow square
+ area of red square.

This is **Pythagoras' theorem**.

● In a right-angled triangle, $c^2 = a^2 + b^2$ where c is the hypotenuse.

Calculate the unknown lengths in these triangles.

a

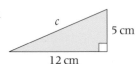

b

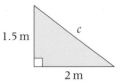

---

a Label the sides.

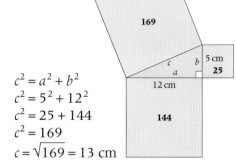

$c^2 = a^2 + b^2$
$c^2 = 5^2 + 12^2$
$c^2 = 25 + 144$
$c^2 = 169$
$c = \sqrt{169} = 13$ cm

b Label the sides.

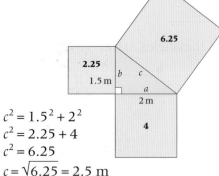

$c^2 = 1.5^2 + 2^2$
$c^2 = 2.25 + 4$
$c^2 = 6.25$
$c = \sqrt{6.25} = 2.5$ m

$\sqrt{}$ means
square root.

$\sqrt{169} = 13$
because
$13 \times 13 = 169$.

1 Calculate the area of these squares. State the units of your answers.

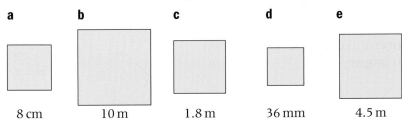

a   b   c   d   e

8 cm   10 m   1.8 m   36 mm   4.5 m

2 Calculate the length of a side of these squares.
State the units of your answers.

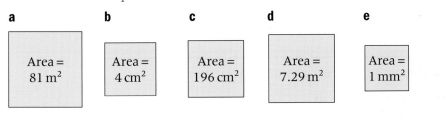

a   b   c   d   e

Area = 81 m²   Area = 4 cm²   Area = 196 cm²   Area = 7.29 m²   Area = 1 mm²

3 Calculate the unknown area for these right-angled triangles.

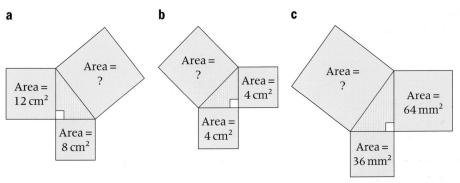

a   b   c

a: Area = 12 cm², Area = ?, Area = 8 cm²

b: Area = ?, Area = 4 cm², Area = 4 cm²

c: Area = ?, Area = 64 mm², Area = 36 mm²

DID YOU KNOW?

Pythagoras was a Greek mathematician most famous for his theorem, who taught his students that 'all things are numbers'.

4 Calculate the length of the hypotenuse in these right-angled triangles. State the units of your answers.

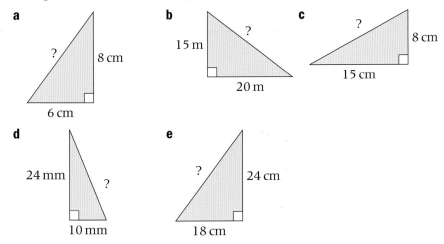

a: ?, 8 cm, 6 cm

b: 15 m, ?, 20 m

c: ?, 8 cm, 15 cm

d: 24 mm, ?, 10 mm

e: ?, 24 cm, 18 cm

More Pythagoras' theorem

This spread will show you how to:

● Understand, recall and use Pythagoras' theorem

Keywords

Hypotenuse
Pythagoras'
  theorem
Right-angled
  triangle
Square
Square root

You use **Pythagoras' theorem** to calculate an unknown length in a **right-angled triangle**.

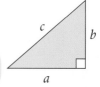

● Pythagoras' theorem states

For any right-angled triangle, $c^2 = a^2 + b^2$ where c is the hypotenuse.

You can use Pythagoras' theorem to find a side given two other sides.

● You add to find the **hypotenuse**.
● You subtract to find the other sides.

The triangle must be right-angled.

Example

Calculate the unknown length in these right-angled triangles.

a

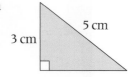

5 cm
3 cm

b

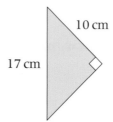

10 cm
17 cm

a Label the sides.

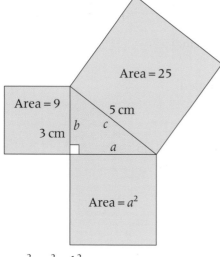

Area = 25
Area = 9
3 cm
5 cm
b   c
a
Area = a^2

$a^2 = c^2 - b^2$
$a^2 = 5^2 - 3^2$
$\quad = 25 - 9$
$a^2 = 16$
$\;a = \sqrt{16} = 4$ cm

b Label the sides.

a
c
b

$b^2 = c^2 - a^2$
$b^2 = 17^2 - 10^2$
$\quad = 189$
$b = \sqrt{189}$
$\quad = 13.7$ cm (to 1 dp)

You don't need to draw the squares on the sides.

1 Calculate the unknown area of the square for these right-angled triangles.

a

Area =
10 cm²

Area =
?

Area =
6 cm²

b

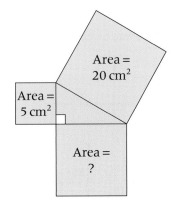

Area =
20 cm²

Area =
5 cm²

Area =
?

2 Calculate the unknown length in these right-angled triangles.
Give the units of your answers.

a

15 cm 12 cm

?

b

? 13 mm

5 mm

c

40 m ?

32 m

d

30 cm 34 cm

?

e

6.5 m ?

6 m

3 Calculate the unknown length in these right-angled triangles.
Give your answers to a suitable degree of accuracy.

a

6 cm

3 cm

?

b

10 m ?

7 m

c

12 cm 8 cm

?

d

? 45 m

28 m

e

41 cm 40 cm

?

f

?

15 cm

36 cm

4 **a** Calculate the perpendicular height of this
right-angled triangle.

b Calculate the perimeter of the triangle.

c Calculate the area of the triangle.

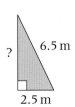

? 6.5 m

2.5 m

This spread will show you how to:

● Calculate the length and midpoint of the line AB

Keywords

Coordinates
Line segment
Midpoint

● The **midpoint M** of a line AB is halfway along it.

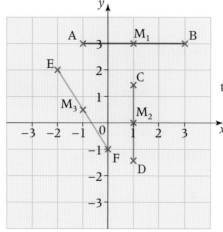

If A = (−1, 3)
and B = (3, 3)
then M_1 = (1, 3)

If C = (1, 1½)
and D = (1, −1½)
then M_2 = (1, 0)

If E = (−2, 2)
and F = (0, −1)
then M_3 = (−1, ½)

M is the midpoint.

● If A = (x_1, y_1) and B = (x_2, y_2) then M = $\left(\dfrac{x_1 + x_2}{2}, \dfrac{y_1 + y_2}{2}\right)$.

The midpoint of AB
is the mean of the
coordinates of
points A and B.

Example

Calculate the coordinates of the midpoint between the points

a (7, 1) and (−3, 5) **b** (4, −1) and (2, −2)

a (7, 1) = (x_1, y_1) and (−3, 5) = (x_2, y_2)
  Midpoint = $(\frac{7-3}{2}, \frac{1+5}{2})$
    = $(\frac{4}{2}, \frac{6}{2})$
    = (2, 3)

b (4, −1) = (x_1, y_1) and (2, −2) = (x_2, y_2)
  Midpoint = $(\frac{4+2}{2}, \frac{-1-2}{2})$
    = $(\frac{6}{2}, \frac{-3}{2})$
    = (3, −1½)

You use Pythagoras' theorem to find the length of a line on a grid.

Example

Calculate the length of the **line segment**
from (2, 4) to (5, 2).

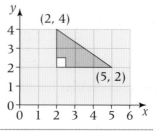

$c^2 = 2^2 + 3^2$
$c^2 = 4 + 9$
$c^2 = 13$
$c = \sqrt{13} = 3.60555 = 3.6$ units (to 1 dp)

Label the sides.

1 a Draw the points A(1, 3) and B(5, 1) on a copy of the grid.

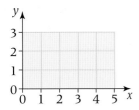

b M is the midpoint of the line AB.
Find the coordinates of the point M.

2 Calculate the coordinates of the midpoint between the points

a (3, 1) and (3, 5)

b (0, 4) and (4, 4)

c (2, −2) and (2, 4)

d (3, 1) and (7, 7)

e (−2, −1) and (6, 7)

3 The point (3, 4) is the midpoint between (x, 6) and (1, y).
Find the values of x and y.

4 Calculate the distance between these points.
Give your answers to a suitable degree of accuracy.

a (1, 2) and (4, 6)

b (2, 2) and (6, 5)

c (1, 2) and (2, 5)

d (0, 5) and (4, 1)

e (3, 6) and (6, 0)

5 a Plot the points A(0, 3), B(3, 6), C(6, 3) and D(3, 0) on square
grid paper.

b What is the name of the shape ABCD?

c Calculate the length of AB.

d Calculate the length of AD.

e Calculate the area of the shape ABCD.

Key objectives

- Use parallel lines, alternate angles and corresponding angles
- Understand, recall and use Pythagoras' theorem in 2-D problems
- Find the coordinates of the midpoint of the line segment AB, given points A and B

1

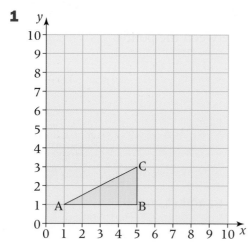

a Calculate the length from A to C. (3)

Give your answer to 1 decimal place.

b Find the coordinates of the midpoint, M, of the line AC. (3)

2 a PQR is a straight line.
SQ = SR.
  i Work out the size of the angle marked $x°$.
  ii Give reasons for your answer. (3)

b DE is parallel to FG.
  i Find the size of the angle marked $y°$.
  ii Give a reason for your answer. (2)

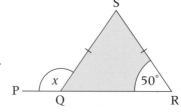

Diagram **not** accurately drawn

(Edexcel Ltd., 2004)

GCSE formulae

In your Edexcel GCSE examination you will be given a formula sheet like this on this page.

Here are the formulae that you are given in your exam.

Area of a trapezium $= \frac{1}{2}(a + b)h$

Volume of prism = area of cross section × length

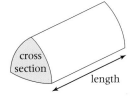

Here are some other formulae that you should learn.

Area of a rectangle = length × width

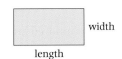

Area of a triangle $= \frac{1}{2} \times$ base × height

Area of a parallelogram = base × perpendicular height

Area of a circle $= \pi r^2$

Circumference of a circle $= \pi d = 2\pi r$

Volume of a cuboid = length × width × height

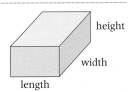

Volume of a cylinder = area of circle × length

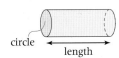

Pythagoras' theorem states,

For any right-angled triangle, $c^2 = a^2 + b^2$
where c is the hypotenuse.

Answers

N1 Before you start ...

1 0.312, 0.35, 0.37, 0.4

2 2.34

3 −8, −5, −3, −1, 2, 4

4 a 7   **b** −10   **c** −12   **d** −3

5 1, 2, 3, 4, 6, 8, 12, 16, 24, 48

N1.1

1 a Four hundred and fifty-six
  b Thirteen thousand, two hundred
  c One hundred and fifteen thousand and twenty
  d Four hundred and sixty thousand, three hundred and forty
  e Four million, three hundred and twenty-five thousand, four hundred
  f Fifty-five million, six hundred and seventy thousand, three hundred and forty-five
  g Forty-five point eight
  h Three hundred and sixty-seven point zero three
  i Four thousand, five hundred and three point three four
  j Two thousand seven hundred point zero two

2 a 538   **b** 2031   **c** 15 603   **d** 280 453
  e 417.3   **f** 1 717 338   **g** 537.403
  h 3.03

3 a 25.5   **b** 1.85   **c** 50   **d** 4.95
  e 1.375   **f** 0.705

4 a 5.007, 5.099, 5.103, 5.12, 5.2
  b 0.5, 0.509, 0.525, 0.545, 0.55
  c 7.058, 7.302, 7.35, 7.387, 7.403
  d 0.4, 0.42, 2.4, 4.2, 42
  e 26.9, 26.97, 27.06, 27.1, 27.6
  f 13.19, 13.3, 13.43, 14.03, 14.15

5 a 320   **b** 4   **c** 1.52   **d** 0.146
  e 23.7   **f** 2430   **g** 0.0123   **h** 4.59
  i 3400   **j** 135.6   **k** 0.0236   **l** 17.45
  m 0.392   **n** 0.728   **o** 0.0124   **p** 8.14

6 a 96.6   **b** 937.3   **c** 22.23   **d** 24 140

N1.2

1 a 3.8   **b** 4.25   **c** 540   **d** 4.8

2 a 6.5 cm   **b** 4.75 kg
  c 1154 °C   **d** 3.24 tonnes

3 a About 7.3 cm   **b** About 68.3 ml
  c About 46.7 mph   **d** About 8.37 °C
  e About 54 g   **f** About 3.3 cm
  g About 3.73 ml   **h** About 2800 °C

4 a 13 : 59   **b** 15 : 21
  c 2 h 7 min   **d** 1 h 20 min

N1.3

1 a −13, −12, −6, 0, 15, 17
  b −8, −7, −6, −5, −3, 0
  c −5, −2, 1, 2, 3, 4
  d −8, −3, −1.5, 2, 3, 9
  e −5, −4.5, −3, −2, 2, 3
  f −9, −1, 2, 3, 6, 8
  g −4.5, −3, −2.5, −1, 0, 5.5
  h −6, −5.8, −5.7, −5.4, −5.1, −5

2 a 16   **b** −7   **c** 4   **d** 37
  e 17   **f** −7   **g** 9   **h** −11
  i −8   **j** 21   **k** −8   **l** −2
  m −18   **n** 4   **o** −5   **p** 2
  q −20   **r** 10   **s** −8   **t** −28
  u −18   **v** −3   **w** −9

3 a 31   **b** −11   **c** 4   **d** −7
  e 5.5   **f** 2.5   **g** 7.5   **h** −0.5

4 a 6, 5, 4, 3
  b 8, 9, 10, 11
  c 13, 12, 11, 10, 9, 8
  d 11, 12, 13, 14, 15, 16
Adding −1 is the same as subtracting 1, and subtracting −1 is the same as adding 1, etc.

5 a 8   **b** −2   **c** 9   **d** 0
  e −13   **f** −14   **g** −14   **h** 20
  i 12   **j** 3   **k** −5   **l** −6
  m 4   **n** −25   **o** −1   **p** 1
  q −9   **r** −23   **s** −9   **t** −23

N1.4

1 a −8, −12, −16   **b** −7, 0, 7, 14, 21, 28

2 a −2   **b** 2   **c** −3   **d** 3
  e −4   **f** 4

3 a 6   **b** 30   **c** −21   **d** 8
  e −20   **f** 24   **g** −24   **h** 42
  i 16   **j** 50   **k** 5   **l** −8
  m 5   **n** 5   **o** −9   **p** −63
  q −49   **r** 72   **s** −9   **t** −6
  u −4   **v** −10   **w** 9   **x** −56
  y −13

4 a $+ \times - = -$, −20   **c** $- \times - = +$, 30
  d $- \times - = +$, 28   **f** $+ \times + = +$, 40
  g $+ \times - = -$, −35   **h** $- \div - = +$, 8
  j $- \times - = +$, 70

5 a −120   **b** 132   **c** −225   **d** −147
  e −117   **f** −133   **g** −414   **h** −40
  i −13   **j** −67.2   **k** −3   **l** 10
  m −6   **n** −50

N1.5

1 a 2, 4, 5, 10, 20   **b** 2, 3, 4, 6, 8, 12, 16
  c 5, 10, 15, 20   **d** 2, 3, 5, 17, 19

2 a $1 \times 24, 2 \times 12, 3 \times 8, 4 \times 6$
  b $1 \times 45, 3 \times 15, 5 \times 9$
  c $1 \times 66, 2 \times 33, 3 \times 22, 6 \times 11$
  d $1 \times 100, 2 \times 50, 4 \times 25, 5 \times 20, 10 \times 10$
  e $1 \times 120, 2 \times 60, 3 \times 40, 4 \times 30, 5 \times 24, 6 \times 20,$
    $8 \times 15, 10 \times 12$
  f $1 \times 132, 2 \times 66, 3 \times 44, 4 \times 33, 6 \times 22,$
    11×12
  g $1 \times 160, 2 \times 80, 4 \times 40, 5 \times 32, 8 \times 20,$
    10×16
  h $1 \times 180, 2 \times 90, 3 \times 60, 4 \times 45, 5 \times 36, 6 \times 30,$
    $9 \times 20, 10 \times 18, 12 \times 15$
  i $1 \times 360, 2 \times 180, 3 \times 120, 4 \times 90, 5 \times 72,$
    $6 \times 60, 8 \times 45, 9 \times 40, 10 \times 36, 12 \times 30,$
    $15 \times 24, 18 \times 20$
  j $1 \times 324, 2 \times 162, 3 \times 108, 4 \times 81, 6 \times 54,$
    $9 \times 36, 12 \times 27, 18 \times 18$
  k $1 \times 224, 2 \times 112, 4 \times 56, 7 \times 32, 8 \times 28,$
    14×16
  l $1 \times 264, 2 \times 132, 3 \times 88, 4 \times 66, 6 \times 44,$
    $8 \times 33, 11 \times 24, 12 \times 22$
  m $1 \times 312, 2 \times 156, 3 \times 104, 4 \times 78, 6 \times 52,$
    $8 \times 39, 12 \times 26, 13 \times 24$
  n $1 \times 325, 5 \times 65, 13 \times 25$
  o $1 \times 432, 2 \times 216, 3 \times 144, 4 \times 108, 6 \times 72,$
    $8 \times 54, 9 \times 48, 12 \times 36, 16 \times 27, 18 \times 24$
3 a 17, 34, 51   **b** 29, 58, 87
  c 42, 84, 126   **d** 25, 50, 75
  e 47, 94, 141   **f** 35, 70, 105
  g 90, 180, 270   **h** 120, 240, 360
  i 95, 190, 285   **j** 208, 416, 624
4 324
5 a 2   **b** 5   **c** 6   **d** 8
  e 15   **f** 18   **g** 25   **h** 12
  i 15
6 a 12   **b** 40   **c** 36   **d** 75
  e 42   **f** 150
7 a 120 seconds   **b** 18 cm × 18 cm

N1 Exam review
1 a

bi 1000   **bii** 0.1387   **biii** ÷   **biv** 1387

2 ai 7 °C   **aii** −10 °C
  bi 6 °C   **bii** 8 °C
  c −7 °C

S1 Before you start …
1 a 600   **b** 71 000   **c** 48   **d** 2630
  e 4500   **f** 6   **g** 75   **h** 6.5
  i 3.2   **j** 0.24
2 a 27   **b** $22\frac{1}{2}$ **c** $10\frac{1}{2}$ **d** 40
  e $9\frac{3}{5}$
3 a 9   **b** 15.5   **c** 7.8
4 a 48 mm   **b** 4.8 cm
5 Perimeter = 26 cm, Area = 40 cm^2
6 5 cubes

S1.1
1 a cm or m **b** ml or cl **c** kg   **d** cm
  e kg   **f** km   **g** ml or cl **h** litre
  i tonne   **j** g
2 a 2 cm   **b** 4 m   **c** 4.5 m   **d** 4 km
  e 5 mm   **f** 4500 g   **g** 6 kg   **h** 6.5 kg
  i 2.5 t   **j** 3000 ml
3 a 10 miles **b** 25 miles **c** 55 miles
  d 52.5 miles
4 a 2.5 cm   **b** 12.5 cm **c** 15 cm
  d 30 cm   **e** 90 cm
5 a 4.4 lb   **b** 88 lb   **c** 110 lb
  d 1.1 lb   **e** 5.5 lb
6 a 180 g butter, 360 g caster sugar
  b 240 g rice, 120 g raisins, 90 g sugar,
    120 g currants
  c 180 g self-raising flour, 60 g corn flour,
    60 g cornflakes, 30 g drinking chocolate,
    180 g margarine, 90 g sugar
7 112 km/h

S1.2
1 a 12 m, 8 m^2 **b** 19 cm, 12 cm^2
  c 39 mm, 81 mm^2 **d** 26.8 cm, 43.2 cm^2
  e 30.4 m, 38.4 m^2
2 a 12 cm^2 **b** 30 m^2 **c** 14 cm^2
  d 72 mm^2 **e** 13.5 cm^2
3 a 5 cm   **b** 9 cm   **c** 12 m
4 a 32 cm, 44 cm^2 **b** 42 cm, 74 cm^2
  c 56 cm, 188 cm^2

S1.3
1 a 6   **b** 12   **c** 3
2 a 6   **b** 6   **c** 8
3 a 80 cm^2 **b** 800 m^2 **c** 120 mm^2 **d** 384 cm^2
4 a 50 cm^2 **b** 375 mm^2 **c** 28 m^2 **d** 160 cm^2
5 a 6 m   **b** 14 cm   **c** 8 mm   **d** 8 cm
6 a $\frac{1}{2} \times 10 \times (10 + 20) = 150$ cm^2
  b $25 + 100 + 25 = 150$ cm^2

S1.4

1 **a** 31.4 cm   **b** 25.12 m   **c** 37.68 cm
   d 62.8 m   **e** 12.56 m   **f** 50.24 cm
   g 9.42 m   **h** 21.98 cm

2 **a** 6 cm   **b** 5 m   **c** 9 cm
   d 15 m   **e** 100 cm

3 **a** 153.86 cm^2 **b** 78.5 m^2 **c** 50.24 cm^2
   d 28.26 m^2 **e** 314 m^2 **f** 200.96 cm^2
   g 113.04 mm^2 **h** 254.34 cm^2

4 **a** 3 m   **b** 9.4 m   **c** 7.1 m^2

S1.5

1 **a** 36 cm^3 **b** 250 m^3 **c** 240 cm^3

2 100

3 **a** 288 m^3 **b** 76.9 cm^3 **c** 55.3 cm^3

4 6 cm

5 **a** 3 cm   **b** 5.7 cm   **c** 8.7 m

6 **a** 1500 cm^3 **b** 440 cm^3 **c** 324 cm^3

S1 Exam review

1 20 cm

2 116.8 cm^2

A1 Before you start …

1 **ai** 3×2 **aii** 6×5 **aiii** 4×10 **aiv** 3×7
   bi 6   **bii** 30   **biii** 40   **biv** 21

2 **ai** 9   **aii** 9   **aiii** 9
   b Order does not matter when adding (commutative).

3 **ai** 30   **aii** 30   **aiii** 30
   b Order does not matter when multiplying (commutative).

4 **a** 5   **b** 9   **c** 4   **d** 10

5 **ai** 1, 2, 3, 6, 9, 18   **aii** 1, 2, 3, 4, 6, 12
   aiii 1, 2, 3, 4, 6, 8, 12, 24
   b 1, 2, 3, 6   **c** 6

A1.1

1 **a** $4b$ **b** $2y$ **c** $3a$
   d $9p$ **e** $3x$ **f** $6z$

2 **a** $5p + 6q$ **b** $9x + 7y$ **c** $2m + 8n$
   d $x + 5y$ **e** $8r - 6s$ **f** $2g - 4f$
   g $2a + 6b + 5c$ **h** $5u - 2v + 3w$ **i** $3x - 4y + 5z$
   j $6r + 5s + 2t$

3 **a** $6t$ **b** $3n$ **c** $4x$

4 **a** $4x$ **b** $4x + 8$

5 **a** $2m$ **b** $3m$ **c** $12m$

6 **a** $6c$ **b** $10d$ **c** $6c + 10d$

7 **a** $50f + 30g$ **b** $80j + 40k$
   c $50x + 60y + 30z$
   d $60p + 80q + 40r$

A1.2

1 **a** y^4 **b** m^6 **c** x^3 **d** p^2

2 **a** $3t^2$ **b** $4pq^2$ **c** $6v^2w^3$ **d** $2r^4s$

3 **a** $6m^2n$ **b** $8y^3z^2$ **c** $12gh^3$ **d** $10xy^4$

4 **a** $6m^2$ **b** $12p^3$ **c** $6xy^2$ **d** $10r^2s^2$

5 **a** n^5 **b** s^7 **c** p^4 **d** t^4

6 **a** x^7 **b** x^8 **c** x^9 **d** x^7

7 **a** r^2 **b** r **c** r^5 **d** r^3

8 **a** m^4 **b** x **c** t^2 **d** y^3

9 **a** x **b** m^2 **c** s^3 **d** v^2
   e q^3 **f** t^4 **g** p **h** y^2

10 $2n^3 = 2 \times n^3$, $2 \times n \times n = 2n^2$, $n^2 = \frac{n^4}{n^2}$, $5 \times n = 5n$

A1.3

1 **a** $3m + 6$ **b** $4p + 24$ **c** $2x + 8$ **d** $5q + 5$
   e $12 + 2n$ **f** $6 + 3t$ **g** $12 + 4s$ **h** $8 + 2v$

2 **a** $6q + 3$ **b** $8m + 4$ **c** $12x + 9$ **d** $6k + 2$
   e $10 + 10n$ **f** $12 + 6p$ **g** $4 + 12y$ **h** $10 + 8z$

3 **a** $n + 5$ **b** $3(n + 5)$

4 **a** $5p + 9$ **b** $7m + 8$ **c** $2x + 4$ **d** $10 + 5k$
   e $9t + 10$ **f** $4r + 7$

5 **a** $s + 6$ **b** $2(s + 6)$ **c** $2s + 19$

6 **a** $5n + 12$ **b** $6p + 10$ **c** $10x + 10$ **d** $18n + 7$

7 **a** $12y$ **b** $y + 2$ **c** $20(y + 2)$ **d** $32y + 40$

8 **a** $4x^2 + x$ **b** $m^3 + 2m$ **c** $2t^3 + 8t$ **d** $3p^3 + 3p$

9 **a** $p^2 + 3p + 2$ **b** $15w^2 + 48w + 9$
   c $-2m^2 + 5m + 3$ **d** $y^2 + 2y + 1$

A1.4

1 **a** $9r$ **b** $4m^2$ **c** $4x$ **d** $8tv$
   e $10mn$ **f** $6xy^2$ **g** $2x^2 + x$ **h** $9w - 8$
   i $z^3 + 3z + 1$

2 **a** $8y + 12$ **b** $6x - 4$ **c** $6k - 6$ **d** $4 - 4n$

3 **a** $k^2 + k$ **b** $m^2 + 7m$ **c** $10t + 5$

4 **a** $2m^2 - 6m$ **b** $8p^2 - 4p$ **c** $r^3 + 3r$ **d** $2s^3 - 8s$

5 **a** $5r + 4$ **b** $2s$ **c** $4j + 5$ **d** $15t - 9$

6 **a** $12m^2 - 9m - 3$ **b** $6p^2 - 14p + 4$
   c $-10q^2 + 15q + 45$ **d** $8v^2 - 20v + 12$

7 **a** $n + 4$, $3(n + 4)$, $4n$, $4n - 2$, $2(4n - 2)$
   b $5n - 16$

A1.5

1 **a** 1, 2   **b** 1, 2, 4   **c** 1, 2, 5, 10
   d 1, 2, 3, 6   **e** 1, 3   **f** 1, 2
   g 1, 2   **h** 1, 2, 4, 8

2 **a** 3   **b** 2   **c** 2   **d** 4

3 **a** y **b** s **c** m **d** $2y$

4 **a** $2(x + 5)$ **b** $3(y + 5)$ **c** $4(2p - 1)$
   d $3(2 + m)$ **e** $5(n + 1)$ **f** $6(2 - t)$
   g $2(7 + 2k)$ **h** $3(3z - 1)$

5 **a** $w(w + 1)$ **b** $z(1 - z)$ **c** $y(4 + y)$
   d $m(2m - 3)$ **e** $p(4p + 5)$ **f** $k(7 - 2k)$
   g $n(3n^2 - 2)$ **h** $r(5 + 3r)$

6 $4(x + 3) = 4x + 12$, $4x^2 - 3x = x(4x - 3)$,
   $3(x - 4) = 3x - 12$, $4x + 3x^2 = x(4 + 3x)$

7 **a** $4(y - 3)$ **b** $x(2x + 3)$ **c** $y(3y - 1)$
   d $5(3 + t^2)$ **e** $3m(1 + 3m)$ **f** $2r(r - 1)$
   g $v(4v^2 + 1)$ **h** $3w(w + 1)$

8 a Kate

b Debbie should have an 8 in front of the x^2-term inside the bracket. If she had included this, she would have been able to take out more factors. Bryn should have $8x$ rather than $8x^2$ as the first term in the bracket. He can take out a further factor of 2.

A1 Exam review

1 a $2x + 2$ **b** $x + x^2$ **c** $x^2 - xy$
2 a $2y$ **b** $3p^2$ **c** $x(x - 3)$

N2 Before you start …

1 a 35 000   **b** 35 300   **c** 35 270
2 a 435   **b** 186
3 32.4 kg
4 a 72   **b** 42   **c** 12   **d** $4\frac{23}{30}$
5 a 1392   **b** 17

N2.1

1 ai 3490   **aii** 3500   **aiii** 3000
  bi 3390   **bii** 3400   **biii** 3000
  ci 14 850 m   **cii** 14 900 m   **ciii** 15 000 m
  di £57 790   **dii** £57 800   **diii** £58 000
  ei 92 640 kg   **eii** 92 600 kg   **eiii** 93 000 kg
  fi £86 190   **fii** £86 200   **fiii** £86 000
  gi 3440   **gii** 3400   **giii** 3000
  hi 74 900   **hii** 74 900   **hiii** 75 000
2 a 4   **b** 29   **c** 469   **d** 369
  e 20   **f** 27   **g** 101   **h** 0
3 ai 3.447   **aii** 3.45   **aiii** 3.4
  bi 8.948   **bii** 8.95   **biii** 8.9
  ci 0.128   **cii** 0.13   **ciii** 0.1
  di 28.387   **dii** 28.39   **diii** 28.4
  ei 17.999   **eii** 18.00   **eiii** 18.0
  fi 10.000   **fii** 10.00   **fiii** 10.0
  gi 0.004   **gii** 0.00   **giii** 0.0
  hi 2785.556   **hii** 2785.56   **hiii** 2785.6
  ii 158.852   **iii** 158.85   **iiii** 158.9
4 ai 8.37   **aii** 8.4   **aiii** 8
  bi 18.8   **bii** 19   **biii** 20
  ci 35.8   **cii** 36   **ciii** 40
  di 279   **dii** 280   **diii** 300
  ei 1.39   **eii** 1.4   **eiii** 1
  fi 3890   **fii** 3900   **fiii** 4000
  gi 0.008 37   **gii** 0.0084   **giii** 0.008
  hi 2400   **hii** 2400   **hiii** 2000
  ii 8.99   **iii** 9.0   **iiii** 9
  ji 14.0   **jii** 14   **jiii** 10
  ki 1400   **kii** 1400   **kiii** 1000
  li 140 000   **lii** 140 000   **liii** 100 000
  mi 3280   **mii** 3300   **miii** 3000

5 a $5 \times 6 = 30$ **b** $18 + 22 = 40$ **c** $\frac{6 \times 3}{9} = 2$
d $35 - 10 = 25$ **e** $\frac{33 \times 5}{3} = 55$
f $(10^2 + 9)^2 \approx 100^2 = 10\,000$

6 ai 66.5 cm   **aii** 67.5 cm
  bi 34.65 litres   **bii** 34.75 litres
  ci 8.355 kg   **cii** 8.365 kg
  di 0.3865 mm   **dii** 0.3875 mm
7 a 2.65 m   **b** 2.55 m

N2.2

1 a 270   **b** 80   **c** 330   **d** 40
  e 3800   **f** 70   **g** 210   **h** 390
2 a 63   **b** 0.6   **c** 0.69   **d** 2.7
3 a 355   **b** 560   **c** 950   **d** 808
  e 567   **f** 889   **g** 14.3   **h** 20.7

4

+	2.9	4.8	3.9	2.5	5.9	5.7
3.1	6	7.9	7	5.6	9	8.8
6.5	9.4	11.3	10.4	9	12.4	12.2
8.2	11.1	13	12.1	10.7	14.1	13.9
4.9	7.8	9.7	8.8	7.4	10.8	10.6
7.1	10	11.9	11	9.6	13	12.8
9.6	12.5	14.4	13.5	12.1	15.5	15.3

5 a 248 km   **b** 263 words
  c 265 marks   **d** 169 minutes
6 a 18.7; 8.7, 10; 5.2, 3.5, 6.5; 4.6, 0.6, 2.9, 3.6
  b 25; 12.7, 12.3; 5.8, 6.9, 5.4; 3.7, 2.1, 4.8, 0.6

N2.3

1 a 36.8   **b** 78.3   **c** 27.1   **d** 42.1
2 a 6.2   **b** 7.1   **c** 8.5   **d** 27.9
3 a 10.72   **b** 19.72   **c** 18.11   **d** 141.99
4 a 8.05   **b** 4.73   **c** 38.74   **d** 18.68
5 a 34.06   **b** 44.71   **c** 3.51   **d** 24.59
  e 17.98   **f** 28.89
6 a 22.08   **b** 47.34   **c** 83.17
7 a 61.98 kg   **b** £221.80   **c** 5.87 m
  d 30.73 kg   **e** 3.525 kg   **f** 7.97 m

N2.4

1 a 56   **b** 7.2   **c** 9.4   **d** 240
  e 72   **f** 0.675   **g** 465   **h** 63
2 a 460   **b** 1.7   **c** 127   **d** 0.0082
3 a 84   **b** 126   **c** 21   **d** 26
  e 187   **f** 279   **g** 32   **h** 174
  i 182   **j** 609   **k** 899   **l** 1485
4 a 17.6   **b** 168   **c** 79.2   **d** 86.8
  e 126   **f** 76.8   **g** 206   **h** 79
5 a 153   **b** 207   **c** 25.3   **d** 97.9
  e 46.2   **f** 111.3   **g** 114.3   **h** 716.1
6 a 86   **b** 22   **c** 568   **d** 216
  e 32   **f** 948   **g** 96   **h** 28

7 a 244   **b** 36   **c** 128   **d** 24
   e 14   **f** 15.3   **g** 10.5   **h** 12.2
8 a 46.2   **b** 46   **c** 18.2   **d** 60
   e 6   **f** 2175   **g** 3   **h** 30
9 a 90 kg   **b** £31

N2.5

1 a 216   **b** 588   **c** 2943   **d** 364
   e 728   **f** 875   **g** 1610   **h** 3888
   i 10 336   **j** 4642   **k** 5320   **l** 9222
2 a 26   **b** 23   **c** 33   **d** 38
   e 37   **f** 68   **g** 15 r 5   **h** 46 r 3
3 a 38.4   **b** 108.1   **c** 147.2   **d** 120.9
   e 153.6   **f** 649.7
4 a 20.02   **b** 27.68   **c** 32.81   **d** 34.5
   e 141.81   **f** 61.56   **g** 83.3   **h** 511.92
   i 769.11
5 a 319.7   **b** 688.5   **c** 1205.4   **d** 805.8
   e 3365.3   **f** 1664.1
6 a £21.06   **b** £36.86   **c** £202.23
   d 39 min 2.4 sec   **e** £80.16
7 a 12   **b** 18   **c** 19   **d** 23
   e 29   **f** 21
8 a 3.8   **b** 5.9   **c** 8.4   **d** 12.4
   e 13.2   **f** 15.4   **g** 13.7   **h** 27.6
   i 43.8

N2 Exam review

1 a 2.7   **b** 20   **c** 11   **d** 28
2 855.4 kg

A2 Before you start …

1 a 8   **b** 11   **c** 7   **d** 6
2 a 7   **b** 6   **c** 15   **d** 2
3 a <   **b** >   **c** >   **d** <
4 16 cm
5 a x **b** m **c** $3n$ **d** $2p$

A2.1

1 ai 14   **aii** $28 \div 2 = 14$
   bi 26   **bii** $33 - 7 = 26$
   ci 21   **cii** $9 + 12 = 21$
   di 42   **dii** $7 \times 6 = 42$
2 a $7 \rightarrow \times 3 \rightarrow 21$ **b** $35 \rightarrow \div 5 \rightarrow 7$
   c $27 \rightarrow -8 \rightarrow 19$ **d** $6 \rightarrow \times 6 \rightarrow 36$
   e $28 \rightarrow +12 \rightarrow 40$ **f** $7 \rightarrow \times 4 \rightarrow 28$
   g $43 \rightarrow -7 \rightarrow 36$ **h** $52 \rightarrow \div 4 \rightarrow 13$
3 a $7 \leftarrow \div 3 \leftarrow 21$ **b** $35 \leftarrow \times 5 \leftarrow 7$
   c $27 \leftarrow +8 \leftarrow 19$ **d** $6 \leftarrow \div 6 \leftarrow 36$
   e $28 \leftarrow -12 \leftarrow 40$ **f** $7 \leftarrow \div 4 \leftarrow 28$
   g $43 \leftarrow +7 \leftarrow 36$ **h** $52 \leftarrow \times 4 \leftarrow 13$
4 a $a = 14$ **b** $b = 25$ **c** $c = 16$ **d** $d = 56$
   e $x = 8$ **f** $f = 40$ **g** $g = 8$ **h** $h = 196$
   i $i = 31$ **j** $j = 25$ **k** $k = 19$ **l** $m = 56$
5 a $c = 8$ **b** $d = 41$ **c** $f = 9$ **d** $g = 24$
   e $h = 20$ **f** $i = 42$ **g** $j = 9$ **h** $k = 22$

   i $l = 15$ **j** $m = 6$ **k** $n = 48$ **l** $q = 7$
   m $r = 32$ **n** $u = 72$
6 a $x - 12 = 11$, $x = 23$ **b** $\frac{x}{5} = 8$, $x = 40$

A2.2

1 a 5   **b** 32   **c** 10   **d** 1
   e $+5$ **f** $\times 5$
2 a $a = 6$ **b** $b = 9$ **c** $e = 28$ **d** $f = 18$
   e $g = 30$ **f** $h = 16$
3 a

	× 4	+ 3
1	4	7
2	8	11
x	$4x$	$4x + 3$
10	40	43

b

	÷ 3	− 1
12	4	3
9	3	2
x	$\frac{x}{3}$	$\frac{x}{3} - 1$
24	8	7

c

	× 5	− 3
1	5	2
2	10	7
x	$5x$	$5x - 3$
11	55	52

4 a $a = 10$ **b** $b = 9$ **c** $e = 2$ **d** $f = 15$
   e $g = 70$ **f** $i = 30$ **g** $j = 60$ **h** $k = 5$
   i $m = 1.5$ **j** $p = -2$
5 a $3x - 1 = 11$ **b** $4n + 7 = 27$
   c $5q + 3 = 33$ **d** $\frac{r}{3} + 15 = 22$
6 ai $2x + 7 = 15$ **aii** $x = 4$
   bi $4x - 5 = 13$ **bii** $x = 4.5$
   ci $\frac{x}{5} + 3 = 11$ **cii** $x = 40$

A2.3

1 a $x = 5$ **b** $x = 5$ **c** $x = 8$ **d** $x = 6$
   e $x = 5.5$ **f** $x = 50$ **g** $y = 18$ **h** $z = 40$
   i $y = 3$ **j** $p = 2$
2 a $m = 7$ **b** $p = -7$ **c** $n = 2$ **d** $q = 5$
   e $r = -11$ **f** $k = 6$ **g** $m = 5$ **h** $a = 8$
3 $16p - 15 = 33$ ($p = 3$, $m = n = 8$)
4 a $6n + 6 = 36$, $n = 5$
   b $5m - 6 = 54$, $m = 12$
5 a $2y + 16 = 36$ **b** $y = 10$
6 a 5 cm   **b** 6 cm   **c** 8 cm
   In **c** all sides are equal.

A2.4

1 a 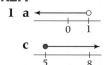   **b**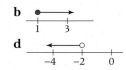
   c 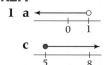   **d**

e
    0 1.5

f
  −4   0

g
  0   3

h
  −3 −1.5 0

2 ai $2x > 10$ **aii** $4x > 20$
  bi $3y \leqslant 18$ **bii** $5y \leqslant 30$
  c $5x \geqslant -20$ **d** $6m < -18$

3 a $x \leqslant 2$ **b** $x < 5$ **c** $x > -2$ **d** $x \geqslant -4$

4 a $3x > 9, x > 3$ **b** $7x > 35, x > 5$
  c $2x \leqslant 2, x \leqslant 1$ **d** $5x \geqslant 15, x \geqslant 3$

5 a $x \leqslant 5$ **b** $x \geqslant 6$ **c** $x \geqslant 2$ **d** $x < 4$
  e $x \geqslant -1$ **f** $x \leqslant 3$ **g** $x > 3$ **h** $x \leqslant 2$

6 a $x \geqslant 3$ **b** $x > 2$ **c** $x \geqslant 0$ **d** $x > -1$
  e $x \geqslant -2$ **f** $x \leqslant 4$ **g** $x \geqslant -2.5$ **h** $x < -7.5$

7 a ii   **b** v   **c** vi   **d** i
  e iv   **f** iii

A2.5

1 a $x < 5$ **b** $y \geqslant 6$ **c** $y \leqslant 4$ **d** $r > 9$
  e $w \leqslant 15$ **f** $s > 2$ **g** $u < -12$ **h** $v \geqslant -4$

2 a $x > 1, x < 5$ **b** $x > -5, x < -1$
  c $x > -2, x < 4$ **d** $x \geqslant -6, x \leqslant -1$
  e $x > 2, x < 7$ **f** $x \geqslant -1, x \leqslant 2$

3 a $-10 \leqslant x < 5$ **b** $5 < y < 12$
  c $-2 < z \leqslant 6$ **d** $-4 \leqslant t \leqslant 2$

4 a
  −5 −3 0 2 5

  b
  −5 −1 0 4 5

  c
  −5 0 1 3 5

  d
  −5 −4 0 5

5 a $-3, -2, -1, 0, 1$ **b** $0, 1, 2, 3, 4$
  c $2, 3$ **d** $-4, -3, -2, -1$

6 a, **b**, **c** and **e**

7 a
  −5 −4 0 5

  b $-4, -3, -2, -1, 0, 1, 2, 3, 4$

8 $1, 2, 3, 4$

9 a $-2, -1, 0, 1, 2$ **b** $-1, 0, 1, 2, 3, 4$
  c $2, 3, 4, 5$

A2 Exam review

1 a $x \geqslant -3$
  b
  −5 −3 0 2 5

2 a $y = 3.5$ **b** $x = 7$

D1 Before you start …

1 a 44, 47, 48, 55, 56, 59, 61, 65
  b 0.5, 0.8, 1.5, 1.7, 2.1, 2.5
  c 13.1, 13.2, 21.3, 23.1, 31.2, 32.1

2 a 81   **b** 179   **c** 105   **d** 205   **e** 441
  f 74   **g** 135   **h** 177   **i** 219   **j** 41

3 a 07.48   **b** 18.17

D1.1

1 a 6, 7, 8, 5, 4   **b** i   **c** u   **d** 30
2 a 5, 4, 7, 4, 2, 2, 1, 2, 3   **b** 5   **c** 92 mm
3 a 9, 17, 11, 3   **b** 808
4 a 28   **b** 67

D1.2

1 a Controlled experiment   **b** Observation
  c Controlled experiment   **d** Data logging
  e Controlled experiment   **f** Observation
  g Observation   **h** Data logging
  i Observation   **j** Data logging

2 a Observation   **b** 1, 21; 2, 11; 3, 3; 4, 4; 5, 1
  c 40   **d** 73

3 a Controlled experiment
  b–c 1, 13; 2, 14; 3, 4; 4, 4; 5, 5; 6, 5
  d 2   **e** 45
  f Yes, the dice seems to be biased in favour of 1 and 2.
  g By increasing the number of rolls.

D1.3

1 a Choices should be given.
  b 'Recently' is too vague.
2 a Which is your favourite fruit?   **b** 100
3 a 30 is in two options and over 40s are missing.
  b The options are too vague.
  c Using more than one shop would improve the reliability of the data.
  d Examples:
    How old are you?
    Under 20 20–29 30–39 40 or over
    How often do you go shopping?
    At most once a month 3 times a month
    At least once a week
4 a Which channel do you watch the most?
  b 30
  c There are far too many 'Other' possibilities.
5 a 'Regularly' is too vague.
  b How many times a week do you buy a newspaper?
    0 1 2 3 4 5 6 7
  c There is no option for less than 1 year. If someone last bought a book a number of years ago, they are unlikely to remember how many years exactly. Better options are:
    Less than a week ago 1–4 weeks ago
    1–6 months ago More than 6 months ago

D1.4

1 a discrete   **b** discrete   **c** continuous
  d discrete   **e** continuous   **f** discrete
  g continuous   **h** continuous   **i** discrete
  j discrete

2 a 4, 9, 16, 11, 10   **b** 50
3 a 8, 6, 7, 10, 3, 6   **b** 40
4 a 0, 4, 7, 6, 8   **b** 25
5 a 8, 13, 10, 9   **b** $1.0 < m \leqslant 2.0$ **c** 40

D1.5

1 **ai** 15   **aii** 12
   bi 39   **bii** 22
   c 58

2 Boys: 12, 5; Girls: 7, 8

3 **a–b** Example:

	Contract	Pay as you go
Black	25	30
Silver	30	15

4

	Sugar	No sugar
Tea		
Coffee		

5

	Part-exchange	Cash
Saloons		
Hatchbacks		

D1 Exam review

1

	Spring	Summer	Autumn	Winter	Total
Girls	3	7	4	1	15
Boys	2	4	8	3	17
Total	5	11	12	4	32

2 **a** There are no 'Bad' options.
   bi The options are too vague.
   bii How much money do you normally spend
     in the canteen?
     £0–£1   £1.01–£1.50   £1.51–£2.00
     More than £2

N3 Before you start …

1 $\frac{1}{3}$

2 **a** $x = 10$ **b** $y = 4$

3 3

4 0.1, $\frac{1}{4}$, $\frac{1}{2} = 0.5$, $23\% = \frac{23}{100}$

5 0.7, 0.75, 0.8, 0.875

N3.1

1 **ai** $\frac{8}{12}$ **aii** $\frac{2}{3}$
   bi $\frac{14}{16}$ **bii** $\frac{7}{8}$
   ci $\frac{12}{20}$ **cii** $\frac{3}{5}$
   di $\frac{10}{15}$ **dii** $\frac{2}{3}$

2 **a** $\frac{1}{3}$ **b** $\frac{3}{4}$ **c** $\frac{3}{5}$ **d** $\frac{4}{9}$
   e $\frac{5}{8}$ **f** $\frac{1}{3}$ **g** $\frac{4}{9}$ **h** $\frac{23}{93}$

3 **a** $\frac{3}{2}$ **b** $\frac{11}{3}$ **c** $\frac{35}{8}$ **d** $\frac{20}{9}$
   e $\frac{41}{7}$ **f** $\frac{39}{5}$ **g** $\frac{96}{11}$ **h** $\frac{88}{7}$
   i $\frac{163}{13}$

4 **a** $1\frac{1}{4}$ **b** $1\frac{3}{5}$ **c** $1\frac{4}{7}$ **d** $2\frac{1}{4}$
   e $2\frac{1}{5}$ **f** $2\frac{6}{7}$ **g** $4\frac{3}{5}$ **h** $3\frac{1}{9}$
   i $8\frac{3}{8}$

5 **a** 8   **b** 27   **c** 56   **d** 56
   e 2   **f** 90   **g** 85   **h** 7

6 **a** $\frac{2}{5} > \frac{1}{3}$ **b** $\frac{1}{3}$, $\frac{7}{18}$, $\frac{4}{9}$

7 **a** $\frac{2}{5}$ **b** $\frac{2}{3}$ **c** $\frac{4}{7}$ **d** $\frac{5}{6}$
   e $\frac{4}{7}$ **f** $\frac{10}{7}$

8 **a** $\frac{3}{15}$, $\frac{1}{3}$, $\frac{2}{5}$ **b** $\frac{1}{2}$, $\frac{15}{28}$, $\frac{4}{7}$ **c** $\frac{4}{7}$, $\frac{5}{8}$, $\frac{9}{14}$

N3.2

1 **a** $\frac{2}{3}$ **b** $\frac{5}{8}$ **c** $\frac{5}{11}$ **d** $\frac{13}{17}$
   e $\frac{3}{23}$ **f** $\frac{13}{27}$

2 **a** 1   **b** $\frac{2}{3}$ **c** $1\frac{2}{11}$ **d** $\frac{7}{13}$
   e $1\frac{2}{3}$ **f** $\frac{2}{3}$ **g** $2\frac{1}{3}$ **h** $3\frac{4}{7}$

3 **a** $\frac{5}{6}$ **b** $\frac{17}{20}$ **c** $\frac{4}{15}$ **d** $\frac{18}{35}$
   e $\frac{23}{24}$ **f** $\frac{38}{45}$ **g** $\frac{59}{99}$ **h** $\frac{94}{105}$

4 **a** $\frac{1}{3}$ **b** $\frac{1}{6}$ **c** $\frac{3}{4}$ **d** $\frac{1}{3}$

5 **a** $1\frac{7}{15}$ **b** $2\frac{1}{10}$ **c** $2\frac{7}{12}$ **d** $1\frac{31}{35}$
   e $2\frac{1}{15}$ **f** $1\frac{7}{8}$ **g** $1\frac{7}{12}$ **h** $\frac{43}{63}$

6 **a** $5\frac{11}{12}$ miles **b** $1\frac{13}{16}$ lb   **c** $1\frac{79}{80}$ kg   **d** $\frac{2}{15}$
   ei $29\frac{9}{28}$ feet   **eii** $62\frac{4}{45}$ feet   **eiii** $16\frac{1}{9}$ m

N3.3

1 **a** $1\frac{1}{2}$ **b** 2   **c** $3\frac{1}{3}$ **d** $2\frac{1}{7}$
   e $2\frac{1}{2}$ **f** $4\frac{1}{3}$

2 **a** 2   **b** 4   **c** $3\frac{1}{3}$ **d** $\frac{7}{12}$
   e $\frac{3}{5}$ **f** 16   **g** 6   **h** $23\frac{3}{8}$

3 **a** 8   **b** 10   **c** 14   **d** 20
   e 48   **f** 220

4 **a** $2\frac{4}{5}$ kg   **b** $2\frac{1}{7}$ m

5 **a** 6   **b** $17\frac{1}{2}$ **c** $2\frac{2}{5}$ **d** 14
   e 48   **f** $6\frac{3}{7}$ **g** 2   **h** $2\frac{1}{7}$

6 **a** $\frac{3}{10}$ **b** $\frac{9}{20}$ **c** $\frac{15}{28}$ **d** $\frac{12}{35}$
   e $\frac{2}{3}$ **f** $\frac{7}{24}$ **g** $\frac{2}{3}$ **h** $2\frac{1}{4}$
   i $\frac{9}{49}$ **j** $\frac{1}{2}$ **k** $2\frac{1}{3}$ **l** $1\frac{37}{40}$

7 **a** 10   **b** $\frac{5}{6}$ **c** $1\frac{1}{15}$ **d** $\frac{6}{7}$
   e $\frac{27}{28}$ **f** $1\frac{1}{5}$ **g** $\frac{1}{4}$ **h** $\frac{4}{35}$

i $\frac{4}{55}$ **j** $2\frac{5}{8}$ **k** $1\frac{1}{6}$ **l** $1\frac{2}{25}$

m 2 **n** $3\frac{3}{8}$ **o** $1\frac{13}{15}$

8 a $3\frac{17}{25}$ **b** $4\frac{4}{55}$

N3.4

1 a $\frac{3}{10}$ **b** $\frac{3}{5}$ **c** $\frac{16}{25}$ **d** $\frac{9}{20}$

e $\frac{3}{8}$ **f** $1\frac{2}{25}$ **g** $3\frac{19}{80}$ **h** $3\frac{1}{16}$

2 a 0.3 **b** 0.44 **c** 1.04 **d** 0.62

e 0.45 **f** 0.52 **g** 0.28 **h** 3.35

3 a 0.44 **b** 0.67 **c** 1.35 **d** 0.73

e 1.14 **f** 1.4 **g** 2.17 **h** 0.85

4 a $\frac{2}{5}$ **b** $\frac{9}{10}$ **c** $\frac{7}{20}$ **d** $\frac{13}{20}$

e $\frac{1}{100}$ **f** $3\frac{31}{50}$ **g** $\frac{61}{400}$ **h** $\frac{17}{800}$

5 a 54% **b** 40% **c** 85% **d** 52%

e 66.7% **f** 24% **g** 120% **h** 44%

6 a 0.37 **b** 0.07 **c** 1.89 **d** 0.45

e 1.45 **f** 0.008 **g** 2.5 **h** 1.232

7 a 72% **b** 20% **c** 125% **d** 3%

e 102% **f** 3.25% **g** 33.3% **h** 137.2%

8 a 68.6% **b** 64% **c** 89.5% **d** 191.7%

e 26.3%

9 a $\frac{1}{7}$ = 0.142 857 142 $\frac{2}{7}$ = 0.285 714 285

$\frac{3}{7}$ = 0.428 571 428 $\frac{4}{7}$ = 0.571 428 571

$\frac{5}{7}$ = 0.714 285 714 $\frac{6}{7}$ = 0.857 142 857

b The first six decimal places recur.

c Again, the first six decimal places recur.

N3.5

1

Fraction	Decimal	Percentage
$\frac{3}{8}$	0.375	37.5%
$\frac{7}{25}$	0.28	28%
$\frac{3}{20}$	0.15	15%
$\frac{3}{8}$	0.375	37.5%
$\frac{4}{5}$	0.8	80%
$\frac{7}{40}$	0.175	17.5%

2 a $\frac{5}{8}$ **b** $\frac{4}{5}$ **c** $\frac{5}{7}$ **d** $\frac{3}{8}$

e $\frac{16}{11}$ **f** $\frac{14}{9}$ **g** $1\frac{7}{23}$ **h** $2\frac{8}{11}$

3 a < **b** > **c** > **d** >

4 a 47%, $\frac{12}{25}$, 0.49 **b** 78%, $\frac{4}{5}$, 0.81

c $\frac{7}{12}$, $\frac{4}{5}$, 66% **d** 29%, 0.3, $\frac{5}{16}$, $\frac{7}{22}$

5 a $\frac{19}{28}$ = 67.9% **b** $\frac{11}{16}$ = 68.8%

c $\frac{19}{24}$ = 79.2% **d** $\frac{1}{3}$ = 33.3%

6 a German, as $\frac{37}{54}$ = 68.5%

b $\frac{7}{31}$ = 23%, so Sarah's class is in accord with the rest of the school.

N3 Exam review

1 a $\frac{7}{20}$ **b** $\frac{23}{24}$ **c** $3\frac{3}{4}$ **d** $7\frac{1}{2}$

2 a $\frac{1}{6}$, $\frac{3}{8}$, $\frac{1}{2}$, $\frac{2}{3}$, $\frac{3}{4}$ **b** $\frac{3}{5}$, 65%, $\frac{2}{3}$, 0.72, $\frac{3}{4}$

S2 Before you start …

1 a 73 **b** 142 **c** 177 **d** 143

e 163

2 a 90 **b** 120 **c** 90

3 a 40° **b** 120°

S2.1

1 a 80° **b** 60° **c** 70° **d** 155°

e 27° **f** 120°

2 a 54° **b** 60° **c** 118°

d $d = 28°$, $e = 104°$ **e** $f = 37°$, $g = 71°$

3 a 23°, isosceles **b** 60°, equilateral

c 90°, right-angled

4 a 71° **b** 66° **c** 60°

S2.2

1 a 50° **b** 50° **c** $c = 70°$, $d = 110°$

d 144° **e** 128°

2 a 90°, rectangle **b** 115°, kite

c 106°, parallelogram **d** 108°, rhombus

e 67°, isosceles trapezium

3 a 70° **b** 50° **c** 100°

S2.3

1 a 60° **b** 60°, 120°, 60°, 120° **c** 360°

2

Number of sides	Number of triangles	Sum of the interior angles
4	2	360°
5	3	540°
6	4	720°
7	5	900°
8	6	1080°
9	7	1260°
10	8	1440°

3 a 1080° **b** 135°

c

Number of sides	Name	Number of triangles	Sum of the interior angles	One interior angle
3	Equilateral triangle	1	180°	60°
4	Square	2	360°	90°
5	Regular pentagon	3	540°	108°
6	Regular hexagon	4	720°	120°
7	Regular heptagon	5	900°	128.6°
8	Regular octagon	6	1080°	135°
9	Regular nonagon	7	1260°	140°
10	Regular decagon	8	1440°	144°

S2.4

1 a 360 **b** 45°

c

Number of sides	Name	Sum of exterior angles	One exterior angle
3	Equilateral triangle	360°	120°
4	Square	360°	90°
5	Regular pentagon	360°	72°
6	Regular hexagon	360°	60°
7	Regular heptagon	360°	51.4°
8	Regular octagon	360°	45°
9	Regular nonagon	360°	40°
10	Regular decagon	360°	36°

2 a 18° **b** 360° **c** 20 **d** 20 sides

3 a 24° **b** 156°

4 a 146° **b** 115°

5 a 45° **b** 135° **c** Octagon

S2.5

1 a 47° (vertically opposite angles)

b 117° (vertically opposite angles)

c $c = 35°$ (vertically opposite angles), $d = 145°$ (angles on a straight line add to 180°)

d $d = 103°$ (vertically opposite angles), $e = 77°$, (angles on a straight line add to 180°), $f = 77°$ (vertically opposite angles)

e 60° (angles at a point add to 360°)

2 a 110° (corresponding angles)

b 47° (alternate angles)

c 115° (alternate angles)

d 63° (corresponding angles)

e 130° (corresponding angles)

f $f = 68°$ (corresponding angles), $g = 112°$ (angles on a straight line add to 180°)

g $h = 50°$ (angles on a straight line add to 180°), $i = 50°$ (corresponding angles)

h $j = 63°$ (alternate angles), $k = 63°$ (vertically opposite angles)

i $l = 118°$ (alternate angles), $m = 118°$ (vertically opposite angles)

3 a $a = 36°$ (alternate angles), $b = 63°$ (alternate angles), $c = 81°$ (angles on a straight line/in a triangle add to 180°)

b $a = 61°$ (corresponding angles), $b = 49°$ (corresponding angles), $c = 70°$ (angles in a triangle add to 180°)

c $a = 113°$ (alternate angles), $b = 67°$ (angles on a straight line add to 180°), $c = 113°$ (corresponding angles), $d = 67°$ (angles on a straight line add to 180°), $e = 113°$ (corresponding/alternate angles)

S2 Exam review

1 80°

2 ai 60° **aii** All angles are equal.

bi 130°

bii The triangle is isosceles, so the other angle at Q is 50°. Angles on a straight line add to 180°.

c 64°

A3 Before you start ...

1 a 3 **b** 6 **c** 5 **d** 6

2 a 3 **b** 4 **c** 5 **d** 4

3 a 4, 8, 12, 16, 20, 24

b 3, 6, 9, 12, 15, 18

c 5, 10, 15, 20, 25, 30

d 6, 12, 18, 24, 30, 36

4 a 14 **b** 9 **c** 3 **d** 7

5 a 4 **b** 16 **c** 25 **d** 9

e 36

A3.1

1 6, 10, 14, 18, 22; 26, 21, 16, 11, 6; 10, 7, 4, 1, −2; −6, −4, −2, 0, 2; −23, −16, −9, −2, 5

2 a 2, 4, 6, 8, 10 **b** 17, 19, 21, 23, 25

c 4, 8, 12, 16, 20 **d** 24, 30, 36, 42, 48

e 7, 12, 17, 22, 27 **f** 1, 4, 9, 16, 25

g 2, 5, 10, 17, 26 **h** 2, 4, 8, 16, 32

3 a 4, 7, 10, 13, 16 **b** 25, 19, 13, 7, 1

c 4, 8, 12, 16, 20 **d** 30, 22, 14, 6, −2

e −16, −10, −4, 2, 8

4 ai 31, 38

aii First term 3, increases by 7 each time

bi 25, 33

bii First term −7, increase by 8 each time

ci −7, −4

cii First term −19, increase by 3 each time

di 11, 27

dii First term 7, increase by 4 each time

ei 11, 19

eii First term 3, increase by 8 each time

fi 1, −4

fii First term 16, decrease by 5 each time

gi −11, 1

gii First term −11, increase by 3 each time

hi 13, −1

hii First term 13, decrease by 7 each time

5 ai 2, 3, 5, 8, 12

aii First term 2, increase by 1, 2, 3, 4

bi 18, 22, 25, 27, 28

bii First term 18, increase by 4, 3, 2, 1

ci −6, −5, −3, 0, 4

cii First term −6, increase by 1, 2, 3, 4

di 6, 8, 11, 15, 20

dii First term 6, increase by 2, 3, 4, 5

ei −24, −23, −21, −17, −9

eii First term −24, increase by 1, 2, 4, 8 (powers of 2)

fi −15, −7, −1, 3, 5

fii First term −15, increase by 8, 6, 4, 2

6 a 1, 3, 5, 7, 9, 11, 13 and 4, 7, 10 (13 could go in the second sequence instead)

b 2, 4, 8, 16, 32 and 7, 11, 15, 19, 23

A3.2

1 a 6, 11, 16; 51   **b** 11, 14, 17; 38

   c 4, 12, 20; 76   **d** −2, 4, 10; 52

   e 22, 20, 18; 4   **f** 10, 5, 0; −35

   g −13, −6, 1; 50   **h** −2, 2, 6; 34

2 a 14, 17, 23, 38   **b** −3, 3, 15, 45

3 a 5, 8, 13, 20, 29   **b** −1, 2, 7, 14, 23

   c 2, 8, 18, 32, 50   **d** 11, 8, 3, −4, −13

4 a 12, 33, 108   **b** −2, 19, 94

   c 15, 57, 207

5 a 5, 9, 13

   b Each term is one more than a multiple of 4.

   c No, 222 is not one more than a multiple of 4.

6 a 3, 9, 19   **b** $2 \times 5^2 + 1 = 51$ not 101

7 a 1, 4, 9, 16, 25   **b** +3, +5, +7, +9

   c

4th square number	16	$1 + 3 + 5 + 7$
5th square number	25	$1 + 3 + 5 + 7 + 9$
6th square number	36	$1 + 3 + 5 + 7 + 9 + 11$

   d 10th square number = 100

A3.3

1 a 8, 6, 4, 2, 0   **b** 1, 0, −1, −2, −3

   c 14, 10, 6, 2, −2   **d** 13, 6, −1, −8, −15

   e 13, 10, 7, 4, 1   **f** 1, −4, −9, −14, −19

   g −7, −9, −11, −13, −15

   h 25, 20, 15, 10, 5   **i** 5, 2, −1, −4, −7

   j 4, −6, −16, −26, −36 **k** 5, 2, −3, −10, −19

   l −8, −2, 8, 22, 40

2 a +4

   b The nth term contains the term $4n$.

   c

Sequence	5	9	13	17	21
$4n$	4	8	12	16	20

   d $4n + 1$

3 a $6n + 5$ **b** $9n − 8$ **c** $7n + 8$ **d** $4n − 14$

   e $23 − 3n$ **f** $19 − 4n$ **g** $24 − 8n$ **h** $39 − 8n$

4 a $4n + 3$ **b** $4n − 10$ **c** $41 − 9n$ **d** $21 − 6n$

5 a Term 3 = 13, Term $n = 3n + 4$

   b Term 4 = 14, Term 10 = 50, Term $n = 6n − 10$

A3.4

1 a

   b 8, 11, 14, 17, 20   **c** 35

2 a

b 10, 14, 18, 22, 26

c Four crosses are added each time – two to the top and two to the bottom

d +4   **e** $4n + 6$

3 a 13, 17 (add 4)   **b** $4n − 3$ **c** 197

4 a 18, 22 (add 4); $4n + 2$; 202

   b 9, 11 (add 2); $2n + 1$; 101

A3.5

1 a 4, 7, 10, 13, 16

   b $3n + 1$

   c The nth pattern has three branches of n dots and one extra dot in the centre.

2 a 6, 11, 16, 21, 26   **b** $5n + 1$

   c The nth pattern has five branches of n beads and one extra bead in the centre.

3 a 3   **b** 5, 8, 11, 14, 17   **c** $3n + 2$

   d Start with two cards leaning against each other, then add three more cards each time (another pair of leaning cards and one bridging card).

   e No, 52 is not two more than a multiple of 3.

4 a Add one vertical and two horizontal posts each time.

   b 16

   c $3n + 1$

   d Start with one vertical post then add three posts each time.

   e 79

5 a

Type of car	Number of days						
	1	2	3	4	5	6	7
Small	70	90	110	130	150	170	190
Medium	85	110	135	160	185	210	235
Large	100	130	160	190	220	250	280

   bi $10 \times 30 + 70 = £370$

   bii $14 \times 25 + 60 = £410$

   biii $20n + 50$

A3 Exam review

1 a $2n − 1$ **b** 1, 3

2 $m = 6n$

D2 Before you start ...

1 a 90°   **b** 130°

2 a 120   **b** 45   **c** 60   **d** 72

   e 6   **f** 20   **g** 30   **h** 18

   i 10   **j** 1.5

2 a ii   **b** i

4 a 661, 665, 714, 741, 746, 751, 756

   b 0.5, 0.9, 1.5, 1.8, 2.1, 2.2

   c 44.6, 45.6, 45.9, 46.4, 49.5

5 a (3, 5)   **b** (5, 1)

D2.1

1 a 1550
  b 3 guitars, 2.5 guitars, 1.5 guitars
2 a 13   **b** 10°
  c Win = 150°, Draw = 80°, Lose = 130°
  d Pie chart with angles given in part **c**
3 a 6°
  b Sunny = 90°, Cloudy = 108°, Rainy = 84°, Snowy = 18°, Windy = 60°
  c Pie chart with angles given in part **b**
4 a 0.75°
  b Pie chart with: Cod 90°, Plaice 75°, Haddock 72°, Sardines 87°, Mackerel 36°

D2.2

1 a 8, 8, 13, 6, 5
  b–c

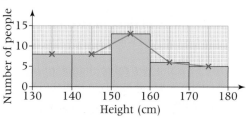

2

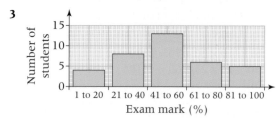

3

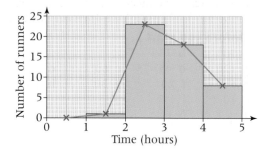

4 b–c

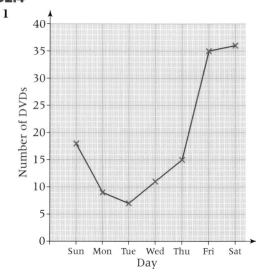

D2.3

1

100	8 8 8
110	0 0 1 2 6 7 7 9 9
120	0 0 1 1 5 5 6 6
130	0 1 4 5 6 7 8
140	0 2 4

Key: | 120 | 5 | means 125 seconds

2

43.0	0 2 3 8 8 9
44.0	0 1 3 4 5 7
45.0	0 0 1 2 6 9
46.0	0 1 3 5 5 9 9

Key: | 44.0 | 7 | means 44.7 seconds

3 a

10	0 4 4 4 7 9 9 9
20	0 0 0 1 2 2 3 3 3 4 5 6 6 6 6 7 8 9 9
30	1 2 4

Key: | 10 | 7 | means 17°C

b

50	0 7 7 7
60	3 6 6 6 8 8 8
70	0 2 2 3 3 3 5 7 9 9 9 9
80	1 2 4 4 8
90	0 3

Key: | 50 | 7 | means 57°F

D2.4

1

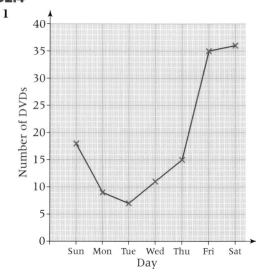

2

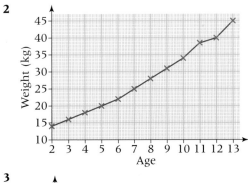

3

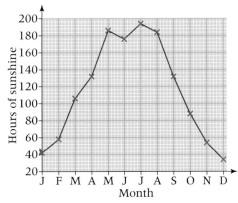

4

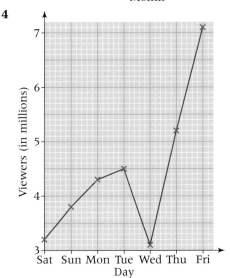

5

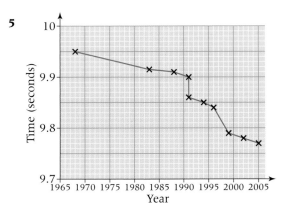

1 a No correlation   **b** Positive correlation
  c Negative correlation

2 a

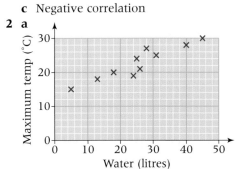

b Positive correlation
ci Increases   **cii** Decreases

3 a

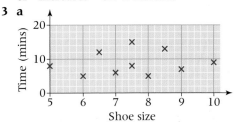

b No correlation   **c** No relationship

D2 Exam review

1 a

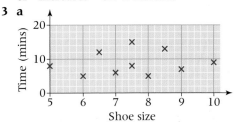

b The higher the mark on paper 1, the higher
  the mark on paper 2 (positive correlation).

2

0	5 7 8 8
10	0 0 0 0 2 5 5 5 6
20	0 0 0 4 5
30	3 5

Key: | 10 | 5 | means 15 minutes

A4 Before you start …

1 a 3, 5, 6, 8   **b** −6, 0, 3, 9
2 a 9   **b** −2   **c** 12   **d** 2

3

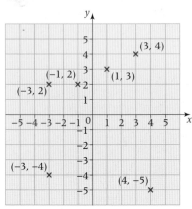

4 a 4   **b** 8

5 a $x = 3$ **b** $x = 2$

A4.1

1 a 0, 5, 10, 15   **b** 0.5, 1, 1.5, 2, 2.5
   c −1, 1, 3, 5, 7   **d** −9, −5, −1, 3, 7
   e −41, −36, −31, −26, −21   **f** −8, −2, 4, 10, 16

2 aii −4, −1, 2, 5, 8   **bii** −8, −3, 2, 7, 12
   cii −7, −5, −3, −1, 1   **dii** −1, 3, 7, 11, 15
   eii 2, 2.5, 3, 3.5, 4   **fii** −17, −14, −11, −8, −5
   gii −3, −2.5, −2, −1.5, −1

3 b $y = 2x + 6$ **c** 0, 2, 4, 6, 8, 10, 12
   d (−3, 0) (−2, 2) (−1, 4) (0, 6) (1, 8) (2, 10) (3, 12)

4 b $y = \frac{1}{2}x - 1$ **c** −2.5, −2, −1.5, −1, −0.5, 0, 0.5
   d (−3, −2.5) (−2, −2) (−1, −1.5) (0, −1)
       (1, −0.5) (2, 0) (3, 0.5)

5 a (ii) (3)   **b** (i) (5)

   c (v) (1)   **d** (iii) (4)

   e (iv) (2)

A4.2

1 a $y = -3, 0, 3, 6, 9$
   b (−2, −3), (−1, 0), (0, 3), (1, 6), (2, 9)
   c–f

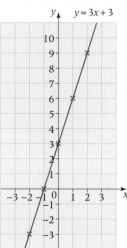

2 a $y = 5, 4, 3, 2, 1$
   b (−2, 5), (−1, 4), (0, 3), (1, 2), (2, 1)
   c–f

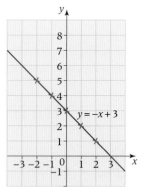

3 a $y = 8, 7, 6, 5, 4$
   b (−2, 8), (−1, 7), (0, 6), (1, 5), (2, 4)
   c–f

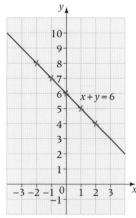

4 a $y = -9, -7, -5, -3, -1$
   b (−2, −9), (−1, −7), (0, −5), (1, −3), (2, −1)
   c–f

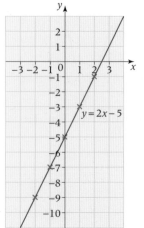

A4.3

1 a–d

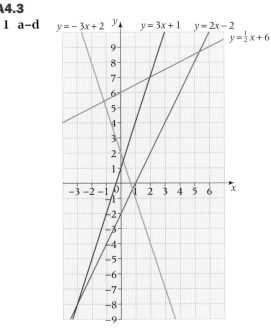

$y = -3x + 2$ $y = 3x + 1$ $y = 2x - 2$ $y = \frac{1}{2}x + 6$

2 a–d

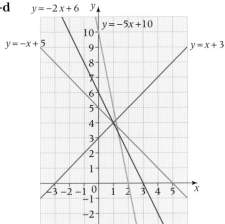

$y = -2x + 6$ $y = -5x + 10$ $y = -x + 5$ $y = x + 3$

3 When $x = 0.5$, $y = 2$; when $y = 0$, $x = 1.5$

4 When $x = -0.5$, $y = -1$; when $y = 7$, $x = 1.5$

5 When $x = \frac{1}{2}$, $y = 2\frac{3}{4}$; when $y = 3\frac{1}{4}$, $x = -\frac{1}{2}$

6 When $x = -2$, $y = 0$; when $y = -5$, $x = 3$

7 a–c

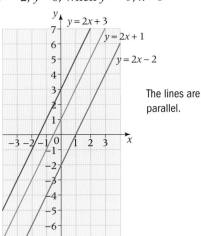

$y = 2x + 3$ $y = 2x + 1$ $y = 2x - 2$

The lines are parallel.

8 a–c

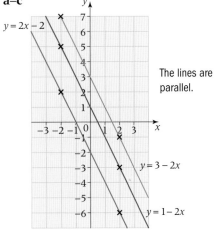

$y = 2x - 2$

The lines are parallel.

$y = 3 - 2x$ $y = 1 - 2x$

9 a $y = 14$ **b** $x = -3$

A4.4

1 a $x = 4$ **b** $x = -2$ **c** $x = 1$ **d** $y = 5$
  e $y = 3$ **f** $y = -1$ **g** $y = -3$ **h** $y = -5$

2 a–e

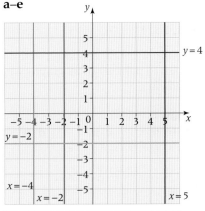

$y = 4$ $y = -2$ $x = -4$ $x = -2$ $x = 5$

3

Horizontal lines	Vertical lines
$y = 4$	$x = 5$
$y = -10$	$x = 15$
$y = -2$	$x = -3$
$y = -6$	$x = 4$

4 a $(-2, 4)$ **b** $(5, -2)$ **c** $(-4, 4)$

5 a $(2, -3)$ **b** $(1, 6)$ **c** $(3, -1)$

6 For example, the lines $x = 2$, $x = -2$, $y = 2$ and $y = -2$ make a square.

7 b x-axis   **c** y-axis

8 a–c

$y = 3x + 1$ $y = 7$ **c** $(2, 7)$

A4.5

1. **a** $m=3$, $c=-1$ **b** $m=2$, $c=5$
   c $m=4$, $c=-3$ **d** $m=\frac{1}{2}$, $c=2$
   e $m=5$, $c=1$ **f** $m=-3$, $c=7$
2. **a** ii   **b** iii   **c** i   **d** iv   **e** v
3. **a** $y=-x+5$ **b** $y=x+3$
   c $y=-x-2$ **d** $y=x-3$
   e $y=-2x+6$ **f** $y=-5x+9$
   g $y=-3x-2$ **h** $y=2x+5$
   i $y=-\frac{1}{2}x+2$ **j** $y=\frac{1}{2}x+4$
   k $y=-\frac{1}{2}x+4$ **l** $y=-3x+4$
4. **a** $y=x+3$ and $y=x-3$ (**b** and **d**)
   b $y=-x+5$ and $y=-x-2$ (**a** and **c**)
   c $y=-3x-2$ and $y=-3x+4$ (**g** and **l**)
   d $y=-\frac{1}{2}x+2$ and $y=-\frac{1}{2}x+4$ (**i** and **k**)
5. **a**, **b** and **e**
6. $y=\frac{1}{2}x-9$, $y=x+11$, $y=2x-2$, $y=3x+1$, $y=4x+3$
7. $y=3x+c$ for any c
8. $y=-4x+c$ for any c
9. $y=\frac{1}{2}x+4$
10. Straight line through $(-2, 2)$ and $(2, -2)$; slopes down from left to right, as do all graphs with negative gradient

A4 Exam review

1. **a** i   **b** iii   **c** ii   **d** iv
2. **a** $y=-1, 1, 3, 5, 7, 9$
   b
   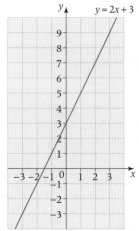
   ci $y=0.4$ **cii** $x=1.2$

D3 Before you start …

1. **a** 2, 3, 5, 7   **b** 1, 4, 9   **c** 1, 3, 6, 10
   d 3, 6, 9   **e** 1, 2, 4, 8
2. **a** $\frac{2}{3}$ **b** $\frac{1}{2}$ **c** $\frac{3}{4}$ **d** $\frac{1}{4}$ **e** 1
3. **a** 1   **b** 1   **c** $\frac{3}{10}$ **d** $\frac{2}{5}$
4. **a** 0.9   **b** 0.4   **c** 0.85
5. **a** 7   **b** 14   **c** 16   **d** 20   **e** 18
6. **a** 0.01   **b** 0.25   **c** 0.35   **d** 0.05   **e** 0.36

D3.1

1. Impossible: **b**, **c**, **e**; Certain: **a**, **d**
2. **a** head, tail   **b** 1, 2, 3, 4
   c c, h, a, n, g, e   **d** yellow, green, blue
   e Mon, Tue, Wed, Thu, Fri, Sat, Sun
3. **Aa** blue, blue, blue, blue
   Ab 1
   Ac 0
   Ad blue
   Ae red
   Ba blue, blue, blue, red
   Bb $\frac{3}{4}$
   Bc $\frac{1}{4}$
   Bd blue
   Be red
   Ca blue, blue, red, red
   Cb $\frac{1}{2}$
   Cc $\frac{1}{2}$
   Cd–e equal chance of each colour
   Da blue, red, red, red
   Db $\frac{1}{4}$
   Dc $\frac{3}{4}$
   Dd red
   De blue
   Ea red, red, red, red
   Eb 0
   Ec 1
   Ed red
   Ee blue
4. **a** $\frac{1}{250}=0.004$ **b** $\frac{10}{250}=\frac{1}{25}=0.04$
5. **a** $\frac{48}{120}=\frac{2}{5}$ **b** $=\frac{3}{5}$

D3.2

1. **a** 0.0   **b** 0.5   **c** 1.0
2. **ai** $\frac{1}{10}$ **aii** $\frac{3}{10}$ **aiii** $\frac{6}{10}=\frac{3}{5}$
   b Yellow 0.1, Green 0.3, Red 0.6
   c Yellow   **d** Red   **e** 1
3. **ai** $\frac{6}{8}=\frac{3}{4}$ **aii** $\frac{2}{8}=\frac{1}{4}$
   b Green 0.25, Pink 0.75
   c Green   **d** Pink   **e** 1
4. 0.99
5. 0.6

D3.3

1. **a** $\frac{20}{50}=\frac{2}{5}$ **b** $\frac{15}{50}=\frac{3}{10}$ **c** $\frac{10}{50}=\frac{1}{5}$ **d** $\frac{5}{50}=\frac{1}{10}$
2. **ai** 24   **aii** 8   **aiii** 16
   aiv 6   **av** 18

bi $\frac{2}{24}=\frac{1}{12}$ **bii** $\frac{12}{24}=\frac{1}{2}$ **biii** $\frac{8}{24}=\frac{1}{3}$

biv $\frac{16}{24}=\frac{2}{3}$ **bv** $\frac{6}{24}=\frac{1}{4}$ **bvi** $\frac{18}{24}=\frac{3}{4}$

3 a $\frac{1}{10}$ **b** $\frac{5}{10}=\frac{1}{2}$ **c** 0 **d** $\frac{2}{10}=\frac{1}{5}$ **e** $\frac{8}{10}=\frac{4}{5}$

D3.4

1 75
2 80
3 9
4 a 25 **b** 20 **c** 15
5 a 0.15
  bi 10, 15, 30, 20, 10, 15
  bii 50, 75, 150, 100, 50, 75
  biii 100, 150, 300, 200, 100, 150
6 £1

D3.5

1 a 11, 16, 14, 9 **b** Red
  ci $\frac{11}{50}=0.22$ **cii** $\frac{16}{50}=0.32$ **ciii** $\frac{40}{50}=0.28$
2 a 9, 10, 6, 9, 6 **b** 2 **c** 40
  di $\frac{9}{40}=0.225$ **dii** $\frac{10}{40}=\frac{1}{4}=0.25$
  diii $\frac{6}{40}=\frac{3}{20}=0.15$ **div** $\frac{9}{40}=0.225$
  dv $\frac{6}{40}=\frac{3}{20}=0.15$
  e 15
3 a 50
  bi $\frac{9}{50}=0.18$ **bii** $\frac{14}{50}=\frac{7}{25}=0.28$
  biii $\frac{27}{50}=0.54$
  c 2 red, 3 green, 5 blue
  d By increasing the number of times a ball is taken out.

D3 Exam review

1 a 0.15, the probabilities add to 1
  b 0, there are no white balls so it is impossible to choose one
2 40

N4 Before you start …

1 $\frac{3}{8}$ **2** £28.00 **3** 1.5
4 4 **5** 68 **6** 50 mph

N4.1

1 ai $\frac{3}{10}$ **aii** 30% **bi** $\frac{5}{8}$ **bii** 62.5%
  ci $\frac{4}{9}$ **cii** 44.4% **di** $\frac{5}{12}$ **dii** 41.7%
  ei $\frac{7}{25}$ **eii** 28%
2 a $\frac{3}{5}$, 61%, 0.63 **b** $\frac{17}{25}$, 69%, $\frac{7}{10}$, 0.71
  c 34%, $\frac{7}{20}$, 0.36, $\frac{3}{8}$, $\frac{2}{5}$ **d** $\frac{2}{5}$, 42%, $\frac{3}{7}$
  e 0.14, 15%, $\frac{3}{19}$, $\frac{1}{5}$ **f** 81%, $\frac{8}{9}$, 0.9, 0.93, $\frac{19}{20}$

3 ai $\frac{3}{5}$ **aii** 60% **bi** $\frac{13}{25}$ **bii** 52%
  ci $\frac{3}{20}$ **cii** 15% **di** $\frac{7}{10}$ **dii** 70%
  ei $\frac{4}{5}$ **eii** 80%

N4.2

1 a 5 **b** 8 **c** 7 **d** 4.5
  e 1.5 **f** 3.3 **g** 3.1 **h** 7.2
  i 6.7 **j** 8.6 **k** 1.8 **l** 1.4
2 a $\frac{1}{3}$ **b** $\frac{1}{2}$ **c** $\frac{3}{10}$ **d** $\frac{1}{4}$ **e** $\frac{3}{8}$
  f $\frac{2}{5}$ **g** $\frac{1}{6}$ **h** $1\frac{1}{2}$ **i** 2 **j** $1\frac{1}{4}$
3 a Column B is 4 times column A.
  b Not in direct proportion.
  c Column F is 1.8 times column E.
  d Column H is 3.1 times column G.
4 £50, £150, £1500, £1900, £2400
5 a £18.75 **b** £5.95 **c** £11.13
  d £6.24 **e** £9.48 **f** 720 Mb
  g £1.87 **h** 12 litres **i** £55.65

N4.3

1 a 2 **b** 3.5 **c** 3.5 **d** 3.33
2 a $\frac{1}{2}$ **b** $\frac{2}{7}$ **c** $\frac{2}{7}$ **d** $\frac{3}{10}$
3 a 2 **b** $\frac{1}{2}$
4 a 1.25 **b** $\frac{4}{5}$
5 a 1.6 **b** $\frac{5}{8}$
6 a £5.60 **b** $\times\frac{7}{5}$, £2.66
  c $\times\frac{20}{9}$, £169.00 **d** 6300 g

N4.4

1 Leonard £7, Pavel £6.75, Andy £11.55
2 a £7.42 per hour
  b 170 bricks per hour
  c 55 km/h
3 £1 = 5 litas, £1 = 11.55 dollars, £1 = 6.3 riyals
4 €345.60, €1036.80, €9072
5 £250, £533.33, £1700

N4.5

1 12 miles/litre, 13 miles/litre, 10.42 miles/litre
2 a 9.2 miles/litre **b** £12.65 per hour
  c 184 kCal per 100 g
3 a 12 inches = 1 foot **b** 2.2 lb = 1 kg
  c 1.6 km = 1 mile
4 a 10.03 m/s, 10.20 m/s, 10.70 m/s, 10.29 m/s, 10.27 m/s, 10.10 m/s
  b Eugene, Victor, Alan, Mark, Janet, Bobby
5 ai 175 km **aii** 16 litres
  bi £321 **bii** 117 hours

N4 Exam review

1 a 8 hours **b** $3\frac{1}{8}$ tins
2 a 100 hamburgers **b** USA by £1.99

S3 Before you start ...

1 a (1, 3) **b** (1, −2) **c** (−3, −2) **d** (−1, 3)
2 a Clockwise **b** Anticlockwise
3 a $x = 2$ **b** $y = 2$ **c** $y = -x$ **d** $y = x$
4 180°

S3.1

1 a 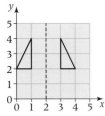 **b**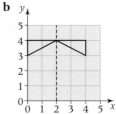

c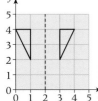

2 a $x = 3$ **b** $y = 1$ **c** $x = -1$
3 a–b

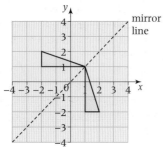

3 c $y = x$
4 a–c

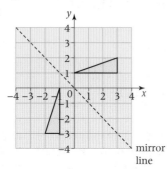

d (−1, 0), (−1, −3), (−2, −3) **e** $y = -x$

S3.2

1 a 90° anticlockwise **b** 90° clockwise
c 180° clockwise **d** 90° anticlockwise
e 90° clockwise **f** 90° clockwise
g 90° anticlockwise **h** 90° anticlockwise
i 180° clockwise **j** 90° clockwise
k 90° clockwise **l** 180° anticlockwise
m 90° clockwise **n** 180° clockwise
o 90° anticlockwise

2

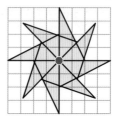

3 b Kite
c Image vertices: (0, 0), (−1, 2), (0, 3), (1, 2)
d (−1, 2) **e** Yes
4 c (−1, −1), (2, −1), (2, −3)

S3.3

1 D, F, H, J

2 A Translation $\begin{pmatrix} 4 \\ 3 \end{pmatrix}$ **B** Translation $\begin{pmatrix} 4 \\ 0 \end{pmatrix}$

C Translation $\begin{pmatrix} 0 \\ 3 \end{pmatrix}$ **D** Translation $\begin{pmatrix} 0 \\ -3 \end{pmatrix}$

E Translation $\begin{pmatrix} 4 \\ -3 \end{pmatrix}$ **F** Translation $\begin{pmatrix} 0 \\ -4 \end{pmatrix}$

G Translation $\begin{pmatrix} -4 \\ 3 \end{pmatrix}$ **H** Translation $\begin{pmatrix} -4 \\ -3 \end{pmatrix}$

3 a Translation $\begin{pmatrix} 5 \\ 0 \end{pmatrix}$ **b** Translation $\begin{pmatrix} 0 \\ 4 \end{pmatrix}$

c Translation $\begin{pmatrix} 0 \\ -4 \end{pmatrix}$ **d** Translation $\begin{pmatrix} 2 \\ -6 \end{pmatrix}$

e Translation $\begin{pmatrix} 3 \\ 2 \end{pmatrix}$ **f** Translation $\begin{pmatrix} -5 \\ 4 \end{pmatrix}$

g Translation $\begin{pmatrix} -2 \\ 6 \end{pmatrix}$ **h** Translation $\begin{pmatrix} -5 \\ 0 \end{pmatrix}$

i Translation $\begin{pmatrix} -3 \\ -6 \end{pmatrix}$ **j** Translation $\begin{pmatrix} 5 \\ -4 \end{pmatrix}$

4 a (−4, 2) **b** Isosceles trapezium
c Image vertices: (1, 0), (4, 0), (2, 2), (3, 2)
d Congruent **e** (1, 0)

S3.4

1 3
2 B
3 a–b **c** Translation $\begin{pmatrix} 1 \\ 4 \end{pmatrix}$

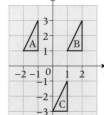

4 a–b

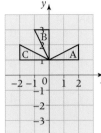

c Rotation through 90° clockwise

5 a–b

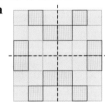

c Rotation through 180°

S3.5

1 Depends on handwriting, for example:

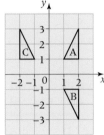

2 a 3   **b** 2   **c** 2   **d** 3
   e 2   **f** 3   **g** 2   **h** 2
   i 2   **j** 2

3 a 3 lines, 4 lines, 5 lines, 6 lines, 8 lines
   b 3, 4, 5, 6, 8

4 a   **b**

5 a 3   **b** 4   **c** 2

S3 Exam review

1 a Reflection in $x = 0$
   b and **d**
   c Rotation through 180°
   d Reflection in $x = 0$

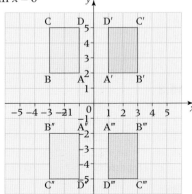

2 a–b

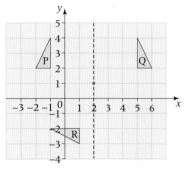

N5 Before you start …

1 a 144   **b** 9
2 a 125   **b** 2
3 a 16   **b** 1 000 000
4 1, 2, 3, 4, 6, 8, 12, 24
5 2, 3, 5, 7, 11, 13
6 a 45   **b** 100

N5.1

1 a 25   **b** 121   **c** 225   **d** 289
2 a 16, 36   **b** 49   **c** 121, 144   **d** 225
3 a 256   **b** 13.69   **c** 2500   **d** 44.89
   e 316.84   **f** 17.64   **g** 3.61   **h** 0.01
   i 15.21   **j** 4.41   **k** 0.49   **l** 175.56
4 a ±23   **b** ±12.53   **c** ±6.40   **d** ±0.4
   e ±2.6   **f** ±28.28   **g** ±36.67   **h** ±6.21
   i ±84.22   **j** ±15.32
5 a 7   **b** 9   **c** 5   **d** 6
   e 11   **f** 12   **g** 3   **h** 2
6 a $(2.645\ 751)^2 = 6.999\ 998$; 2.645 751 is only accurate to 6 d.p. so its square is not exactly 7.
   b 56 and 57
7 a 4.5
   bi 6.3   **bii** 7.7   **biii** 9.7

N5.2

1 a 343   **b** 1000   **c** 2197   **d** 6859
2 a Square: 4, 16; Cube: 27
   b Square: 64, 144; Cube: 64
   c Square: 196, 256; Cube: 216
   d Square: 900; Cube: 1000
3 a 512   **b** 13.82   **c** 8000   **d** 59.32
   e 1601.61   **f** −21.95   **g** 704.97   **h** 0.125
   i −157.46   **j** 970.30   **k** −0.001   **l** 4784.09
4 a 9   **b** 4.64   **c** 4   **d** 4.41
   e 1.97   **f** 1.39   **g** 1.1   **h** 3.83
   i 23   **j** −6   **k** −4.12   **l** 0.25
   m −8.26   **n** −2.06   **o** 7.01
5 ai 2.7   **aii** 3.7   **aiii** 4.3
   aiv 5.3   **av** 6.7   **avi** 7.9
   avii 9.7   **aviii** 11.4

N5.3

1 a 16   **b** 32   **c** 125   **d** 2401   **e** 729
2 a 3375   **b** 729   **c** 1024   **d** 217 678.23
   e 2197

3 a 25   **b** 40   **c** 259 947

   d 8000   **e** $\frac{5}{256}$ or 0.01953

4 a 3   **b** 4   **c** 4   **d** 7

   e 23

5 a 340   **b** 76 600   **c** 0.085   **d** 23 000

   e 312 000   **f** 56 200   **g** 2.96

6 a 3^4 **b** 7^5 **c** 2^{12} **d** 10^3

   e 3^4 **f** 4^7 **g** 10^{10} **h** 7^6

   i 2^6 **j** 10^5 **k** 4^0

7 a 0.1   **b** 0.125   **c** 0.001   **d** 0.333 …

   e 0.142857 …   **f** 0.076923 …

8 a 1   **b** $\frac{1}{5} = 0.2$ **c** 1

9 a 5.4   **b** 3   **c** 10^4

   d 1 730 000

10 a y^5 **b** 4^{10} **c** w^5 **d** 4^{y-2}

   e g^4 **f** 576

N5.4

1 a 10^2 **b** 10^1

   c 10^5 **d** 10^0

2 a 2×10^2 **b** 8×10^2 **c** 9×10^3

   d 6.5×10^2 **e** 6.5×10^3 **f** 9.52×10^2

   g 2.358×10 **h** 2.5585×10^2

3 a 500   **b** 3000   **c** 100 000

   d 250   **e** 4900   **f** 3 800 000

   g 750 000 000 000

   h 8 100 000 000 000 000 000

4 a 6×10^2 **b** 4.5×10^4

   c 6.5×10^0 **d** 5×10^6

5 a 4×10^5 **b** 9×10^7

   c 2.5×10^8 **d** 2.4×10^{13}

6 a 2×10^2 **b** 2×10^4

   c 5×10 **d** 7.5×10^2

7 a 9.75×10^9 **b** 1.37×10^4

   c 4.01×10^{11} **d** 2.06×10^8

8

Planet	Mean distance from Sun (m)	Light travel time
Mercury	5.79×10^{10}	3 minutes 13 seconds
Earth	1.50×10^{11}	8 minutes 20 seconds
Mars	2.28×10^{11}	12 minutes 40 seconds
Jupiter	7.78×10^{11}	43 minutes 13 seconds
Pluto	5.90×10^{12}	5 hours 27 minutes 47 seconds

N5.5

1 a 75   **b** 40   **c** 63   **d** 180   **e** 441

2 a 2×3^2 **b** $2^3 \times 3$ **c** $2^3 \times 5$

   d 3×13 **e** $2^4 \times 3$ **f** 2×41

   g $2^2 \times 5^2$ **h** $2^4 \times 3^2$ **i** $2^2 \times 3^2 \times 5$

   j $3^2 \times 5 \times 7$ **k** $2^2 \times 3 \times 37$ **l** $2 \times 3^3 \times 5^2$

3 a 7 missing in the answer; $126 = 2 \times 3^2 \times 7$

   b Divided 105 by 5 but recorded it as 3;

     $210 = 2 \times 3 \times 5 \times 7$

   c 221 is not prime, so he should not have

     stopped; $221 = 13 \times 17$

4 a e.g. 8, 12, 20   **b** e.g. 16, 24, 54, 90

   c e.g. 112, 120, 176, 200   **d** e.g. 64

5 a 3   **b** 5   **c** 6   **d** 48

   e 3   **f** 17

6 a 72   **b** 120   **c** 72   **d** 60

   e 180   **f** 432

7 a $\frac{3}{4}$ **b** $\frac{2}{3}$ **c** $\frac{5}{8}$ **d** $\frac{2}{3}$

   e $\frac{9}{13}$ **f** $\frac{2}{5}$

N5 Exam review

1 a 81   **b** 9   **c** $\frac{1}{9}$

2 a $2^2 \times 3^3$ **b** 12

A5 Before you start …

1 a 6   **b** 11   **c** 9   **d** 6

2 a $3x + 3$ **b** $2x - 2$ **c** $8x + 12$ **d** $12x - 6$

3 a $x = 4$ **b** $y = 6$

4 a $4(x + 2)$ **b** $2(3x + 1)$ **c** $3(y - 3)$

5 2, 3, 5, 7, 11, 13, 17, 19

A5.1

1 a 24   **b** 6   **c** 18   **d** 8

   e 27   **f** 5   **g** −2   **h** 16

2 a −12   **b** 15   **c** 14   **d** 9

3 ai 19   **aii** −5   **bi** 2   **bii** −10

   ci 12   **cii** 9   **di** 23   **dii** −13

   ei 16   **eii** 4   **fi** 36   **fii** 12

4 a $x = 6$ **b** $y = 11$ **c** $x = -2$

   d $y = 1$ **e** $b = 3$ **f** $c = -4$

   g $f = 2$ **h** $g = -4$

5 b $3x - 6$ **c** $6 + 2x$ **d** $10 - 5x$

6 a $4(2m + 1)$ **b** $3(4n - 3)$ **c** $5(3p + 11)$

   d $q(q + 2)$ **e** $4(4r - 7)$ **f** $2q(2p - 5)$

7 a Identity   **b** Function   **c** Formula

   d Equation   **e** Expression   **f** Formula

   g Formula   **h** Function

A5.2

1 a 60 cm^2 **b** 100 cm^2 **c** 5 m^2 **d** 11.5 m^2

2 ai £4   **aii** £7.25   **aiii** £3.10   **b** 10p

3 a £115   **b** £290

4 a 13   **b** 48

5 144

6 a 47.5   **b** 84

7 a 2   **b** 2

8 4

9 a 3   **b** 2

10 a 2   **b** 2

11 Paul; when $x = 6$, $2x^2 = 2 \times 36 = 72$

A5.3

1 a $C = 35 + 20h$ **b** £95

2 a $C = 2 + 0.6m$ **bi** £5   **bii** £11

3 a $C = 75 + 35d$ **b** €320   **c** 12 days

4 a $P = 2b + 2$ **b** 12 pencils

   c 18 pencils   **d** 23

5 14 children

6 5 days

7 a $C = 3n + 1.5m$ **b** $m = 4 \times n$

  c $C = 9n$ **d** 6 adults

A5.4

1 a 8   **b** -2

2 a 4   **b** 14

3 a 11   **b** 6.5

4 a 60   **b** 144

5 a $\frac{1}{2}$ **b** 4

6 a $x = \frac{y - c}{m}$ **b** $t = \frac{v - u}{a}$ **c** $x = 2(y - d)$

  d $y = \frac{4 - x}{3}$

7 a $t = \frac{s + 6}{3}$ **b** $t = \frac{2x - 9}{5}$ **c** $t = \frac{3x - 12}{2}$

8 a $y = \frac{2 - 4x}{6}$ **b** $y = \frac{2x + 6}{3}$ **c** $y = \frac{3x - z}{5}$

9 a $n = \frac{P - 1}{4}$

  bi 9   **bii** 13   **biii** 57

10 a 200   **b** 150   **c** 570

A5.5

1 $A = \text{length} \times \text{width} = m(m + 2) = m^2 + 2m$

2 a $x(x + 2)$ **b** $x(x - 2)$

  c $A = x(x + 2) - x(x - 2) = x^2 + 2x - x^2 + 2x = 4x$

3 a odd, even; even + even = even;

    odd + odd = even; odd + even = odd

  b For any two consecutive numbers, one is odd and one is even. odd + even = odd.

  c odd + even + odd + even

    = (odd + even) + (odd + even)

    = odd + odd = even

4 a odd   **b** $2n(2n + 1)$ **c** $4n^2 + 2n$

  d $4n^2 \div 2 = 2n^2$, multiple of 2

  e $4n^2$ and $2n$ are even, so $4n^2 + 2n$ is even + even = even.

5 a e.g. if $x = 2$, $3x = 6$ which is even

  b e.g. if $x = 2$, $x^2 = 4$ which is even

  c e.g. if $x = 2$ and $y = 3$, $x^2 + y^2 = 13$ which is odd

A5 Exam review

1 a $x = \frac{3(y - 5)}{2}$ **b** 3

2 a Bryani; $4x^2 = 4 \times 3^2 = 4 \times 9 = 36$ **b** 64

S4 Before you start ...

1 a is acute, b is obtuse

2 a $(2, 3)$ **b** $(1, -2)$ **c** $(-2, 0)$ **d** $(-3, 2)$

3 4

4 48 cm²

S4.1

1 a 60°, equilateral   **b** 90°, right-angled

  c 33°, isosceles   **d** 79°, scalene

  e 45°, right-angled isosceles

2 a e.g. $(1, 1)$ **b** e.g. $(3, 0)$ **c** e.g. $(3, 2)$

  d e.g. $(-2, 0)$ **e** $(1, 1.5)$ **f** e.g. $(3, 0)$

3 a 60°, 60°, 60°   **b** 30°, 30°, 120°

4 a 5   **b** 5   **c** 5

  d 5   **e** 5   **f** 5

5 a 6 cm²   **b** 6 cm²   **c** 6 cm²

  d 6 cm²   **e** 6 cm²

6 No, the angles sum to 180°, so none of the angles can be greater than 180°.

S4.2

1 a 90°   **b** $b = 100°$, $c = 80°$

  c 10°   **d** $d = 125°$, $e = 55°$

  e 105°   **f** $f = 110°$, $g = 70°$, $h = 110°$

2

Shape	Equal in length	Bisect each other	Perpendicular
Rectangle	✓	✓	✗
Kite	✗	✗	✓
Isosceles trapezium	✓	✗	✗
Square	✓	✓	✓
Parallelogram	✗	✓	✗
Rhombus	✗	✓	✓
Ordinary trapezium	✗	✗	✗

3 a $(-1, 2)$ **c** 6 square units

S4.3

1 a Triangular prism   **b** Square-based pyramid

  c Sphere   **d** Cuboid

  e Pentagon-based pyramid

  f Cone   **g** Cylinder

  h Cube   **i** Tetrahedron

  j Pentagonal prism

2 a   **b**   **c**

3 a 8   **b** 12   **c** 6

4 a

Name of solid	No. of faces (f)	No. of edges (e)	No. of vertices (v)
Triangular prism	5	9	6
Square-based pyramid	5	8	5
Tetrahedron	4	6	4
Pentagonal prism	7	15	10
Square-based prism	6	12	8
Cube	6	12	8
Hexagonal pyramid	7	12	7
Octagonal prism	10	24	16
Pentagonal pyramid	6	10	6

  b $e + 2 = f + v$

5 For example,

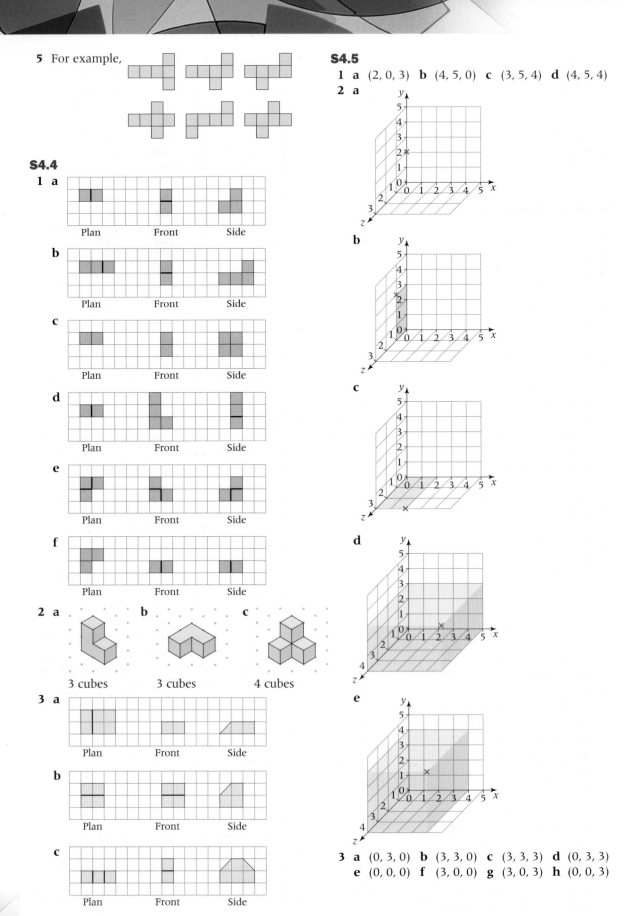

S4.4

1 a

Plan   Front   Side

b

Plan   Front   Side

c

Plan   Front   Side

d

Plan   Front   Side

e

Plan   Front   Side

f

Plan   Front   Side

2 a   **b**   **c**

3 cubes   3 cubes   4 cubes

3 a

Plan   Front   Side

b

Plan   Front   Side

c

Plan   Front   Side

S4.5

1 a $(2, 0, 3)$ **b** $(4, 5, 0)$ **c** $(3, 5, 4)$ **d** $(4, 5, 4)$

2 a

b

c

d

e

3 a $(0, 3, 0)$ **b** $(3, 3, 0)$ **c** $(3, 3, 3)$ **d** $(0, 3, 3)$
e $(0, 0, 0)$ **f** $(3, 0, 0)$ **g** $(3, 0, 3)$ **h** $(0, 0, 3)$

4 **a** $p = 4$, $q = 5$, $r = 2$
   b A(0, 5, 0), B(4, 5, 0), C(4, 5, 2), D(0, 5, 2),
     E(0, 0, 0), F(4, 0, 0), G(4, 0, 2), H(0, 0, 2)
   c 40 cubic units

S4 Exam review
1 **a** Isosceles **b** 70°
2 **a** Cylinder, cone
   b Cuboid, square-based pyramid

N6 Before you start …
1 47
2 **a** 1.3   **b** 0.3
3 **a** 42   **b** 35
4 **a** 48   **b** 3.8
5 $7 \times 12 \div 4$

N6.1
1 **a** 26   **b** 37   **c** 52   **d** 10
   e 33   **f** 5   **g** 180   **h** 9
2 **a** 28   **b** 72   **c** 5   **d** 16
   e 2   **f** 75
3 **a** $5 \times (2 + 1) = 15$ **b** $5 \times (3 - 1) \times 4 = 40$
   c $20 + 8 \div 2 - 7 = 17$ **d** $2 + 3^2 \times (4 + 3) = 65$
   e $2 \times (6^2 \div 3) + 9 = 33$ **f** $(4 \times 5 + 5) \times 6 = 150$
4 **a** Pete, because the contents of the brackets are
     $2 \times 9 - 4 = 18 - 4 = 14$.
   b No; $(5 \times 4)^2 = 20^2 = 400$, whereas
     $5 \times 4^2 = 5 \times 16 = 80$.
   ci 55.7685 **cii** 55.8
5 **a** 1   **b** 2   **c** 2   **d** 14   **e** 40
   f 7
6 **a** 14 **b** 10 **c** 2 **d** 12 **e** 91
   f 112 **g** 70 **h** 37 **i** 11 **j** 3
7 **a** 170 **b** 0.58 **c** 1.78

N6.2
1 **ai** 2000   **aii** 1500   **aiii** 1550
   bi 6000   **bii** 5800   **biii** 5790
   ci 18 000   **cii** 17 800   **ciii** 17 790
   di 35 000   **dii** 35 100   **diii** 35 130
   ei 237 000   **eii** 236 900   **eiii** 236 870
2 **ai** 4.356   **aii** 4.36   **aiii** 4.4   **aiv** 4
   bi 9.857   **bii** 9.86   **biii** 9.9   **biv** 10
   ci 0.937   **cii** 0.94   **ciii** 0.9   **civ** 1
   di 19.496   **dii** 19.50   **diii** 19.5   **div** 19
   ei 26.808   **eii** 26.81   **eiii** 26.8   **eiv** 27
   fi 20.000   **fii** 20.00   **fiii** 20.0   **fiv** 20
   gi 0.005   **gii** 0.00   **giii** 0.0   **giv** 0
   hi 3896.657 **hii** 3896.66
   hiii 3896.6 **hiv** 3897
   ii 249.763 **iii** 249.76
   iiii 249.8 **iiv** 250
3 **a** 0.3   **b** 150   **c** 0.08   **d** 280
   e 38   **f** 0.04   **g** 92.3   **h** 4460
4 **a** 10^2 **b** 0.01   **c** 0.01   **d** 1000
   e 0.1   **f** 0.01   **g** 0.01

5 **ai** 9.48   **aii** 9.5   **aiii** 9
   bi 27.7   **bii** 28   **biii** 30
   ci 46.7   **cii** 47   **ciii** 50
   di 388   **dii** 390   **diii** 400
   ei 2.41   **eii** 2.4   **eiii** 2
   fi 4910   **fii** 4900   **fiii** 5000
   gi 0.009 48 **gii** 0.0095 **giii** 0.009
   hi 3490   **hii** 3500   **hiii** 3000
   ii 9.88   **iii** 9.9   **iiii** 10
   ji 25.1   **jii** 25   **jiii** 30
   ki 2310   **hii** 2300   **hiii** 2000
   li 237 000 **lii** 240 000 **liii** 200 000
   mi 4390   **mii** 4400   **miii** 4000
6 **a** 2.4   **b** 0.56   **c** 50   **d** 20
   e 0.48   **f** 400
7 **a** $4 \times 4 = 16$ **b** $20 \times 20 = 400$
   c $\frac{5 \times 8}{20} = 2$ **d** $54 \div 9 = 6$
8 **a** $\frac{30 \times 40}{3 \times 4} = 100$ **b** $\frac{16 \times 0.5}{0.2 \times 32} = 1.25$
   c $(25 + 4)^2 \approx 30^2 = 900$ **d** $\frac{64 \times 4}{4} = 64$
   e $\sqrt{2 \div 0.04} = \sqrt{50} \approx 7$ **f** $\sqrt{30 \div 0.6} = \sqrt{50} \approx 7$

N6.3
1 **a** 63   **b** 12.1   **c** 5.4   **d** 24.2
   e 360   **f** 4.3   **g** 236   **h** 0.0078
2 **a** 15.4   **b** 189   **c** 58.3   **d** 114.8
   e 133   **f** 63.6   **g** 49   **h** 69
   i 35.2   **j** 173.6   **k** 134.1   **l** 784.3
   m 112   **n** 34   **o** 18   **p** 19.8
3 **a** 11.9   **b** 65.1   **c** 111.2   **d** 93.6
   e 100.8   **f** 211.2   **g** 43   **h** 73
4 **a** 11.6   **b** 35.6   **c** 148.6   **d** 153.9
   e 140.4   **f** 100.3
5 **a** 49.3   **b** 726   **c** 67.2   **d** 66.7
   e 26.6   **f** 67.5   **g** 12   **h** 40
6 **a** £116.91 **b** 30.38 m² **c** £35.76
   ai 101 430 **aii** 1 014 300 **aiii** 1014.3
   aiv 10.143 **av** 1.0143 **avi** 1014.3
   avii 1.0143 **aviii** 0.10143
   bi 65.49 **bii** 654.9 **biii** 3.7 **biv** 17.7
7 **ai** 9331 **aii** 0.9331 **aiii** 217 **aiv** 430
   bi 78.72 **bii** 7872 **biii** 0.48 **biv** 16.4

N6.4
1 **a** 26.08   **b** 32.71   **c** 2.81   **d** 31.99
   e 26.47   **f** 13.49   **g** 9.17   **h** 67.54
2 **a** 51   **b** 100.8   **c** 109.2   **d** 174.8
   e 117.6   **f** 475.3
3 **a** 3.9   **b** 6.1   **c** 8.8   **d** 12.3
   e 13.3   **f** 14.9
4 **a** 161.98 kg **b** 19.22 g **c** 1.102 kg
5 **a** 4.002   **b** 4.4   **c** 75.31   **d** 14.7
   e 41.673   **f** 181.64   **g** 15.13   **h** 4.4712
   i 3.5991
6 **a** £3.33 **b** £11.31 **c** 75 trees **d** £79.25

N6.5

1 **a** $2.4 \times (4.3 + 3.7) = 19.2$
   b $6.8 \times (3.75 - 2.64) = 7.548$
   c $(3.7 + 2.9) \div 1.2 = 5.5$
   d $(2.3 + 3.4^2) \times 2.7 = 37.422$
   e $5.3 + 3.9 \times (3.2 + 1.6) = 24.02$
   f $3.2 + 6.4 \times (4.3 + 2.5) = 46.72$
   g $(3.2 + 6.4) \times (4.3 + 2.5) = 65.28$
2 **a** 178.412 383 5   **b** 0.196 708 95
   c 3.210 178 253   **d** 3.350 190 476
   e 1.157 007 415   **f** 0.135 604 5
3 **ai** 15.3 m^2 **aii** £103.40   **b** £66.67
4 **a** £21.13   **b** £16.37
   c Yes, the new bill is cheaper than the old bill.

N6 Exam review

1 **ai** 3.7   **aii** 6.8   **aiii** 0.7   **aiv** 11.5
   b $(1.5 + 2.2) \times 3.1 = 11.47$
2 **a** 1.962 631 579   **b** 1.96 or 2.0

A6 Before you start ...

1 **a** $2x + 8$ **b** $3y - 6$ **c** $10x + 15$ **d** $-6x + 2$
2 **a** 12   **b** 16
3 **a** $x = 5$ **b** $y = 4$
4 **a** 3   **b** 4   **c** 2   **d** 5
5 **a** $6n$ **b** $\frac{1}{2}n$

A6.1

1 **a** $4x + 12$ **b** $2y - 8$ **c** $15 - 5a$ **d** $6 - 3b$
2 **a** $x = 4$ **b** $s = 6$ **c** $t = 3$ **d** $v = 3$
3 **a** $-2c - 8$ **b** $-3d + 9$ **c** $8m - 2$ **d** $12 - 8n$
4 **a** $a = -6$ **b** $b = -1$ **c** $c = 2$ **d** $d = -2$
5 **a** $e = 1.5$ **b** $f = \frac{2}{3}$ **c** $g = 0.75$ **d** $h = -0.5$
6 **a** $x = -8.5$ **b** $y = 2.5$ **c** $z = 2.5$
   x is the odd one out.
7 **a** $3(x - 2)$ **b** $x = 6$
8 **a** $4(2y + 5)$ **b** $y = 1$
9 $4(z - 6), z = 8$

A6.2

1 **a** $m = 5$ **b** $p = 3$ **c** $t = 3$ **d** $n = 7$
   e $q = 8$ **f** $s = 8$
2 **a** $s = -3$ **b** $t = -4$ **c** $u = -2$ **d** $v = -1$
3 **a** $a = 5$ **b** $b = -4$ **c** $c = 2.5$ **d** $d = -3$
4 **a** $x = 7.5$ **b** $x = -3$ **c** $x = 0.25$ **d** $x = -1.5$
5 **a** $21 = 2n + 5$ **b** $4n - 11 = 21$
   c $2n + 5 = 4n - 11$ **d** $n = 8$
6 **a** $n = 10$ **b** $5n - 8 = 2n + 10, n = 6$
   c $3n + 4 = 5n + 12, n = -4$

A6.3

1 **a** $r = 4$ **b** $s = -3$ **c** $t = 2$ **d** $v = -5$
2 **a** $a = 3$ **b** $b = -2$ **c** $c = 5$ **d** $d = -4$
3 **a** $x = 6$ **b** $y = -6$ **c** $z = 5.5$ **d** $m = 2$
4 **a** $e = 3.5$ **b** $f = 0.5$ **c** $g = -1.5$ **d** $h = -1$

5 **a–d**

	$3x - 2$	$4x + 1$	$8x - 3$
$2(x + 3)$	$x = 8$	$x = 2.5$	$x = 1.5$
$4(2x - 1)$	$x = 0.4$	$x = 1.25$	No solution
$3(4x + 1)$	$x = -\frac{5}{9}$	$x = -0.25$	$x = -1.5$

6 **a** $3x + 9$ **b** $4x + 4$
   c $4x + 4 = 3x + 9$ **d** $x = 5$
7 **a** $4(x + 2)$ **b** $8x = 4(x + 2)$ **c** $x = 2$
8 **a** $4m$ **b** $3(m + 2)$
   c $4m = 3(m + 2), m = 6$ **d** 8

A6.4

1 **a** $x = 15$ **b** $m = -8$ **c** $n = -18$ **d** $m = 20$
2 **a** $s = 9$ **b** $t = 6$ **c** $u = -10$ **d** $v = 12$
3 **a** $x = 6$ **b** $y = 6$ **c** $z = 15$ **d** $q = -8$
4 **a** $x = 1$ **b** $x = 11$ **c** $x = -17$ **d** $x = 6$
5 **a** $x = 12$ **b** $x = 6$ **c** $x = 7$ **d** $x = 5$
6 **a** $\frac{n}{4} + 6$ **b** $\frac{n}{4} + 6 = 10$ **c** $n = 16$
7 **a** $\frac{n}{3} - 4 = 7, n = 33$ **b** $\frac{n}{2} + 8 = 3, n = -10$
8 **a** $\frac{2x + 6}{3}$ **b** $x = 9$
9 $\frac{4 + x}{4} = 10, x = 36$

A6.5

1 **a**

x	x^2	Too big or too small
5.5	30.25	Too big
5.4	29.16	Too big

   d $x = 5.4$
2 $x = 4.1$
3 $x = 5.2$
4 **a** 0, 6, 24   **b** x is between 2 and 3.
   e $x = 2.2$
5 $x = 4.1$

A6 Exam review

1 **a** $x = 5.3$
2 **a** $x = 8$ **b** $y = 6.5$ **c** $p = \frac{5}{8}$

D4 Before you start ...

1 **a** 26   **b** 18   **c** 5.6
2 **a** 4, 5.5, 6.5, 7, 8
   b 2.3, 2.4, 3.2, 3.4, 4.2, 4.3
   c 7.5, 7.9, 8.3, 8.6, 9.1
3 **a** 6, 6, 7, 8, 8, 9, 9, 9, 9, 9
   b 100, 100, 101, 102, 102, 104, 104, 104, 104, 104
4 **a** 3   **b** 8   **c** 42   **d** 47   **e** 52

D4.1

1 **a** Discrete   **b** Discrete   **c** Continuous
   d Continuous   **e** Continuous   **f** Discrete
   g Continuous   **h** Continuous   **i** Discrete
   j Continuous   **k** Discrete   **l** Discrete
2 **a** 5   **b** 4   **c** 9   **d** 1   **e** 7
   f 5   **g** 17   **h** 7   **i** 2   **j** £3.85

3 a 2   **b** 3   **c** 30
4 41 kg
5 a 31 °F   **b** 34 °F
6 23 or 42

D4.2

1 a 4
  b–d

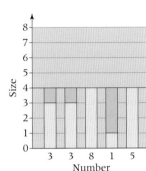

2 a 11, 4, 25   **b** Car
3 a 38p, 85p, £1.12, £2.15, £2.47   **b** £1.12
4 a 80.4 °F   **b** 80 °F   **c** 80 °F
5 a 5.0   **b** 5.8

D4.3

1 a 3, 3, 3, 3, 4, 4, 5, 5
  b Range = 2, Mode = 3, Median = 3.5,
    Mean = 3.75
2 a 1, 1, 1, 1, 2, 2, 2, 2, 2, 3, 3, 4, 4, 4, 4, 4, 5,
    5, 5, 5, 5, 5, 5, 5
  b 8
  c Range = 4, Mode = 5, Median = 4,
    Mean = 3.28
3 a 2.4   **b** 1   **c** 2   **d** 3
4 a 2.7   **b** 4   **c** 3   **d** 3
5 a 3, 4, 0, 3, 3, 3, 3, 0
  b Mean = 5.85, Mode = 4, Median = 6,
    Range = 7

D4.4

1 a 2, 4
  b Number 47's data is more spread out than
    Number 45's.
2 a 1, 3, 4, 1, 1   **b** 1.8, 2, 2
  c On average, houses in Ullswater Drive have
    more cars than those in Ambleside Close.
3 a Ireland: 22, 23, 24, 24, 24, 25, 26, 26, 26, 27,
    27, 28
    Spain: 2, 5, 6, 7, 10, 10, 10, 11, 11, 11, 11, 12
  b Ireland 25.5, Spain 10
  c On average, Ireland has more days of rain
    than Spain.
  d Ireland 6, Spain 10
  e There is a bigger spread or larger variation in
    the number of rainy days in Spain.

D4.5

1 a 1, 6, 8, 3, 3, 3   **b** 70 to 74   **c** 70 to 74

2 a 3   **b** 23, 28, 33, 38
  c 23, 168, 66, 38; Mean speed = 29.5 mph
3 a 30 students   **b** $160 < h \leq 170$
  c $170 < h \leq 180$ **d** 163.3 cm

D4 Exam review

1 a 32   **b** $150 < h \leq 160$ **c** 157.2 cm
2 a 1   **b** 3   **c** 2.1

S5 Before you start …

1 a 42°   **b** 123°   **c** 230°
2 360°
3 Circle with 4.6 cm diameter
4 10 cm²
5 a 67 mm   **b** 6.7 cm

S5.1

1 a Rectangle, 27.3 cm   **b** Rhombus, 22.4 cm
  c Rectangle, 27.9 cm
2 a 057° **b** 168° **c** 237° **d** 276° **e** 348°
3 a   **b** 2.4 km **c** 13.8 km

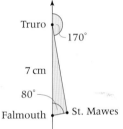

Scale: 1cm represents 2 km

S5.2

1 a 8.2 cm   **b** 5.3 cm   **c** 11.6 cm
2 a 5.7 cm, 5.7 cm **b** 7.6 cm, 5.0 cm
  c 5.8 cm, 3.4 cm
3 a 60°   **b** 76°   **c** 90°
4 a 5.7 cm, 55° **b** 6.0 cm, 45° **c** 6 cm, 67°

S5.3

For examples of constructing perpendicular
bisectors, see page 246.
  1 d 4 cm
  4 c 90°
  5 The diagonals are perpendicular bisectors of
    each other if each line is divided into two equal
    parts and they meet at right angles. Use your
    ruler, compasses and protractor to check.

S5.4

For examples of constructing angle bisectors,
see page 248.
  6 c

7 d perpendicular
 e The obtuse angles are equal (vertically opposite angles) and the acute angles are equal (vertically opposite angles). One acute angle and one obtuse angle sum to 180° (angles on a straight line). The angle between the bisectors is half an acute angle and half an obtuse angle, so it is half 180°, which is 90°.
8 e 2.2 cm

S5.5

See page 246, for examples of constructing perpendicular bisectors.
See page 248, for examples of constructing angle bisectors.
See page 250, for examples of loci and using loci in problem solving.

1 b Angle bisector
2 b Angle bisector
3 b Perpendicular bisector
4 Circle of radius 3 cm
5 A parallel line centred between the existing parallel lines
6 A semicircle of radius 2 m
7 b Perpendicular bisector
 c The region to the left of the perpendicular bisector

S5 Exam review

1 School 048°, church 130°, park 215°, café 254°, cinema 312°

2

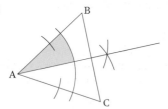

N7 Before you start ...

1 £33 **2** $43 **3** 57 kg
4 £5.40 **5** £367.50

N7.1

1 a $2\frac{1}{2}$ **b** 2 **c** $2\frac{2}{3}$ **d** $1\frac{6}{7}$ **e** 2 **f** $1\frac{1}{3}$
2 a 4 **b** $3\frac{3}{4}$ **c** 4 **d** $4\frac{2}{3}$ **e** $2\frac{1}{4}$
 f $22\frac{2}{5}$ **g** $13\frac{1}{3}$ **h** $8\frac{5}{9}$ **i** 10
3 a $\frac{4}{5}$ kg **b** $3\frac{1}{2}$ kg **c** $7\frac{1}{5}$ litres **d** $14\frac{2}{5}$ kg
4 a €12 **b** £28 **c** $37\frac{1}{2}$ m **d** $36\frac{4}{7}$ km
 e £375 **f** $58\frac{1}{3}$ mm **g** 1375 m **h** $18\frac{6}{13}$ g
5 a 264 kg **b** $4500 **c** 4.44 kg **d** 952 cups
 e 21.67 tonnes **f** 96° **g** 139.35°
 h 0.87 hours or 52 minutes **i** £260.67
 j 20 hours
6 a $\frac{2}{3}$ **b** $\frac{3}{5}$ **c** $\frac{1}{5}$ **d** $\frac{11}{60}$
7 a £24 **b** £7.50 **c** 73 days

N7.2

1 a £150 **b** 2 kg **c** £40
 d 18.5 kg **e** £0.30 or 30p **f** 34.28 m
2 a £9 **b** 82 kg **c** $5
 d £0.75 or 75p **e** £31.50 **f** 0.19 m
3 a £51 **b** 72 Mb **c** £45
 d £40 **e** 136.5 m **f** £22
 g 1099 mm **h** 6.3 kg **i** 31.5 mm
 j 24 litres
4 a Find 10% by dividing by 10; find 5% by halving 10%; add the two answers together.
 b Find 10% and then halve it.
 c Find 10% and times by 3; find 5% by halving 10%; add the two answers together.
 d Find 10%; halve 10% to find 5%; halve 5% to find 2.5%; add the three answers together.
 e Find 10% and halve it to find 5%; subtract 5% from 100% (the original amount).
5 a 11.2 Mb **b** 13.2 tonnes **c** 90.85 km
 d £98.28
6 a £2.04 **b** 13.92 km **c** £3.04
 d €108.80 **e** 11.05 m **f** 33.58 cm
 g 125.8 m **h** £1.53 **i** €2.13

N7.3

1 a 4.5 kg **b** 10.2 m **c** 54°
 d 0.74 cm **e** 331.5 ml **f** 63°
 g 18.2 kg **h** 85.87 kg **i** 5.544 kg
 j 3.96 m²
2 a £385 **b** 70.3 kg **c** £550.20
 d 491.4 km **e** 1128 kg
3 a £397.80 **b** 524.9 kg **c** £1758.96
 d 599.56 km **e** $3423.55
4 New wage: £364, £296.92, £428.74, £217.64, £206.59
5 a 492.8 ml **b** £166.50 **c** £250 185
 d 1081 students

N7.4

1 Selling price: £10.20, £25.96, £7.96, £28.12, £176.49
2 a £116.33 **b** £2.10 **c** £36.74 **d** £21.89
3 aii 742.4 ml **aiii** 740 ml
 bii 4.914 m **biii** 4.9 m
 cii 2.7356 tonnes **ciii** 2.7 tonnes
 dii 519.6 g **diii** 520 g
4 Payment by installments costs £189.36, so cash payment is cheaper by 36p.

N7.5

1 a £612.50 **b** £2335.80 **c** £26 684.80
2 a £1358.20 **b** £8828.30 **c** £4658.63
 d £2634.91
3 a £790 **b** £1109.25 **c** £54.60
 d £132.43
4 a £477.30 **b** £14 105 **c** £149 582
 d £20 622.15
5 a £8820 **b** £15 099.37 **c** £43 24.91

N7 Exam review

1 a $\frac{7}{20}$ b £17.50

2 £9720

D5 Before you start ...

1 a 360°   b 270°   c 95°

2 a 30   b 20   c 15   d 10   e 3

3 a 14, 24, 10, 20   b 6, 2, 5, 10   c 7, 3, 5, 13

4 a (1, 3)   b (4, 1)

D5.1

1 ai 24   aii 12   aiii 36   aiv 4   av 76

   b Cotton

2 ai £20   aii £10   b Children

   c 4 × World Single Trip = £20, which is cheaper than World Annual insurance.

3 ai 1 person   aii 3 people

   b 28 tickets

4 a 120°   b 3°   ci 30   cii 50   ciii 40

D5.2

1 ai Cooking and washing up

   aii Washing and ironing

   bi Cooking and washing up   bii DIY

2 ai 100 million   aii 1000 million

   b India   c UK

3 ai 2   aii 1

   b 85–90 m   c 70–75 m   d 10 athletes

4 The women jumped further, on average. The men had a greater spread of long jumps than the women.

D5.3

1 a 10, 16, 22, 22, 24, 26, 28, 29, 30

   bi 23   bii 22   biii 24   biv 20

2 a

0	7 9
10	7 9 2 1 5 8 7
20	5 5 1 5 3
30	1 2 7
40	3 0 1

b

0	7 9
10	1 2 5 7 7 8 9
20	1 3 5 5 5
30	1 2 7
40	0 1 3

   ci 23.4   cii 25   ciii 22   civ 36

3 a 128 sec   b 120 sec   c 126 sec   d 31 sec

4 a 49   b 16   c $\frac{1}{4}$

5 a Long jump

   b High jump 26 cm, long jump 15 cm; there is a greater spread of distances for the high jump than there is for the long jump.

D5.4

1 a 0900   b 22 °C, 1500   c 2 °C, 0300   d 20 °C

2 There were always more bus passengers than train passengers from 1970 to 2000. The number of bus passengers was decreasing during this period, whereas the number of train passengers was increasing.

3 a Increasing rapidly   b Decreasing slowly

   c An alternative form of energy supply

D5.5

1 a Negative correlation   b No correlation

   c Positive correlation

2 a A: Poor exam mark, lots of revision; B: Very good exam mark, lots of revision; C: Very good exam mark, little revision; D: Poor exam mark, little revision; E: Average exam mark, average amount of revision

   b A: Not much pocket money, equal eldest; B: Lots of pocket money, equal eldest; C: Lots of pocket money, equal youngest; D: Not much pocket money, equal youngest; E: Average pocket money, middle age

   c A: Low fitness level, lots of hours in gym, B: Good fitness level, lots of hours in gym, C: Good fitness level, few hours in gym, D: Low fitness level, few hours in gym, E: Medium fitness level, medium hours in gym

3 a 16   b 24

4 a, c

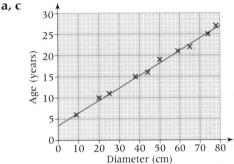

   b Positive correlation   d 20 years

D5 Exam review

1 ai 2.5 kg, 1.1 kg   aii 2.3 kg, 1.1 kg

   b Boys are heavier, on average. The spread of weights is the same for boys and girls.

2 a, c

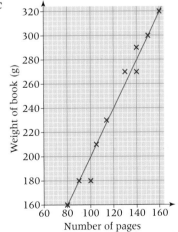

   b The greater the number of pages, the heavier the book (positive correlation).

   di 140 pages   dii 240 g

S6 Before you start ...

1 a 40 cm² **b** 30 cm² **c** 113.04 cm²
2 450 cm³
3 a 250 **b** 6300 **c** 41 **d** 250 **e** 3500
f 4 **g** 5.6 **h** 40 **i** 4.1 **j** 5.2
4 a ii **b** iii **c** i

S6.1

1 a 48 cm² **b** 32 cm² **c** 24 cm² **d** 208 cm²
2 a 136 cm² **b** 38 m² **c** 160 cm² **d** 118 cm²
e 188 cm²
3 a 24 cm² **b** 40 cm² **c** 32 cm² **d** 6 cm²
e 108 cm²
4 a 528 cm² **b** 189 cm²

S6.2

1 a 160 cm³ **b** 108 m³ **c** 134.4 m³
2 a 203.125 m³ **b** 9.3 cm³ **c** 3.125 m³
3 a 24 cm², 120 cm³ **b** 3 m², 30 m³
c 4 m², 20 m³ **d** 32 cm², 256 cm³
4 a 50.3 cm² **b** 28.3 cm²
c 201 cm² **d** 78.5 cm²
5 a 402 cm³ **b** 170 cm³
c 503 cm³ **d** 157 cm³

S6.3

1 a 1800 mm **b** 4.5 cm **c** 3.5 m
d 2 km **e** 3.5 km **f** 4.5 m
g 0.85 m **h** 250 cm **i** 2.5 m
j 0.8 km
2 a 8 m² **b** 80 000 cm²
3 a 24 m² **b** 240 000 cm²
4 a 400 mm² **b** 730 mm² **c** 1090 mm²
d 250 mm² **e** 40 000 mm²
5 a 6 cm² **b** 12 cm² **c** 8.5 cm²
d 65 cm² **e** 100 cm²
6 a 4 m² **b** 8.5 m² **c** 100 m²
d 12.5 m² **e** 0.5 m²
7 a 50 000 cm² **b** 100 000 cm² **c** 65 000 cm²
d 77 500 cm² **e** 6000 cm²
8 a 4 km² **b** 18 km² **c** 0.5 km²
d 1.5 km²
9 a 1000 litres **b** 6000 litres **c** 7500 litres

S6.4

1 2.5 mph
2 a 8 **b** 15 **c** 150 **d** 40 **e** 2.5
3 37.5 miles
4 a 320 **b** 175 **c** 270 **d** 50 **e** 125
5 2.5 hours
6 a 2 **b** 2.5 **c** 3.5 **d** 4.5 **e** 3.33
7 a 70 km/h **b** 14 km/litre
8 a 333.3 m/min **b** 5.6 m/s
9 912.5 g

S6.5

1 a Area **b** Volume

c Length **d** None of these
e Volume **f** None of these
g Length **h** Volume
i Area **j** None of these
k Length **l** Length
m None of these **n** None of these
o None of these **p** Area
q Area **r** None of these
s Volume **t** Volume
2 a Area **b** Length **c** Volume
d Area **e** Area **f** Length
g Length **h** Length
3 c, as it has dimensions L³
4 c, as it has dimensions L²

S6 Exam review

1 a Length **b** Volume **c** Area
d Area **e** Volume
2 £75.30

A7 Before you start ...

1

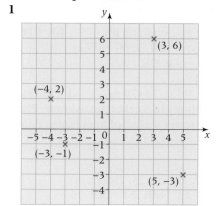

2 $y = 1, 3, 5, 7, 9$
3 a, b, e, f
4 c
5 a $y = 2x - 5$ **b** $y = 4 - 2x$

A7.1

1 a $y = -1, 3, 5, 7, 11$
b

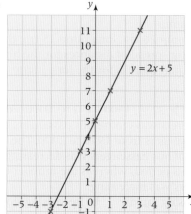

2 a–d

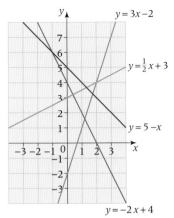

$y = 3x - 2$
$y = \frac{1}{2}x + 3$
$y = 5 - x$
$y = -2x + 4$

3 a–d

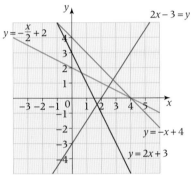

$y = -\frac{x}{2} + 2$
$2x - 3 = y$
$y = -x + 4$
$y = 2x + 3$

4 a–d

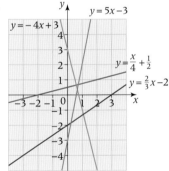

$y = 5x - 3$
$y = -4x + 3$
$y = \frac{x}{4} + \frac{1}{2}$
$y = \frac{2}{3}x - 2$

5 $4x + 2y = 1$ is the odd one out, as it gives
$y = \frac{1}{2} - 2x$ not $y = 2x + \frac{1}{2}$

6 a   **bi** 5.5   **bii** −1.5

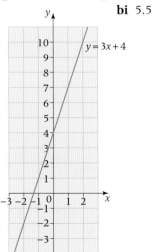

$y = 3x + 4$

7 a–d

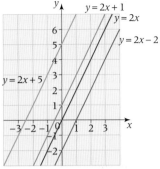

$y = 2x + 1$
$y = 2x$
$y = 2x - 2$
$y = 2x + 5$

The lines are all parallel.

8 a–c

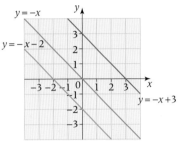

$y = -x$
$y = -x - 2$
$y = -x + 3$

The lines are all parallel.
$y = -x + 1$ would lie between $y = -x$ and
$y = -x + 3$, with the same slope and
passing through $(0, 1)$.

A7.2

1 a ii   **b** iv   **c** i   **d** v   **e** iii
2 a $y = 2x + 3$ **b** $y = -3x + 1$ **c** $y = 3x - 1$
   d $y = 3x + 5$ **e** $y = 3x + 2$ **f** $y = -2x - 1.5$
3 $y = 3x - 1$, $y = 3x + 5$, $y = 3x + 2$
4 $12x - 3y = 9$
5 b, c, d, a, e
6 e ratio = 4, ratio = gradient/slope of line
   h ratio = 4

A7.3

1 a $y = 2$ **b** $y = 8$ **c** $x = 2$ **d** $x = -3$
2 a   **b** $x = 8$
                         c $(2, 4)$ and $(-3, 3.5)$

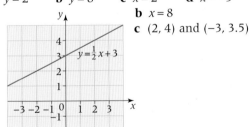

$y = \frac{1}{2}x + 3$

3 a $y = 4x - 7$ **b** $x = -2$
5 ai $x = 1.5$ **aii** $x = 5$ **aiii** $x = -3$
   b $3x + 2 = 11$, $x = 3$
6 a $x = 2$
   bi $x = 4$ **bii** $x = -4.5$ **biii** $x = 1.5$

A7.4

1 a $(2, 3)$ **b** $(-1, -4)$ **c** $(3, 7)$ **d** $(-2, -4)$
   e $(7, -2)$ **f** $(4, 1)$

2 a Yes **b** Yes **c** No **d** Yes

3 b $y = 2x + 1$ and $y = 4x + 2$ cross at $(-\frac{1}{2}, 0)$, $y = 3$
  and $y = x + 1$ cross at $(2, 3)$, $y = x$
  and $y = -x$ cross at $(0, 0)$

4 b $(1, 1)$
  c No, because the lines do not cross at $(1, 2)$.

5 b $(3, 2)$

6 b $x = 4$, $y = 2$

7 a $5x + 2y = 9$

b–c

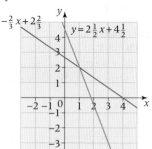

$y = -\frac{2}{3}x + 2\frac{2}{3}$

$y = 2\frac{1}{2}x + 4\frac{1}{2}$

d $(1, 2)$
e £1
f £2

A7.5

1 a $y = 9, 1, 0, 1, 9$

b–d

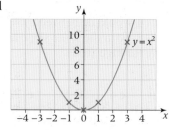

$y = x^2$

2

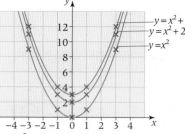

$y = x^2 + 3$
$y = x^2 + 2$
$y = x^2$

$y = x^2 + 2$ is the same shape as $y = x^2$ but shifted up 2; $y = x^2 + 3$ is the same shape as $y = x^2$ but shifted up 3.

3

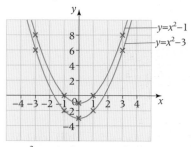

$y = x^2 - 1$
$y = x^2 - 3$

$y = x^2 - 1$ is the same shape as $y = x^2$ but shifted down 1; $y = x^2 - 3$ is the same shape as $y = x^2$ but shifted down 3.

4 a iv **b** i **c** ii **d** iii

5 a

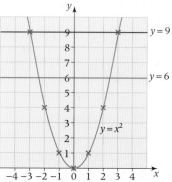

$y = 9$
$y = 6$
$y = x^2$

b $(3, 9)$ and $(-3, 9)$ **c** $x = -3, 3$
e $x = -2.4, 2.4$ **f** $y = 3$
g No, because the curve $y = x^2$ does not cross the line $y = -9$.

A7 Exam review

1 ai Gradient 3, y-intercept 2
  ai Gradient 1, y-intercept -1
  ai Gradient 1, y-intercept 0
  b $y = x - 1$ and $2y = 2x$, because they are parallel.

2 a $5, -1$

b

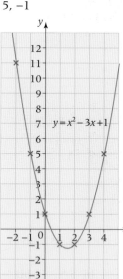

$y = x^2 - 3x + 1$

c $-1\frac{1}{4}$

N8 Before you start …

1 $2 : 3$

2 12

3 £9 : £21

4 240 miles

5 15 miles

6 a 0.23 m **b** 240 000 cm

N8.1

1 a $1 : 2$ **b** $8 : 5$ **c** $8 : 5$ **d** $3 : 2$
  e $19 : 9$ **f** $1 : 6$ **g** $2 : 4 : 3$ **h** $4 : 5 : 8$

2 a 2 : 5 **b** 11 : 16 **c** 5 : 2 **d** 5 : 3
e 5 : 3 **f** 8 : 5
3 a 1 : 3 **b** 7 : 3 **c** 15 : 2 **d** 9 : 100
4 a 1 : 3 **b** 3 : 2 **c** 2 : 1 **d** 3 : 4
5 a 1 : 2.5 **b** 1 : 3.85 **c** 1 : 4.17 **d** 1 : 41.67
e 1 : 23.68 **f** 1 : 150 **g** 1 : 12.5
6 a 1 : 50 **b** 1 : 20 000 **c** 1 : 36
7 a 35 kg **b** 28 kg

N8.2

1 b 3 : 1; height of 144 cm = 3 × width of 48 cm; width of 48 cm = $\frac{1}{3}$ × height of 144 cm

c 16 : 7; limousine length of 6.4 m = $\frac{16}{7}$ × car length of 2.8 m; car length of 2.8 m = $\frac{7}{16}$ × limousine length of 6.4 m

d 3 : 4; can containing 330 ml = $\frac{3}{4}$ × can containing 0.44 litre; can containing 0.44 litre = $\frac{4}{3}$ × can containing 330 ml

2 a 15 girls **b** 88 kg
c 60 purple flowers **d** 504 students
3 a 1.2 cm **b** 44 teachers **c** 39 cm
4 a 325 m **b** 0.6 cm
5 a £27 : £63 **b** 287 kg : 82 kg
c 64.5 tonnes : 38.7 tonnes
d 19.5 litres : 15.6 litres
e £6 : £12 : £18

N8.3

1 a 42 women **b** 240 g
c 63 feet **d** 430 pages
2 a £40 : £35 **b** £350 : £650
c 260 days : 104 days **d** 142.86 g : 357.14 g
e 214.29 m : 385.71 m
3 ai 66.66% **aii** 360 cm
bi 120% **bii** 102 kg
4 ai 72 g **aii** 115 g Copper, 69 g Aluminium
b $\frac{11}{50}$

N8.4

1 a 9 **b** 4 **c** 8 **d** 26 **e** 21
2 ai Sandra £156, Steve £351
aii $\frac{4}{13}$ **aiii** $2\frac{1}{4}$
bi Kirsty £60 000, Steve £24 000
bii $\frac{5}{7}$ **biii** $\frac{2}{5}$
3 ai 5 : 2 **aii** $2\frac{1}{2}$
bi 11 : 12 **bii** $\frac{11}{12}$
4 a 10 **b** 54 **c** 225 cl
5 ai 144 miles **aii** 3.5 hours
bi 18 275 kg **bii** 0.068 m³

N8.5

1 a £7.15 **b** £124.19 **c** £10.62 **d** £33.60
2 a Pie chart angles: Green Day 120°, Red Hot Chili Peppers 45°; Blue 195°

b Pie chart angles: Walk 216°, Bus 60°, Cycle 24°, Taxi/minibus 48°, Car 12°
3 a 3.6 m **b** 12.5 miles **c** 13.9 m/s
d 18 mph **e** 0.014 m²
4 9.6 cm, 7.2 cm
7 a £7 **b** £350

N8 Exam review

1 3 : 1
2 a 12 g **b** 280 g

S7 Before you start …

1 a 47° **b** 123°
2 a 35 mm **b** 3.5 cm
4 a 40 cm, 75 cm² **b** 12 cm, 6 cm²
5 200 cm²

S7.1

1 a 40 cm **b** 100 cm **c** 5 cm
d 65 cm **e** 125 cm
2 a 110 cm **b** 80 cm
3 75 cm by 200 cm
4 a 6 m, 9 m, 18 m **b** 162 m²
5 a 1000 m **b** 4000 m **c** 5000 m
d 250 m **e** 7250 m

S7.2

1 a 2 **b** 3 **c** 2 **d** 2
e 2 **f** 3 **g** 5 **h** 2
2 a A: Yes, 2; D: Yes, 3; B, C, E: No **b** A, D
3 a A: Yes, 2; C: Yes, 3; B, D, E: No **b** A, C

S7.3

1 a 2 **b** 2 **c** 3 **d** 2
2 a 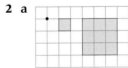 **b**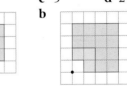

c

d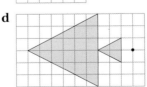

e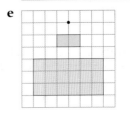

f

g

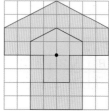

h

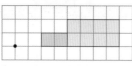

i

j

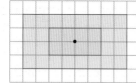

S7.4

1 a $a = 40°$, $b = 50°$
  b $c = 20°$, $d = 40°$
  c $h = 75°$, $i = 75°$, $j = 30°$, $k = 75°$, $l = 75°$
  d All 60°

2 a Yes, 2 **b** Yes, 5 **c** No **d** No
  e Yes, 4 **f** No

3 a 2, 8 cm **b** 3, 12 cm

4 a 6 cm **b** 12 cm

S7.5

1 a 16 cm **b** 12 cm²
  c Length = 30 cm, width = 10 cm
  d 80 cm **e** 300 cm² **f** 5, 25

2 a 32 cm³ **b** 6 cm, 12 cm, 12 cm
  c 864 cm³ **d** 27

3 a 30 cm² **b** 120 cm²

4 a 250 cm³ **b** 2000 cm³

5

Scale factor	Multiplier for length	Multiplier for area	Multiplier for volume
4	4	16	64
5	5	25	125
6	6	36	216
7	7	49	343

6 56 cm, 160 cm²

S7 Exam review

1

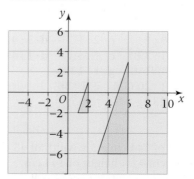

2 a 12.5 cm **b** 7.2 cm

D6 Before you start …

1 a 11, 13, 17, 19 **b** 16 **c** 15
  d 12, 16, 20 **e** 20

2 a $\frac{1}{3}$ **b** $\frac{2}{3}$ **c** $\frac{9}{10}$ **d** $\frac{1}{4}$ **e** $\frac{1}{4}$

3 a 1 **b** $\frac{4}{5}$ **c** $\frac{1}{5}$ **d** $\frac{7}{10}$

4 a 40 **b** 160 **c** 35 **d** 16 **e** 3

5 a 0.9, 1.0, 1.1, 1.3, 1.8, 2.1
  b £450, £540, £1300, £1450, £1540

D6.1

1 a Any impossible event
  b Any event that will definitely happen

2 a $\frac{2}{5}$ or 0.4 **b** $\frac{3}{5}$ or 0.6

3 a $\frac{3}{10}$, 0.35, $\frac{3}{8}$, $\frac{2}{5}$, 45%
  b

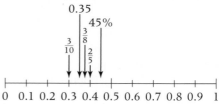

4 a $\frac{3}{8}$ **b** Red **c** Blue
  d 8 red, 2 blue, 6 green

5 a Green 0.2, Red 0.27, Blue 0.25, Yellow 0.28
  b 25

D6.2

1 a Yes **b** Yes **c** No **d** Yes
  e No **f** Yes **g** No **h** Yes

2 a $\frac{1}{4}$ **b** $\frac{1}{4}$ **c** $\frac{1}{2}$

3 a $\frac{2}{5}$ **b** $\frac{1}{2}$ **c** $\frac{1}{10}$ **d** $\frac{1}{2}$ **e** $\frac{3}{5}$
  f 1

4 a $\frac{1}{5}$ **b** $\frac{1}{5}$ **c** $\frac{2}{5}$ **d** $\frac{2}{5}$ **e** $\frac{4}{5}$

5 a 30, 5, 5, 10
  bi $\frac{3}{5}$ **bii** $\frac{1}{10}$ **biii** $\frac{3}{10}$

D6.3

1 a £250, £300, £450, £600, £700, £1200, £1300, £1400, £1400, £1500

b 1.2 GHz, 1.2 GHz, 1.3 GHz, 1.6 GHz, 1.6 GHz, 1.7 GHz, 1.8 GHz, 2.0 GHz, 2.3 GHz, 2.4 GHz

c 1   **d** 6

ei 3, 5, 6, 10   **eii** 4, 5, 6, 7, 8, 9, 10

eiii 5, 6, 7, 8

f 5

2 a Biased, as each name is not equally likely to be chosen.

b Biased, as each name is not equally likely to be chosen.

c Random, as each card is equally likely to be picked.

d Biased, as each height is not equally likely to be chosen.

e Biased, as each person is not equally likely to find the star.

f Biased, as only students 1 to 6 will have an equal chance of being selected.

g Biased, as student 30 has no chance of being picked.

D6.4

1 AB, AC, BC, BA, CA, CB

2 a AD, AE, AF, BD, BE, BF, CD, CE, CF

b $\frac{1}{9}$ **c** $\frac{4}{9}$

3 a HH, HT, TH, TT

b

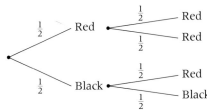

1st spin   2nd spin

c $\frac{1}{4}$ **d** $\frac{3}{4}$ **e** 25

4 a Red Red, Red Black, Black Red, Black Black

b First selection   Second selection

c $\frac{1}{2}$

D6.5

1 a RA, RB, RC, RD, RE, YA, YB, YC, YD, YE, GA, GB, GC, GD, GE, PA, PB, PC, PD, PE

b

	R	Y	G	P
A	(R, A)	(Y, A)	(G, A)	(P, A)
B	(R, B)	(Y, B)	(G, B)	(P, B)
C	(R, C)	(Y, C)	(G, C)	(P, C)
D	(R, D)	(Y, D)	(G, D)	(P, D)
E	(R, E)	(Y, E)	(G, E)	(P, E)

c $\frac{1}{20}$

2 a

	1	2	3	4
Heads	(1, H)	(2, H)	(3, H)	(4, H)
Tails	(1, T)	(2, T)	(3, T)	(4, T)

bi $\frac{1}{8}$ **bii** $\frac{1}{4}$

3 a

	Club (C)	Diamond (D)	Spade (S)	Heart (H)
Club (C)	(C, C)	(D, C)	(S, C)	(H, C)
Diamond (D)	(C, D)	(D, D)	(S, D)	(H, D)
Spade (S)	(C, S)	(D, S)	(S, S)	(H, S)
Heart (H)	(C, H)	(D, H)	(S, H)	(H, H)

b $\frac{1}{4}$

4 a

	1	2	3	4	5	6
1	(1, 1)	(2, 1)	(3, 1)	(4, 1)	(5, 1)	(6, 1)
2	(1, 2)	(2, 2)	(3, 2)	(4, 2)	(5, 2)	(6, 2)
3	(1, 3)	(2, 3)	(3, 3)	(4, 3)	(5, 3)	(6, 3)
4	(1, 4)	(2, 4)	(3, 4)	(4, 4)	(5, 4)	(6, 4)
5	(1, 5)	(2, 5)	(3, 5)	(4, 5)	(5, 5)	(6, 5)
6	(1, 6)	(2, 6)	(3, 6)	(4, 6)	(5, 6)	(6, 6)

P(Double six) = $\frac{1}{36}$

D6 Exam review

1 ai $\frac{1}{6}$ **aii** $\frac{5}{6}$ **aiii** $\frac{5}{12}$

b 0; there are no purple balls, so it is impossible to pick one

2 a No, you would expect approximately 100 sixes.

b Red dice   Blue dice

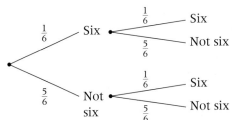

A8 Before you start ...

1 10 miles = 16 km, 20 miles = 32 km

2 10 m = 1000 cm, 20 m = 2000 cm

3 7 km

4 3.8 litres

5 4.5 kg

A8.1

1 a 4.8 km **b** 6.25 miles
c 7.2 km **d** 1.25 miles
1 mile is longer than 1 km.
2 a 2.7 kg **b** 4.5 kg **c** 8.8 lbs
d 4 lbs **e** 3.2 kg **f** 1 lb
g 5.5 kg **h** 11 lb
1 kg is heavier than 1 lb, as 1 kg ≈ 2.2 lb
3 ai 68 °F **aii** 14 °C **aiii** 86 °F **aiv** −7 °C
b 32 °F
c 28 °F, 36 °F, 43 °F, 54 °F, 75 °F

A8.2

1 a e.g. 0 cm = 0 mm, 10 cm = 100 mm
b 100 mm
2 a 0 lbs, 22 lb, 11 lb
ei 4.5 kg **eii** 2.3 kg
eiii 6.6 lb **eiv** 5.5 lb
3 a e.g. £0 = $0, £10 = $17, £20 = $34
b $51
di $8.50 **dii** £17.60
4 b The NZ cap is cheapest.

A8.3

1 a 1 pm **b** 60 miles
c $1\frac{1}{2}$ hours **d** 25 miles
e

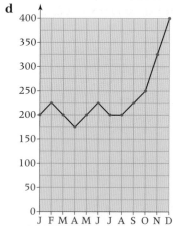

2 a F **b** C **c** D **d** A
e G **f** B **g** E
3 a 8 hours **b** 260 miles **c** 2 hours
d $\frac{1}{2}$ hour **e** 2 hours

A8.4

1 a 80 km **b** 5 hours **c** 16 km/h
d $\frac{50}{2}$ = 25 km per hour
e 15 km/h **f** first **g** faster
2 a 5 miles **b** $\frac{1}{2}$ hour
c 2:30 pm to 3 pm, as the graph is steeper here.
d 5 mph **e** 10 miles **f** $\frac{1}{2}$ hour
g 20 mph **h** 15 miles

i

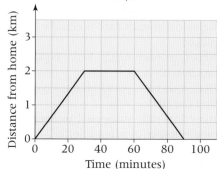

j 4:45 pm
3 a 2 km **b** 4 km/h
c

A8.5

1 a 200 **b** 225 **c** 25
d

e Sales rose sharply – due to Christmas season.
f Increase in sales
2 a 0.7 m **b** 0.5 m **c** 1.9 m **d** 0.1 m
e No, as growth has slowed down.
3 a iii **b** ii **c** i

A8 Exam review

1 a 12 m **b** 50 m
2 a 09:05 **b** 7 km **c** 10 minutes
d 21 km/h

S8 Before you start …

1 a 360°   **b** 180°

2 a   **b**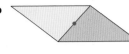

3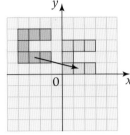

4 100 cm²

5 a 3.7   **b** 3.9   **c** 8.8   **d** 13.6   **e** 3.0

S8.1

1 a 120°
  b 3 × 120° = 360°, so three hexagons fit together at a point.
2 $x = 135°$
3 $a = 60°$, $b = 120°$
4 $a = 30°$, $b = 60°$
5 a 120°
  b The hexagon has equal angles, so it is regular.
6 No; the interior angle is 108°, which is not a factor of 360°.

S8.2

1 a 47° (alternate angles)
  b 63° (corresponding angles)
  c $c = 56°$ (alternate angles), $d = 43°$ (corresponding angles)
  d $e = 52°$ (alternate angles), $f = 48°$ (corresponding angles), $g = 80°$ (angles in a triangle/on a straight line add to 180°)
  e 125°
2 a 45°   **b** 54°   **c** 40°
  d $d = 75°$, $e = 105°$ **e** 70°
3 a $a = b = c = 61°$
  b $d = e = f = 70°$, $g = 40°$
  c $h = 36°$, $i = j = 108°$, $k = 36°$
  d $l = m = n = o = p = 60°$
  e $q = r = s = t = 25°$
4 a 75°   **b** 82°   **c** 34°

S8.3

1 a 64 cm²   **b** 100 m²   **c** 3.24 m²
  d 1296 mm²   **e** 20.25 m²
2 a 9 m   **b** 2 cm   **c** 14 cm
  d 2.7 m   **e** 1 mm
3 a 20 cm²   **b** 8 cm²   **c** 100 mm²
4 a 10 cm   **b** 25 m   **c** 17 cm
  d 26 mm   **e** 30 cm

S8.4

1 a 4 cm²   **b** 15 cm²
2 a 9 cm   **b** 12 mm   **c** 24 m
  d 16 cm   **e** 2.5 m
3 a 5.2 cm   **b** 7.1 m   **c** 8.9 cm
  d 53 m   **e** 9 cm   **f** 39 cm
4 a 6 m   **b** 15 m   **c** 7.5 m²

S8.5

1 a   **b** (3, 2)

2 a (3, 3)   **b** (2, 4)   **c** (2, 1)
  d (5, 4)   **e** (2, 3)
3 $x = 5$, $y = 2$
4 a 5 units   **b** 5 units   **c** 3.2 units
  d 5.7 units   **e** 6.7 units
5 a

  b Square   **c** 4.2 units
  d 4.2 units   **e** 18 square units

S8 Exam review

1 a 4.5 units   **b** (3, 2)
2 ai 130°
  aii Triangle SQR is isosceles, so the other angle at Q is 50°. Angles on a straight line sum to 180°.
  bi 64°   **bii** Alternate angles

Index